October – 1977
Moab, Utah

CHILTON'S Repair and Tune-Up Guide

Jeep
Universal
1953–76

ILLUSTRATED

Prepared by the

Automotive Editorial Department

Recreational Vehicles

Chilton Book Company

Chilton Way
Radnor, Pa. 19089
215–687-8200

president and chief executive officer **WILLIAM A. BARBOUR;** executive vice president **K. ROBERT BRINK;** vice president and general manager **WILLIAM D. BYRNE;** associate editorial director **GLEN B. RUH;** managing editor **JOHN H. WEISE, S.A.E.;** assistant managing editor **PETER J. MEYER;** senior editor **KERRY A. FREEMAN;** editor **ROBERT J. BROWN**

CHILTON BOOK COMPANY   RADNOR, PENNSYLVANIA

Manufactured in the United States of America

1234567890   5432109876

Chilton's Repair & Tune-Up Guide: Jeep Universal 1953–76
ISBN 0-8019-6555-1
ISBN 0-8019-6556-X (pbk.)

Library of Congress Catalogue Card No. 76-20410

ACKNOWLEDGMENTS

The CHILTON BOOK COMPANY wishes to express appreciation
to the following firms for their generous assistance in the prepa-
ration of this book:

Jeep Corporation
A Division of American Motors Corporation
Detroit, Michigan

Kaiser Jeep Corporation
Toledo, Ohio

Willys Motors, Inc.
Toledo, Ohio

Watkins Motor Trucks, Inc.
Chester, Pennsylvania

Warn Industries
Seattle, Washington

Jack Kane's 4 Wheel Drive Center
Routes 3 and 320
Broomall, Pennsylvania 19008

Contents

1 · General Information, Lubrication, and Maintenance

Introduction

The first "Jeep," as we know it today, was produced in 1941 for the military services. It was a basic utility vehicle with four-wheel-drive (4wd) and bore the military title "4 x 4 G.P." This meant that it was a 4wd General Purpose vehicle.

The actual term "Jeep" came from the name of a prewar cartoon character which supposedly had supernatural powers and, reportedly, always told the truth. Since the name "G.P.," which the military used, sounds so much like the word "Jeep,"

when said quickly, the short nickname universally replaced the cumbersome military designation. When Henry Kaiser bought the rights to manufacture the vehicle from the Willys Motor Company, this nickname was made a legitimate trademark and was included in the company name, the Kaiser Jeep Corporation.

Model Identification

The first Jeep was the Model MB Military. It was produced from 1941 until 1945

Model MB Military 1941—45

and was available only to the military. The distinguishing characteristics were an L head, four-cylinder engine, no tailgate, a 6 volt (6 V) electrical system, split windshield, rear-mounted spare tire, and a timing chain.

The next model produced was the CJ-2A. It was made from 1945 to 1949 and was the first Jeep made available directly to the public. This is the civilian version of the MB Military. In fact, the letters CJ stand for Civilian Jeep. The distinguishing characteristics of this model are the L head, four-cylinder engine, split windshield, and 6 V electrical system. The civilian version differs from the Model MB Military in that the spare tire is mounted on the side of the vehicle and the newer model CJ-2A has a tailgate.

The CJ-3A was brought out in 1948. The only difference between this model and the CJ-2A is that the CJ-3A has a one-piece windshield. This model was produced until 1953.

The military services received a new model Jeep in 1950; the Model MC-M38 Military. This Jeep had a 24 V electrical system, a four-cylinder L head engine, no tailgate, brush guards over the headlights, a one-piece windshield, and a rear-mounted spare tire. This model was only produced until 1951.

In 1951 the Model MD-M38A1 Military replaced the Model MC-M38 Military. The newer model had rounded front fenders and was made until 1968.

A new civilian Jeep, the Model CJ-3B, was introduced in 1953. It can be distin-

Model CJ-2A 1945–49

Model CJ-3A 1948–53

Model MC-M38 Military 1950–51

Model MD-M38A1 Military 1951–68

Model CJ-3B 1953–64

guished by its high flat hood but also had a four-cylinder, F head engine, side-mounted spare tire, one-piece windshield, tailgate, angular fenders (like all of the earlier models), and a 6 V or 12 V electrical system. The CJ-3B was made until 1964.

The CJ-5, a civilian version of the MD-M38A1 was released in 1955. It has a tailgate, a 6 V or 12 V electrical system, and rounded fenders. Two engines were offered for the first time in the Universal series with this introduction. The traditional four-cylinder F head was offered as well as the V6 engine that was made by Buick but installed by Kaiser. The V6 was available from 1965 to 1971. The CJ-5's spare is usually mounted on the side. In 1972 the wheelbase of the CJ-5 was lengthened

Model CJ-5 1955–76

Model CJ-6 1955–76

Model CJ-7 1976

from 81 to 34 in. to accommodate the larger American Motors engines that are presently used.

A longer version of the CJ-5 was also introduced in 1955. This was the CJ-6 with a wheelbase of 101 in. It was, and is still, identical to the CJ-5 except for the longer wheelbase. The CJ-6 also had its wheelbase elongated (to 104 in.) in 1972 to accommodate the larger American Motors engines.

For the 1976 model year, the CJ-6 was discontinued in the U.S. and Canada, although still exported. A new model, the CJ-7, featuring a one-piece removable plastic hardtop, automatic transmission, steel side doors with roll-up windows and the full-time 4WD system, Quadra-Trac, was introduced. The CJ-5 remained the same with its 83.5 in. wheelbase, while the CJ-7 has a wheelbase of 93.5 in.

Serial Number Identification

VEHICLE

Each Jeep model series has one or more serial number prefixes to identify it. Identification of a specific vehicle requires a prefix plus a serial number which will be consecutive for each prefix grouping. The

following chart identifies the Jeep model by the serial number prefix.

Model Identification by Serial Number

Model	Prefix	Serial Number
CJ-3B	453-GB2	5 digit S/N *
	454-GB2	5 digit S/N
	57348	5 digit S/N
	8105	5 digit S/N
CJ-5	57548	5 or 6 digit S/N
	8305	5 digit S/N
CJ-5A	8322	5 digit S/N
CJ-6	57648	5 digit S/N
	8405	5 digit S/N
CJ-6A	8422	5 digit S/N

* S/N Serial Number

Any prefix that is not given here indicates that yours is a special vehicle with differences that are not covered in this book.

The vehicle serial number is located on a metal plate mounted on the firewall under the hood. It is on the left side on CJ-5, CJ-6, and CJ-7 models and on the right on CJ-3B models.

When American Motors Corporation took over the Jeep Corporation, the numbering system was changed to the American Motors 13-digit alpha-numerical Vehicle Identification Number (VIN).

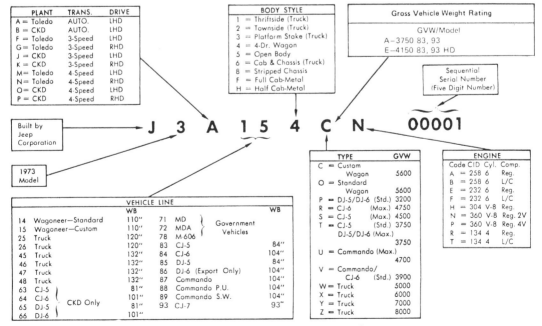

American Motors Jeep serial number code

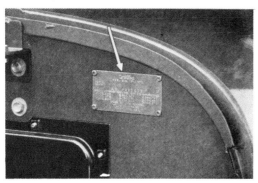

Serial number plate location on CJ-5, CJ-6, and CJ-7

Serial number plate location on CJ-3B

Engine serial number location on the F-head engine

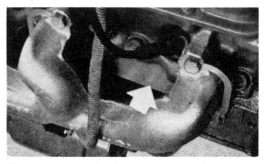

Engine serial number location on the V6 engine

Engine serial number location on the straight 6 engine

This number is also stamped on a metal plate on the left side of the firewall on the Universal series.

The serial number is interpreted in the following manner. The first digit, "J," signifies that the vehicle was made by the Jeep Corporation. The second digit, a number, signifies the year of production. The third digit, a letter, tells you where the vehicle was assembled, the type of transmission, and whether it is right-hand or left-hand drive. The next two digits, which are numbers, tell you what model you have. The next digit in the serial number, a number, tells the body style. The following digit, a letter, tells you the type of vehicle and the gross vehicle weight (GVW). The next digit, a letter, explains which engine the vehicle uses. The last five digits are sequential numbers indicating sequence in production.

ENGINE SERIAL NUMBER IDENTIFICATION

All CJ-3B, CJ-5, and CJ-6 Jeeps came with the F head, four-cylinder engine as standard equipment until 1965 when the

V6 engine was made available as an option. The engine serial number on the F head is located on the water pump boss at the front of the engine. It consists of a five- or six-digit number. The engine code prefix for the F head, four-cylinder engine is "4J."

The engine number for the V6 engine is located on the right side of the engine, on the crankcase, just below the head. The code is "KLH."

The American Motors engine code is, of course, found on the identification plate on the firewall. The second location is on the engine itself, on a machined surface of the block between number two and three spark plugs on the six-cylinder engines. On the 304 cu in. V8, the number is located on a tag attached to the right valve cover. (For further identification, the displacement is cast into the side of the block.) The letter in the code identifies the engine by displacement (cu in.), carburetor type, and compression ratio.

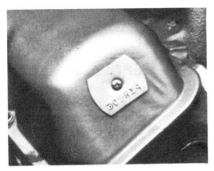

Engine serial number location on the V8 engine

Code	CID	Carb.	Comp. Ratio
A (standard)	258	1V	8.0 : 1
B (optional)	258	1V	7.6 : 1
E (standard)	232	1V	8.0 : 1
F (optional)	232	1V	7.5 : 1
H	304	2V	8.4 : 1
R	134	1V	Regular
T	134	1V	Low

It is sometimes necessary to machine oversized or undersized clearances for cylinder blocks and crankshafts. If your engine is equipped with oversized or undersized parts, it is necessary to order parts that will match the old parts. To find out if your engine is one with odd-sized parts, check the engine number. If it is followed by a letter or a series of letters, odd part sizes are involved. This applies to all Jeeps. The following chart explains just what the letters indicate on engines in Jeeps made prior to 1972.

Letter A (10001-A) indicates 0.010 in. undersized main and connecting rod bearings.
Letter B (10001-B) indicates 0.010 in. oversized cylinder bore.
Letter AB (10001AB) indicates the combination of the above specifications.
Letter C (10001C) indicates 0.002 in. undersized piston pin.
Letter D (10001D) indicates 0.010 in. undersized main bearing journals.
Letter E (10001E) indicates 0.010 in. un-

dersized connecting rod bearing journals.

Before you replace any of these parts, refer to this chart so the proper tolerances and clearances may be maintained and the right replacement parts may be obtained.

The code for vehicles with American Motors engines is as follows:

Letter B indicates 0.010 in. oversized cylinder bore.
Letter M indicates 0.010 in. undersized main bearings.
Letter P indicates 0.010 in. undersized connecting rod bearings.
Letters PM indicates a combination of the above specification for P and M.
Letter C indicates 0.010 in. oversized camshaft block bores.

The parts size code is located on the boss directly above the oil filter on the straight sixes and on the tag adjacent to the engine number on V8s.

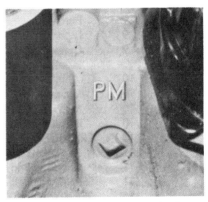

Location of the Parts Size letter code for 6 cylinder American Motors engines; on the boss directly above oil filter

TRANSMISSION IDENTIFICATION

There is a tag attached to the transmission case that identifies the manufacturer and model of the transmission. It is necessary to have the information on this tag before ordering parts. When reassembling the transmission, be sure that this tag is replaced on the transmission case so identification can be made in the future.

The following chart correlates engine, transmission, model number, and transmission number, and notes the number of speeds, shifter location, and starting and stopping serial numbers.

Model	Model of Borg-Warner Trans	Trans No.	Notes
CJ-3B, CJ-5, CJ-6 (4 Cyl)	T-90	644315	Used on vehicles up to serial number 57348–93447, 57548–151236, 57748–23457.
	T-90	946109	After above numbers *
CJ-5, CJ-6 (V6)	T-86AA	946112	Floorshift (3 spd)
	T-14A	947216	Floorshift (3 spd)
	T-18	994753	Floorshift (4 spd)
CJ-5, CJ-6 (American Motors engines)	T-14A	——	Floorshift (3 spd)
	T-15A	——	Floorshift (3 spd)
	T-18	——	Floorshift (4 spd)
CJ-5, CJ-7	T-150	——	Floorshift (3 spd)
	T-18A	——	Floorshift (4 spd)

* Some vehicles use 931790, 944316, or 944344; all parts are the same as on 946109 except the countershaft cluster gear. See 946109 for parts.

Routine Maintenance

AIR CLEANER

It is very important that particular attention be paid to the air cleaner. When the vehicle is used on the highway where there is little or no dust visible in the air, the maintenance required is very little. If the vehicle is used most frequently on highways, the oil in an oil bath air filter should be changed every 2,000 miles. If the vehicle is operated under dusty conditions, the air filter should have clean oil installed every other day or even every day. If the conditions are extremely dusty, it might be best to change the oil twice a day.

While the necessity of such frequent changes is uncommon, it could be warranted under extremely dirty conditions such as a dusty field.

Use the same viscosity of oil for an oil bath air filter as you use in the engine crankcase. If it is cold and you are using a light-viscosity oil in the engine, use a light-viscosity oil in the air filter. If you are using a heavier oil in the crankcase for warm weather, use the same, heavier oil in the oil bath air cleaner.

To service the oil bath type air cleaner, first stop the engine. On the F head, four-cylinder engine, first unscrew the oil cup clamp and remove the oil cup from the cleaner body. Remove the oil from the cup and scrape out all the dirt inside, on the bottom. Wash the cup with a safe solvent such as kerosine. Refill the oil cup and replace it on the air cleaner body.

To service the air cleaner body (less the oil cup), loosen the hose clamp and remove the hose from the cleaner. Detach the breather hose from the fitting on the cleaner. Remove the two wing nuts and lift the cleaner from the vehicle. Agitate the cleaner body thoroughly in a cleaning solution to clean the filtering element and then dry the element with compressed air. Reinstall the air cleaner body and replace the oil cup. The air cleaner should be serviced every 2,000 miles.

To service the oil bath type air cleaner on V6 engines, first remove the air cleaner from the engine by unscrewing the wing nut on top of the air cleaner. Remove the oil cup from the body of the air cleaner and remove all of the oil from the oil cup. Remove all of the dirt from the inside of the oil cup with a safe solvent. Wash the filter element in solvent, air dry it, and then fill the oil cup to the indicated level with clean oil. Assemble the air cleaner element to the oil cup, making sure that the gasket is in place between the two pieces. Mount the air cleaner assembly to the carburetor, making sure that the gasket between the air cleaner and the carburetor is in place and making a good seal. Secure the air cleaner to the carburetor with the wing nut. This air cleaner should be serviced every 6,000 miles or more frequently in dusty areas.

The air filter on the newer Jeeps consists of an outside polyurethane element that is soaked in oil and an inner paper element. The air cleaner should be serviced in accordance with the instructions on the

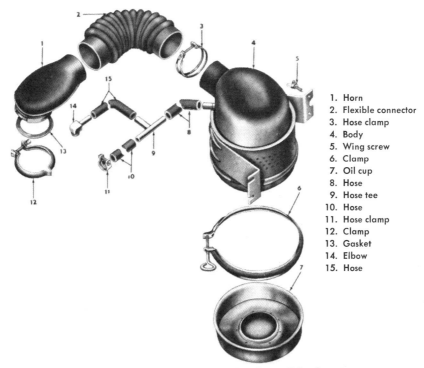

1. Horn
2. Flexible connector
3. Hose clamp
4. Body
5. Wing screw
6. Clamp
7. Oil cup
8. Hose
9. Hose tee
10. Hose
11. Hose clamp
12. Clamp
13. Gasket
14. Elbow
15. Hose

Exploded view of an oil bath oil filter for an F-head engine

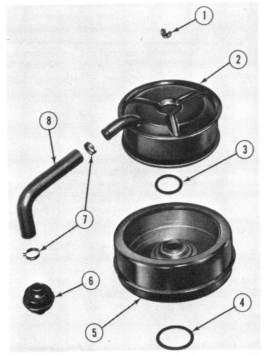

Exploded view of an oil bath oil filter for a V6 engine

1. Wing nut
2. Cover
3. Rubber gasket
4. Cork gasket
5. Oil cup
6. Breather
7. Clamps
8. Vent tube

decal attached to the air cleaner housing. If the decal is missing, follow the directions and recommendations below.

The air cleaner element should be cleaned every 6,000 miles. If the vehicle is operated in dusty areas, check the air cleaner every day and clean it if it is dirty. The paper element should be replaced initially at 18,000 miles and every 30,000 miles thereafter. If there is evidence of plugging or damage, replace the paper element.

Polyurethane and paper element type air filter

To clean the polyurethane element, first carefully remove the element from the air cleaner housing. Separate the paper element from the polyurethane one. Take care not to rip or tear either of them.

Wash the polyurethane element in a safe solvent such as kerosine. Wrap the polyurethane element in a dry, clean cloth and squeeze it to remove all solvent. Do not twist the element because you could very easily tear it. After cleaning the element and drying it, oil it liberally with engine oil. Use SAE 10W-30. Squeeze the polyurethane element to evenly distribute the oil and remove any excess oil. The element should be just damp with oil, not dripping.

To clean the paper cartridge, first shake out the accumulated dirt. Do not wash the paper element in water or any other liquid because liquid will destroy a paper element. Blow compressed air through the element in the reverse direction of the normal air flow (from the inside out). Be careful not to blow a hole in the paper element.

Install the paper cartridge inside the polyurethane element. Make sure that the edges of the polyurethane element are over the plastic end plates of the paper cartridge.

PCV VALVE

The PCV valve, which is the heart of the positive crankcase ventilation system, should be changed initially at 18,000 miles and every 30,000 miles thereafter. However, it is possible to clean a PCV valve in solvent once or twice before having to replace it. The main thing to keep in mind is that the valve should be free of dirt and residue and should be in working order. As long as the valve is kept clean and is not showing signs of becoming worn or gummed up, it should perform its function properly. When the valve cannot be cleaned sufficiently or becomes sticky and will not operate freely, it should be replaced.

The PCV filter, which is located at the air filter housing on the six-cylinder models, should be checked along with the PCV

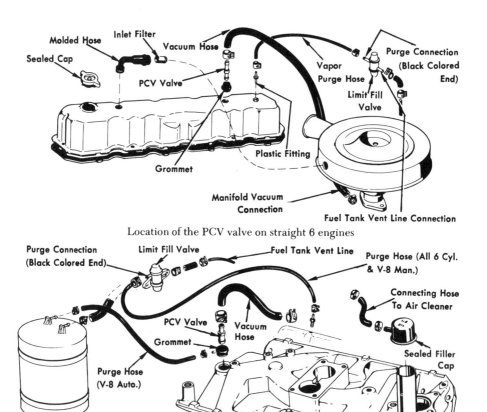

Location of the PCV valve on straight 6 engines

Location of the PCV valve on the V8 engines

valve. Just blow out the screen with compressed air in the reverse direction of the normal air flow. Check to see that the screen forms a good seal around the edges of the air cleaner housing so no dirt can pass. If the screen is torn or clogged, or if it is seated improperly and cannot be repaired, replace it.

On V8 engines, the air being drawn into the PCV system passes through a polyurethane foam filter located in the oil filler cap. The filler cap is vented only by a hose connected to the air cleaner. The foam filter in the oil filler cap should be cleaned with safe solvent every 30,000 miles.

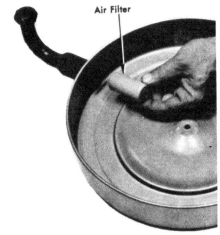

The PCV air filter

FLUID LEVEL CHECKS

Engine Oil

It is first necessary to make sure that your vehicle is on a level surface to ensure an accurate reading. Then, raise the hood, position the hold-up rod, and measure the oil with the dipstick which is on the right side of four-cylinder and V8 engines and on the left of six-cylinder engines (facing rear of vehicle). Add oil through the filler pipe on the right side of F head engines, through the valve cover filler hole on six-cylinder engines, and through the filler pipe at the front of the engine on V8s.

If the oil is below the ADD mark, add a quart of oil, then recheck the level. If the level is still not reading full, add only a half of a quart at a time, until the dipstick reads FULL. Do not overfill the engine.

When you check the oil in *any* engine, make sure that you allow sufficient time for all of the oil to drain back into the crankcase after stopping the engine or else you will only measure a fraction of the actual amount. A minute or so should be enough time.

Earlier CJ-3B models had engine oil pressure gauges on the dash. An oil pressure gauge is standard equipment on the Renegade and is optional on other new-model Jeeps.

There is a red tell-tale lamp in the instrument cluster of later models which is connected to a pressure-sensitive switch. The light should glow red when the ignition switch is on and should go out when the engine is started and running, indicating that the oil pressure has reached a safe level. The light goes on when the ignition switch is turned on to tell you that the light is not burned out. The switch is sensitive to the minimum oil pressure of 6 lbs. As long as the pressure remains at 6 lbs, the light will not come on. The main disadvantage of an oil pressure light is that the pressure may be within the acceptable range, but not acceptable for the speed of the engine. The oil could be at 6 lbs pressure at 2,000 rpm. This is dangerous because the engine needs more pressure at this speed to be lubricated properly. At the other extreme, excessive oil pressure can be equally hazardous. There is an oil pressure relief valve (set at 75 lbs for both sixes and V8s). The advantages of an oil pressure gauge are obvious.

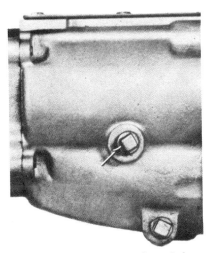

The filler hole (arrow) and the drain hole on the transmission

Manual Transmissions

The level of lubricant in the transmission should be maintained at the filler hole on all manual transmissions. This hole is located on the left side of the transmission on vehicles prior to 1972, and on the right side on later vehicles. Even though the transfer case and the transmission are linked together (on all three-speed transmissions) by passages that allow the oil from each unit to flow into the other, check each separately at their fill holes. When you check the level in the transmission, make sure that the vehicle is level so that you get a true reading. When you remove the filler plug, the lubricant should run out of the hole. If there is lubricant present at the hole, you know that the transmission is filled to the proper level. Replace the plug quickly for a minimum loss of lubricant. If lubricant does not run out of the hole when the plug is removed, lubricant should be added until it does. Replace the plug as soon as the lubricant reaches the level of the hole.

Automatic Transmission

The fluid level in automatic transmissions is checked with a dipstick which is located in the filler pipe at the right rear of the engine. The fluid level should be maintained between the ADD and FULL marks on the end of the dipstick with the automatic transmission fluid at normal operating temperatures. To raise the level from the ADD mark to the FULL mark, requires the addition of one pint of fluid. The fluid level with the fluid at room temperature (75° F) should be approximately ¼ in. below the ADD mark.

NOTE: *In checking the automatic transmission fluid, insert the dipstick in the filler tube with the markings toward the center of the car. Also, remember that the FULL mark on the dipstick is the indication of the level of the automatic transmission fluid when it is at operating temperature. This temperature is only obtained after at least 15 miles of expressway driving or the equivalent of city driving.*

To check the automatic transmission fluid level, follow the procedure given below. This procedure is applicable either when the fluid is at room temperature or at operating temperature.

1. With the transmission in Park, the engine running at idle speed, the foot brake applied and the vehicle resting on level ground, move the transmission gear selector through each of the gear positions, including Reverse, allowing time for the transmission to engage. Return the shift selector to the Park position and apply the parking brake. Do not turn the engine off, but leave it running at idle speed.

2. Clean all dirt from around the transmission dipstick cap and the end of the filler tube.

3. Pull the dipstick out of the tube, wipe it off with a clean cloth, and push it back into the tube all the way, making sure that it seats completely.

4. Pull the dipstick out of the tube again and read the level of the fluid on the stick. The level should be between the ADD and FULL marks. If fluid must be added, add enough fluid through the tube to raise the level to between the ADD and FULL marks. Do not overfill the transmission because this will cause foaming and loss of fluid through the vent and malfunctioning of the transmission.

NOTE: *Use only Dexron® or Dexron II® transmission fluid.*

Brake Master Cylinder

Check the level of fluid in the hydraulic brake master cylinder every 2,000 miles on older Jeeps, such as the early CJ-3B and the early CJ-5 and CJ-6, and every 6,000 miles on 1972 and later versions. On all

Location of the master cylinder and the steering shaft universal on 1972 and later models

early-model Jeeps, prior to 1972, the master cylinder is located under the left side of the front floor space. To check the level of the brake fluid in the master cylinder, remove the floor plate that covers the master cylinder. Clean the area around the master cylinder of all dirt so that, when you remove the cover, no dirt will fall in and contaminate the brake fluid. Dirt in the hydraulic system could score the inside of the master cylinder or wheel cylinder and cause leakage or brake failure. Unscrew the lid of the master cylinder with a wrench. The fluid level should be within ½ in. from the top of the reservoir chamber. Use only heavy-duty brake fluid and keep it away from any other fluids or vapors that could contaminate it.

On 1972 and later Jeeps, the master cylinder is located under the hood, on the left side of the firewall. The possibility of getting dirt in the master cylinder is less with this type of arrangement. To check the fluid, use a screwdriver to pry off the retaining clip from the lid of the reservoir. The fluid level should be within ½ in. of the top of the reservoir.

Replace the caps when you have finished checking the fluid level in the master cylinder and have finished replenishing the supply.

If the master cylinder is less than half-full, there is probably a leak somewhere in the hydraulic system. Investigate the problem before driving the vehicle.

Coolant

The coolant level should be maintained about ½ in. below the filler neck of the radiator with F head engines. The cooling systems in four-cylinder engines carry 5–7 lbs of pressure.

On the American Motors engines (six-cylinder and V8), the coolant level should be maintained 2 in. below the bottom of the filler cap when the engine is cold (room temperature). Since operating temperatures reach as high as 205° F for the six, and 195° F for the V8s, coolant could be forced out of the radiator if it is filled too high. The radiator coolant level should be checked regularly, such as every time you fill the vehicle with gas. Never open the radiator cap of an engine that hasn't had sufficient time to cool or else the pressure inside the radiator can blow off the cap and send out sprays of scalding water.

Location of the filler hole in the rear axle. It is in the same approximate position on the front axle

Front and Rear Axle

The front and rear axle differentials hold approximately 2½ pt of either SAE 80 or SAE 90 gear oil. Either is acceptable for use in the differential housing. Check the level of the oil in the differential housing every 5,000 miles under normal driving conditions and every 3,000 miles if the vehicle is used in severe driving conditions. The level should be up to the filler hole. When you remove the filler plug, the oil should start to run out. If it does not, replenish the supply until it does.

Manual Steering Gear

Check the steering gear lubricant level every 5,000 miles, sooner on older models. The level should be at the filler hole. Use SAE 80 gear oil to replenish the supply if it is needed. Don't forget to replace the filler bolt. If level is abnormally low, check for leaks.

Power Steering Reservoir

On models with power steering, check the fluid in the power steering pump every 5,000 miles. The level of the fluid should be at the correct point on the dipstick attached to the inside of the lid of the power steering pump. Replenish the supply with

Remove Bolt
to Lubricate

Steering gear filler hole

DEXRON automatic transmission fluid. If the pump is abnormally low on fluid, check all the power steering hoses and connections, and the hydraulic cylinder for possible leaks.

Transfer Case (Except Quadra-Trac)

The transfer case should be checked in the same manner and frequency as the manual transmissions. The level should be up to the filler hole. Use the same viscosity oil as is being used in the transmission. The filler hole is located on the left side of the vehicle on Jeeps made prior to 1972. On 1972 and later models, the fill hole is on the right side. Check the oil level at the top hole; the bottom one is for draining.

Quadra-Trac Transfer Case

Fluid levels in the Quadra-Trac transfer case and low range reduction unit, if so equipped, should be checked at the same time every 5,000 miles. The lubricant levels are checked at the filler plug holes. The filler plug holes are located on the rear side of the transfer case assembly, just below center in the middle of the case housing and to the right of center of the reduction unit housing. The lubricant should be level with each filler plug hole. If not, replenish lubricant with a mixture of AMC/Jeep Lubricant Concentrate, Jeep Part No. 8123004, 5356068, 8997156, or Lubrizol® 762 and

SAE 30W nondetergent motor oil (Ashland Valvoline® preferred). See "Lubrication—Oil Changes" for the proper mixture quantities.

NOTE: *Do not mix concentrate 8997156 with concentrate 8123004.*

FRONT HUB ASSEMBLY

Wheel Bearings

The front wheel bearings should be repacked with new grease every 6,000 miles, or once a year, whichever comes first. The procedure for servicing the front wheel bearings is as follows:

1. Jack up the vehicle so the front wheels clear the ground. Chock the back wheels so the Jeep won't roll off the jack. Remove the wheel/tire assembly.

2. Remove the dust cap. Remove the cotter pin from the center of the axle nut, or bend the lip of the lockwasher. Remove the axle nut and lockwasher or the snap-ring—depending on what type of device is used.

3. Unscrew the bolts and washers that attach the drive axle flange to the hub. Remove the drive axle flange from the hub, along with the gasket.

4. Remove the two bearing nuts and their lockwashers from the spindle.

5. Remove the hub from the spindle. Be careful not to damage the bearings.

Capacities

Engine No. Cyl Displacement (cu in.)	Engine Crankcase Add 1 Qt for New Filter	TRANSMISSION Pts to Refill After Draining				Drive Axle (pt)		Gasoline Tank (gal)	COOLING SYSTEM (qt)	
		Auto-matic	Manual 3 Speed	4 Speed	Transfer Case	Front	Rear		With Heater	Without Heater
4—134	4	——	2.5	6.75	3.5	2.5	2.5	10.5	12	11
6—225	4	——	2.5	6.75	3.5	2.5	2.5	10.5	10	9
6—232	5	——	2.5④	6.5	3.25	2.5①	2.5①	16	10.5②	9.5②
6—258	5	10⑤	2.5④	6.5	3.25③	2.5①	2.5①	16	10.5②	9.5②
8—304	5	10⑤	2.75④	6.5	3.25③	2.5①	2.5①	16	14②	13②

① 3 pt with a Model 44 front or rear differential, 4 pts with an AMC model rear axle—1976
② When the radiator cores are increased from two to three tube cores on some heavy-duty applications, the capacity is increased by approximately 1.5 pt.
③ 3.5 pts with Quadra-Trac, 4.5 with Quadra-Trac and reduction unit. Includes 8 oz of additive.
④ 3 pts—1976
⑤ 22 pts after an overhaul

6. Remove the bearings from the hub.

7. Clean the bearings in a cleaning solution. Remove all of the old grease and dirt with a clean, stiff brush. Set the cleaned bearings on a clean, dry cloth and allow them to dry completely.

8. Pack the wheel bearings with good wheel bearing grease. Force the grease in and around the rollers in their cages. It is a good idea to replace the grease seals, even if they are not leaking, since they are relatively cheap and replacing them could save you some grief later. Chances are it was damaged on removal of inner bearing anyway.

9. Make sure that the hub races and the spindle are clean before replacing the bearings. Replace the bearings and seal in the hub.

10. To reinstall the hub and wheel assembly to the axle, reverse the steps from no. 5.

NOTE: *See Chapter 9 "Brakes, Wheel Bearings," for more details.*

Steering Knuckle

The axle shaft universal joints are located in the steering knuckle and are bathed in oil as they turn. To check the fluid level in the steering knuckle, remove the filler plug from the inside of the knuckle. The fluid should be at the level of the hole. If it is not, replenish the supply. Examine the knuckle for leaks if the level is abnormally low. A leak should be readily visible.

NOTE: *This does not apply to 1972 and later models with left-hand drive.*

Front axle steering knuckle filler plug

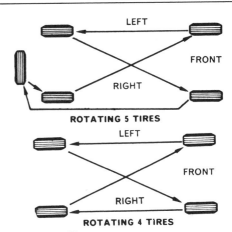

Tire Rotation Chart

TIRE AND WHEELS

Tire Rotation

Tires should be rotated every 6,000 miles. If no spare is used, follow the "rotating four tires" diagram. If you have a spare and are including it in your tire rotating sequence, follow the "rotating five tires" diagram.

NOTE: *Radial tires must be kept on the same side of the vehicle on which they were originally installed when rotated.*

If uneven tire wear occurs before 6,000 miles, rotate the tires sooner. If the tires show abnormal wear patterns, have the axle alignment checked. Inflation pressures should be adjusted whenever tires are rotated. Tires should also be balanced or rebalanced when they are rotated.

Tire Inflation Chart

| Model | Tire Size | Ply Rating | Pressure (psi)▲ | |
			Front	Rear
CJ-5	7.35 X 15	4	20	20
CJ-6	8.55 X 15	4 or 8	20	20
	H78 X 15	4	20	20
	6.00 X 16	6	30	30
CJ-3B	6.00 X 16	4	26	28
CJ-5				
CJ-6				

▲ Pressures given are for normal loads and under sustained speeds of under 65 mph. For maximum loads (GVWR) or sustained speeds of over 65 mph, increase pressure to maximum for tire (DOT rating).

Tire Life and Safety

Common sense and good driving habits will afford maximum tire life. Fast starts and stops, and hard cornering are hard on tires and will shorten their useful life span. If you start at normal speeds, allow yourself sufficient time to stop, and take corners at a reasonable speed, the life of your tires will increase greatly. Also make sure that you don't overload your vehicle or run with incorrect pressure in the tires. Both of these practices increase tread wear.

Inspect your tires frequently. Be especially careful to watch for bubbles in the tread or side wall, deep cuts, or underinflation. Remove any tires with bubbles. If the cuts are so deep they penetrate to the cords, discard the tire. Also look for uneven tread wear patterns that indicate that the front end is out of alignment or that the tires are out of balance.

Wider Treads and Radial Ply Tires

The main thing to remember when you have decided to install a different type tire on your vehicle is that you have to install at least four. Your spare tire should be of the same size and tread design as the rest.

Radial tires must not be mixed with belted or conventional tires because of the unusual handling characteristics that will result. Radial tires are not designed for vehicles that carry a substantial load, once again, because of the unusual handling characteristics that will result. Make sure that the tires you select will provide adequate clearance between the fender wells, the fenders themselves, and all suspension and steering components. Also, oversize flotation type tires require wider rims than stock.

Mud and snow tires should be operated at full inflation pressures and not at sustained speeds over 75 mph for one hour or more.

FUEL FILTER

The in-line fuel filter, which is located at the carburetor, should be cleaned (pre-1972) or replaced every 15,000 miles. If the vehicle is driven in abnormally dirty conditions or if dirty gasoline was put in the gas tank, the filter could become clogged before 15,000 miles. If there is evidence of foreign material (e.g., water, dirt) in the fuel sediment bowl, on early models, remove and empty it. Wipe it dry with a clean, dry cloth and replace it.

BATTERY

Check the level of the water in the battery every time you fill the gas tank. The water level should meet the bottom of the filler hole. Minimally, it should at least cover the plates.

Pushing, Towing, and Jump Starting

To push-start your vehicle, (*manual transmissions only*) follow the procedures below. Check to make sure that the bumpers of both vehicles are aligned so neither will be damaged. Be sure that all electrical system components are turned off (headlights, heater, blower, etc.). Turn on the ignition switch. Place the shift lever in Third or Fourth and push in the clutch pedal. At about 15 mph, signal the driver of the pushing vehicle to fall back, depress the accelerator pedal, and release the clutch pedal slowly. The engine should start.

When you are doing the pushing or pulling, make sure that the two bumpers match so you won't damage the vehicle you are to push. Another good idea is to put an old tire in between the two vehicles. If the bumpers don't match, perhaps you should tow the other vehicle. Decide whether or not you are going to use 4wd or low range. Do the road surface conditions warrant its use? If the other vehicle is just stuck, use first gear to slowly push it out. Tell the driver of the other vehicle to go slowly too. Try to keep your Jeep right up against the other vehicle while you are pushing. If the two vehicles do separate, stop and start over again instead of trying to catch up and ramming the other vehicle. Also try, as much as possible, to avoid riding or slipping the clutch. Low range makes this easy. When the other vehicle gains enough traction, it should pull away from your vehicle.

If you have to tow the other vehicle, make sure that the tow chain or rope is sufficiently long and strong, and that it is attached securely to both vehicles at a strong place. Attach the chain at a point on the frame or as close to it as possible. Once again, go slowly and tell the other driver to do the same. Warn the other driver not to allow too much slack in the line when he gains traction and can move under his own power. Otherwise he may run over the tow line and damage both vehicles.

If your Jeep must be towed, follow these guidelines:

1. A Jeep with a manual transmission can be towed with either all four wheels or either axle on the ground for any distance at a safe speed with both the transmission and transfer case in Neutral.

2. To tow a Jeep with an automatic transmission and Quadra-Trac, the driveshaft to to the axle(s) remaining on the ground must be disconnected. Be sure to index mark the driveshafts and yoke flanges for alignment upon assembly. Also, the driveshafts must be tied securely up out of the way or removed completely while the vehicle is being towed.

3. A Jeep equipped with an automatic transmission and Quadra-Trac with the optional low range reduction unit can be towed with all four wheels on the ground without disconnecting the driveshafts. Place the transmission shift lever in Park, the low range reduction unit shift lever in Neutral, and the emergency drive control knob in the Normal position. If the emergency drive system was engaged when the engine was shut down, it will have to be restarted and the emergency drive control knob turned to the Normal position to disengage the system since the control mechanism is vacuum-operated.

CAUTION: *Never tow the Jeep with the emergency drive system engaged or the reduction unit in low range.*

In all cases, unnecessary wear and tear can be avoided by disconnecting the driveshafts at the differentials and either tying them up out of the way or removing them altogether. Be sure to index mark the driveshafts and yoke flanges for proper alignment during assembly. If the Jeep is equipped with free-running front hubs (manual transmission only), there is no need to remove the front driveshaft, simply disengage the hubs.

Jacking and Hoisting

Scissors jacks or hydraulic jacks are recommended for the Jeep Universal. To change a tire, place the jack beneath the spring plate, under the axle, near the wheel to be changed.

Make sure that you are on level ground, that the transmission is in Reverse or Park, the parking brake is set, and the tire diagonally opposite to the one to be changed is blocked. Loosen the lug nuts before you jack the wheel to be changed completely free of the ground.

If you use a hoist, make sure that the pads of the hoist are located in such a way as to lift on the Jeep's frame and not on a shock absorber mount, floor boards, oil pan, or any other part that cannot support the full weight of the vehicle.

Lubrication

FUEL AND OIL RECOMMENDATIONS

NOTE: *All 1975–76 models must use lead-free gasoline only.*

All Jeep engines (except 1975–76) are designed to operate on regular grade gasoline. If the vehicle is being used for heavy-duty service, do not use lead-free gas. If the Jeep is being used in light-duty service, a tank of lead-free gas can be used without any problems, in 1972–74 models. If your vehicle pings or knocks, use a higher octane fuel or retard the timing of the engine, but not more than three degrees from the setting required for proper operation. This is only recommended for an emergency situation—until you can get some higher octane fuel. A little knocking at low speeds is acceptable, but continued knock at high speeds can damage your engine.

Oil Type

Many factors help to determine the proper oil for your Jeep. The big question is what viscosity to use and when. The whole matter of viscosity revolves around the lowest anticipated ambient temperature to be encountered before your next oil change. The recommended viscosity ratings for temperatures ranging from below 0° F to above 32° F are listed below. They are broken down into multiviscosities and single-viscosities. Multiviscosity oils are recommended because of their wider range of acceptable temperatures and driving conditions.

Lowest Air Temperature Anticipated	Multiviscosity Engine Oil
Above 40° F	SAE 10W-30, 40 or 20W-40
Above 32° F	SAE 10W-30 or 10W-40
Above 0° F	SAE 10W-30 or 10W-40
Below 0° F	SAE 5W-20 or 5W-30

	Single-Viscosity Engine Oil
Above 40° F	SAE 30 or 40
Above 32° F	SAE 20W-20
Above 0° F	SAE 10W *
Below 0° F	SAE 10W *

* A sustained speed of 55 mph or higher should not be maintained with SAE 10W oil in the engine because the engine will force oil past the piston rings and burn it in the combustion chamber. Oil consumption will be higher than normal.

OIL CHANGES

Engine

The engine oil is to be changed every 2,000 miles for the F head engine. For the V6 and all of the American Motors engines, the recommended interval is 5,000 miles. The oil should be changed more frequently, however, if the vehicle is being used in very dusty areas. Before draining the oil, make sure that the engine is at operating temperature. Hot oil will hold more impurities in suspension and will flow better, allowing it to remove more oil and dirt. To get the engine hot enough, drive the vehicle for 15 minutes at expressway speeds or the equivalent in city driving.

Drain the oil into a suitable receptacle. After the drain plug is loosened, unscrew the plug with your fingers, using a rag to shield your fingers from the heat. Push in on the plug as you unscrew it so you can feel when all of the screw threads are out of the hole. You can then remove the plug quickly with the minumum amount of oil running down your arm and you will also have the plug in your hand and not in the bottom of a pan of hot oil. Be careful of the oil. If it is at operating temperatures it is hot enough to burn you or at least make you uncomfortable.

Manual Transmission

The lubricant in the transmission should be changed every 18,000 miles. (30,000 miles on newer models). All you have to do is remove the drain plug which is located at the bottom of the transmission or else on the side near the bottom. Allow all the lubricant to run out before replacing the plug. Replace the oil with the correct oil, usually SAE 80 or SAE 90 gear lubricant. If you are experiencing hard shifting and the weather is very cold, use a lighter oil in the transmission. If you don't have a pressure gun to install the oil, use a suction gun.

Automatic Transmission

The automatic transmission fluid should be changed every 25,000 miles of normal driving and every 10,000 miles of heavy-duty driving such as pulling a trailer or continuous off-road operation. If, when the transmission fluid level is checked, the fluid is noticed to be discolored from a clear red to brown and has a burned smell or there is water present, the fluid should be changed immediately.

1. Drive the vehicle for at least 20 minutes at expressway speeds or the equivalent to raise the temperature of the fluid to its normal operating range.

2. Drain the automatic transmission fluid into an appropriate container before it has cooled. The fluid is drained by loosening the transmission oil pan and allowing the fluid to run out around the edges. It is best to loosen only one corner of the pan and allow the majority of the oil to drain out.

3. Remove the remaining oil pan screws, and remove the pan and pan gasket.

4. Remove the oil strainer and discard it.

5. Remove the O-ring seal from the pick-up pipe and discard it.

6. Install a new O-ring seal on the

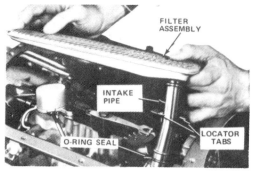

Installing a new filter and intake pipe assembly on an automatic transmission

pick-up pipe and install the new oil strainer and pipe assembly.

7. Thoroughly clean the bottom pan and position a new gasket on the pan mating surface. Use petroleum jelly on the gasket to hold it in place and help seal it.

8. Install the pan and tighten the attaching screws to 10–13 ft lbs.

9. Pour about 5 qts of Dexron or Dexron II automatic transmission fluid down the filler pipe. Make sure that the funnel, container, hose, or any other item used to assist in filling the transmission is clean.

10. Start the engine with the transmission in Park. Do NOT race it. Allow the engine to idle for a few minutes.

11. After the engine has been running for a few minutes, move the selector lever through all of the gears.

12. With the selector lever in Park, check the transmission fluid level and adjust as necessary. Remember the transmission fluid must be warm when at the Full mark.

Front and Rear Axle

Drain and refill the front and rear axle housings every 20,000 miles. Remove the oil by loosening the differential housing cover or with a suction gun. Refill the axle housings with SAE 90W gear oil until the lubricant level meets the fill hole.

Transfer Case (Except Quadra-Trac)

The transfer case is to be serviced at the same time and in the same manner as the transmission. It has its own drain plug which should be opened. Don't rely on the transmission drain plug to completely drain the transfer case. The transfer case and the transmission are not interconnected in Jeeps with four-speed transmissions as they are in some vehicles with three-speed transmissions. You will have to remove the transfer case drain plug if you want to drain it.

Quadra-Trac Transfer Case

Quadra-Trac transfer cases do not require periodic or scheduled lubrication. However, if a "stick-slip" condition develops in the transfer case, a full 8 fluid ounces of lubricant concentrate, Jeep Part Number 8123004, 5356068, 8997156 or Lubrizol 762, should be added to the Quadra-Trac unit. This applies to units also equipped with reduction units. It may be necessary to drain (minimum) a slight amount of lubricant at the drain plug to permit the addition of the full amount of concentrate through the fill hole. If the addition of the concentrate does not cure the "stick-slip" condition, the unit(s) should be drained and refilled.

NOTE: *There is no substitute for the Quadra-Trac lubricant concentrate, Jeep Part Number 8123004, 5356068, 8997156 or Lubrizol 762.*

The "slip-stick" condition which is the cause of having to add additional special lubricant additive is described as follows: When the clutch elements of the Quadra-Trac transfer case stick, it is under a torque wind-up condition as in a conventional transfer case. Sudden release of the clutch under this condition, results in a constant, pulsating, grunt-like or rasping noise. This is a low-frequency "stick-slip" noise that, if it occurs, is evident to the driver at slow or crawl speeds—such as when slowly turning a corner or when maneuvering to park. If the vehicle is not driven for a week or more, the "slip-stick" condition may occur when the vehicle is first driven. This is considered normal and should be of no concern, as the noise should disappear with continued driving.

Should it become necessary to drain the Quadra-Trac unit, simply remove the drain plug from the transfer case and allow it to drain completely. If the transfer case is equipped with a reduction unit, it will be necessary to loosen the 5 bolts on the reduction unit housing, so that it can be pulled back far enough to allow the lubricant to flow out. Let the reduction unit drain completely. Torque the 5 bolts holding the reduction unit to the transfer case to 15–25 ft lbs. Pour a full 8 fluid ounces of the special lubricant concentrate, Jeep Part Number 8123004, 5356068, or Lubrizol 762 into the reduction unit, if so equipped, or directly into the transfer case. Replace the reduction unit fill plug, if so equipped, and top off the transfer case with a good quality SAE 30 *Non-Detergent* motor oil (Ashland Valvoline preferred). For units without reduction units: 3.5 pts are required; with reduction units: 4.5 pts are required.

NOTE: *Be careful not to overtighten the drain and fill plugs. It is very easy to strip the threads in the aluminum housing of the Quadra-Trac units.*

OIL FILTER CHANGES

The oil filter should be changed every 5,000 miles or sooner if the vehicle is driven in dusty areas. Change the oil filter when you change the oil. The engine should be at operating temperatures when the filter is changed. On the older four-cylinder Jeeps, the oil filter is located on the right side and on the forward half of the engine. When you open the hood, the oil filter is on your left, facing toward the rear. It has the appearance of a tin can mounted on the side of the engine with a bolt going down through the center of the lid. To change the element, remove the bolt, remove the lid, and remove and discard the element. Clean out the cup with a clean, dry cloth and flushing oil or clean, light-viscosity engine oil. Clean the lid in the same manner and remove and discard the old gasket from the lid. Replace it with a new one. Do not use a solvent that could get into the oil and dilute it. Place the new filter element in the cup. Place the lid on the cup and the bolt down through the center. Tighten the bolt to 10–15 ft lbs.

Start the engine and look for leaks. If a leak does develop, turn off the engine and remove the oil filter lid. Inspect the gasket to see if it is seated properly. Adjust the gasket if needed. Replace the lid, start the engine, and check for leaks. If the leak persists, tighten the bolt further.

On the newer F head, V6, straight six, and V8 engines, the oil filter is the spin-on type. On the F head engines, the filter is located in the same place as the former cartridge type filter was located. On the V6 engine, the filter is located on the right side of the engine just below the alternator. On the straight six engines, the filter is located on the lower, center right side of the engine. On the V8 engines, the filter is located on the lower, front right side of the engine.

An oil filter wrench

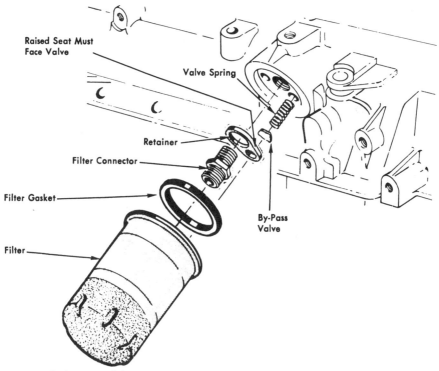

The location of the spin-on type oil filter on the straight 6 and V8 engines

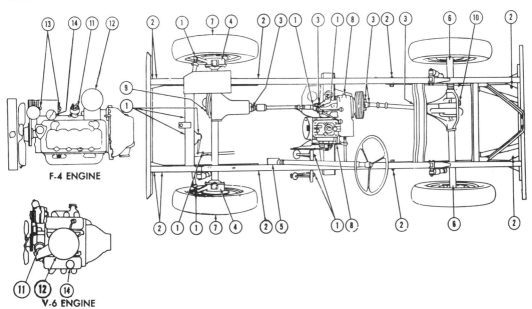

Lubrication chart. Lubrication points for the straight 6 and the V8 are basically the same as illustrated here for the F-head 4 cylinder and the V6 (This chart is primarily for pre-1972 models).

Chart Number	Item to be Lubricated	Frequency
1.	Chassis bearings	Every 1,000 miles
2.	Spring shackle bushings	With lube fittings; every 1,000 miles
	Spring pivot bolt bushings	Without lube fittings; no lubrication
	Universal joints	Every 1,000 miles
3.	Propeller shaft	Check every 1,000 miles
4.	Front axle shaft	Change every 12,000 miles
5.	Steering gear housing	Check every 1,000 miles
6.	Rear wheel bearings	With lube fittings; sparingly every 2,000 miles. Without lube fittings; disassemble to lubricate every 12,000 miles
7.	Front wheel bearings	Disassemble to lubricate every 12,000 miles
8.	3 Speed transmission and transfer case	Check every 1,000 miles and change every 10,000 miles
	4 Speed transmission and transfer case [1]	Check every 1,000 miles and change every 10,000 miles
9.	Differentials	
	Front	Check every 1,000 miles and
	Rear	change every 10,000 miles
10.	Speedometer cable	Disassemble to lubricate every 12,000 miles
11.	Distributor	
	Oiler	Every 1,000 miles several drops engine oil
	Wick	Every 1,000 miles one drop of engine oil
	Pivot	Every 1,000 miles one drop of engine oil
	Cam	Every 1,000 miles 2 cc of cam lubricant
12.	Air cleaner	Change every 2,000 miles
13.	Generator	Every 1,000 miles
14.	Engine	Change every 2,000 miles

[1] The 4 speed transmission and transfer case require separate lubrication on each unit.
NOTE: On some models there are more grease fittings on the driveshafts than are indicated on this chart. Check carefully to make sure that you didn't miss any.

To replace the filter, you may need an oil filter wrench since the filter may have been screwed on too tightly and the heat from the engine may have made it even tighter. A filter wrench can be obtained at an auto parts store and is well worth the investment since it will save you a lot of grief. Loosen the filter with the filter wrench. With a rag wrapped around the filter, unscrew the filter from the oil pump housing. Be careful of hot oil that might run down the side of the filter, especially on the straight sixes and V8s. On the F head, four-cylinder engines, the filter is mounted with the open side facing downward so you won't have to worry about oil running down on your hand. Make sure that you have a pan under the filter before you start to remove it from the engine so you won't make a mess and, if some of the hot oil does happen to get on you, you will have a place to dump the filter in a hurry.

Wipe the base of the mounting plate with a clean, dry cloth. When you install the new filter, smear a small amount of oil on the gasket with your finger, just enough to coat the entire surface where it comes in contact with the mounting plate. When you tighten the filter, turn it only a quarter of a turn after it comes in contact with the mounting plate.

CHASSIS GREASING

The following charts indicate where the grease fittings are located on the vehicles and how often they are to be serviced. The charts are for the CJ-3B, CJ-5, and CJ-6. These are the manufacturer's service recommendations. Of course it wouldn't hurt if the chassis was serviced more often than stated—especially if the vehicle is operating in dusty areas, deep water, or under heavy-duty conditions.

2 · Tune-Up and Troubleshooting

AMC Breakerless Inductive Discharge (BID) Ignition System

COMPONENTS

The AMC breakerless inductive discharge (BID) ignition system consists of five components:

Control unit
Coil
Breakerless distributor
Ignition cables
Spark plugs

The control unit is a solid-state, epoxy-sealed module with waterproof connectors. The control unit has a built-in current regulator, so no separate ballast resistor or resistance wire is needed in the primary circuit. Battery voltage is supplied to the ignition coil positive (+) terminal when the ignition key is turned to the "ON" or "START" position; low voltage is also supplied by the control unit.

The coil used with the BID system requires no special service. It works just like the coil in a conventional ignition system.

The distributor is conventional, except for the lack of points, condenser and cam.

Advance is supplied by both a vacuum unit and a centrifugal advance mechanism. A standard cap, rotor, and dust shield are used.

In place of the points, cam, and condenser, the distributor has a sensor and trigger wheel. The sensor is a small coil which generates an electromagnetic field when excited by the oscillator in the control unit.

Standard spark plugs and ignition cables are used.

OPERATION

When the ignition switch is turned on, the control unit is activated. The control unit then sends an oscillating signal to the sensor which causes the sensor to generate a magnetic field. When one of the trigger wheel teeth enters this field, the strength of the oscillation in the sensor is reduced. Once the strength drops to a predetermined level, a dimodulator circuit operates the control unit's switching transistor. The switching transistor is wired in series with the coil primary circuit; it switches the circuit off when it gets the demodulator signal.

From this point on, the BID ignition system works in the same manner as a conventional ignition system.

The ignition timing is adjusted in the same manner as for a conventional system.

Tune-Up Procedures

SPARK PLUGS

Spark plugs ignite the air and fuel mixture in the cylinder as the piston reaches the top of the compression stroke. The controlled explosion that results forces the piston down, turning the crankshaft and the rest of the drive train.

The average life of a spark plug is 12,-000 miles. This is, however, dependent on a number of factors: the mechanical condition of the engine; the type of fuel; driving conditions; and the driver.

When you remove the spark plugs, check their condition. They are a good indicator of the condition of the engine. It is a good idea to remove the spark plugs at regular intervals, such as every 3,000 or 4,000 miles, just so you can keep an eye on the mechanical state of your engine.

A small deposit of light tan or gray material on a spark plug that has been used for any period of time is to be considered normal. Any other color, or abnormal amounts of deposit, indicate that there is something amiss in the engine.

The gap between the center electrode and the side or ground electrode can be expected to increase not more than 0.001 in. every 1,000 miles under normal conditions.

When a spark plug is functioning normally or, more accurately, when the plug is installed in an engine that is functioning properly, the plugs can be taken out, cleaned, regapped, and reinstalled in the engine without doing the engine any harm.

When, and if, a plug fouls and begins to misfire, you will have to investigate, correct the cause of the fouling, and either clean or replace the plug.

There are several reasons why a spark plug will foul and you can learn which reason by just looking at the plug. A few of the most common reasons for plug fouling, and a description of the fouled plug's appearance, is listed in the "Troubleshooting" section, which also offers solutions to the problems.

DISTRIBUTOR WIRING SEQUENCES AND FIRING ORDERS

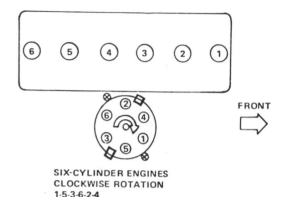

SIX-CYLINDER ENGINES
CLOCKWISE ROTATION
1-5-3-6-2-4

American Motors Sixes—circles indicate the position of the distributor cap latches on 1972–74 models; squares indicate the latches on 1975–76 models.

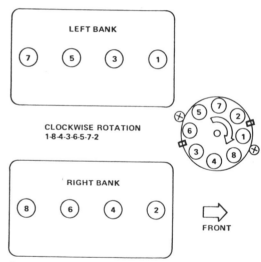

American Motors 304 V8—circles indicate the position of the distributor cap latches on 1972–74 models; squares indicate the latches on 1975–76 models.

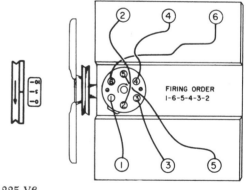

225-V6

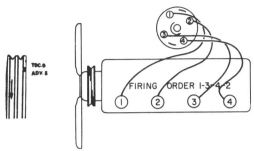

F-head 4 cylinder engine

Firing positions for the F-head 4 cylinder engine

Removal

1. Number the wires so you won't cross them when you replace them.

2. Remove the wire from the end of the spark plug by grasping the wire by the rubber boot. If the boot sticks to the plug, remove it by twisting and pulling at the same time. Do not pull the wire itself or you will most certainly damage the delicate carbon core.

3. Use a $\frac{13}{16}$ in. spark plug socket to loosen all of the plugs about two turns.

4. If compressed air is available, blow off the area around the spark plug holes. Otherwise, use a rag or a brush to clean the area. Be careful not to allow any foreign material to drop into the spark plug holes.

5. Remove the plugs by unscrewing them the rest of the way from the engine.

INSPECTION

Check the plugs for deposits and wear. If they are not going to be replaced, clean the plugs thoroughly. Remember that any kind of deposit will decrease the efficiency of the plug. Plugs can be cleaned on a

Measuring spark plug gap

spark plug cleaning machine, which can sometimes be found in service stations, or you can do an acceptable job of cleaning with a stiff brush.

Check spark plug gap before installation. The ground electrode must be parallel to the center electrode and the specified size wire gauge should pass through the gap with a slight drag. If the electrodes are worn, it is possible to file them level.

Installation

1. Insert the plugs in the spark plug hole and tighten them hand-tight. Take care not to cross-thread them.

2. Tighten the plugs to the torque figure specified in the "Tune-Up" section at the end of this chapter.

3. Install the spark plug wires on their plugs. Make sure that each wire is firmly connected to each plug.

BREAKER POINTS AND
CONDENSER

The points and condenser function as a circuit breaker for the primary circuit of the ignition system. The ignition coil must boost the 12V of electrical pressure supplied by the battery to as much as 25,000V in order to fire the plugs. To do this, the coil depends on the points and the condenser for assistance.

The coil has both primary and second-

Tune-Up Specifications

Year	Model	SPARK PLUGS Type	Gap (in.)	DISTRIBUTOR Point Dwell (deg)*	Point Gap (in.)	Ignition Timing (deg)▲	Cranking Comp. Pressure psi●	VALVES Tappet Hot Clearance (in.) Intake	Exhaust	Intake Opens (deg)	Fuel Pump Pressure psi	Idle Speed rpm
1953–71	4 Cyl—134 cu in., F Head	Champ J8	0.030	40	0.020	5B	90–110	0.018 Cold	0.016 Cold	9B	3	600
1965–71	6 Cyl—225 cu in.	AC-44S	0.035	30	0.016	5B	165	Zero	Zero	24B	5	550
1972–76	6 Cyl—232 cu in.	Champ N12Y	0.035	32	0.016	5B①	145	Zero	Zero	12½B	4–5	700②
1972–76	6 Cyl—258 cu in.	Champ N12Y	0.035	32	0.016	3B①	145	Zero	Zero	12½B	4–5	700④
1972–76	V8—304 cu in.	Champ N12Y	0.035	32③	0.016	5B①⑤	185	Zero	Zero	14¾B	5–6½	700–800

* Breakerless Inductive (BID) ignition system 1975–76; no points
▲ With vacuum advance disconnected.
● Readings must be within 10 lbs of all other cylinders.
B Before top dead center.

① At 550 rpm 1971–73, 700 rpm 1974–76
② 650–700 rpm in 1972, 550–650 rpm in 1974
③ 30 deg in 1974
④ 550–650 rpm 1974–75, 500–700 rpm TCS disconnected manual trans 1976, 450–650 rpm in Drive auto trans 49 states 1976, 600–800 rpm in Drive auto trans California 1976
⑤ 10°B with auto trans 1976

ary circuits. When the ignition is turned on, the battery supplies voltage to the coil which passes the voltage on to the points. The points are connected to ground, completing the primary circuit.

As the cam in the distributor turns, the points open and the primary circuit collapses. The magnetic force in the primary circuit of the coil cuts through the secondary circuit, increasing the voltage to a level sufficient to fire the spark plugs. When the points open, the electrical charge in the primary circuit jumps the gap created between the two open contacts of the points. If this electrical charge were not transferred elsewhere, the material on the contacts of the points would melt and the gap between the points would start to change. If this gap is not maintained, the points will not break the primary circuit. If the primary circuit is not broken, the secondary circuit will not fire the spark plugs.

Condenser

The function of the condenser is to absorb excessive voltage from the points when they open and thus prevent the points from becoming pitted or burned.

It is interesting to note that the above cycle must be completed by the ignition system every time a spark plug fires. On a four-cylinder engine, such as the F head, two of the plugs must fire each time the crankshaft turns once. So if the engine is turning at an idle speed of 600 rpm, the points are opening and closing 1,200 times a minute. Just think what they are doing at 65 mph.

There are two ways to check the breaker point gap; it can be done with a feeler gauge or a dwell meter. Either way you set the points, you are basically adjusting the amount of time that the points remain closed or open. The time is measured in degrees of distributor rotation. When you measure the gap between the breaker points with a feeler gauge, you are setting the maximum amount the points will open when the rubbing block on the points is on a high point of the distributor cam. When you adjust the points with a dwell meter, you are adjusting the number of degrees that the points will remain closed before they start to open as a high point of the distributor cam approaches the rubbing block.

When you replace a set of points, always replace the condenser at the same time.

When you change the point gap or the dwell, you will also have changed the ignition timing. So, if the point gap or dwell is changed, the ignition timing must be adjusted.

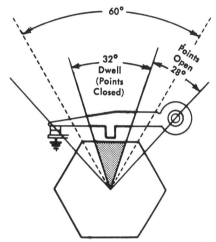

Diagram of point dwell. These angles are for the 232 cu in. and 258 cu in. sixes

INSPECTION OF THE POINTS

1. Disconnect the high-tension wire from the top of the distributor and the coil, and unsnap the distributor retaining caps.

2. Remove the distributor cap by prying off the spring clips on the F-head, or depressing and turning the hold-down screws on the side of the cap on all other engines.

3. Remove the rotor from the distributor shaft by pulling it straight up. On the 304 cu in. V8 and 225 cu in. V6, the rotor is attached to the distributor shaft by screws. Remove the screws to remove the rotor. Examine the condition of the rotor. If it is cracked or the metal tip is excessively worn or burned, it should be replaced.

4. Pry open the contacts of the points

Replace Contact Set
When Transfer Has
Exceeded .020"

Contact point material transfer

with a screwdriver and check the condition of the contacts. If they are excessively worn, burned, or pitted, they should be replaced.

5. If the points are in good condition, adjust them, and replace the rotor and the distributor cap. If the points need to be replaced, follow the replacement procedure below.

Replacement of the Breaker Points and Condenser

1. Remove the coil high-tension wire from the top of the distributor cap. Remove the distributor cap from the distributor and place it out of the way. Remove the rotor from the distributor shaft.

2. Remove the dust cover that is in the top of the distributor on some models, covering the points. It is pressed in hand-tight.

3. Loosen the screw that holds the condenser lead to the body of the breaker points. Remove the condenser from the points.

4. Remove the screw that holds and grounds the condenser to the distributor body. Remove the condenser from the distributor and discard it.

5. Remove the points assembly attaching screws and adjustment lockscrews. A screwdriver with a holding mechanism

will come in handy here so you don't drop a screw into the distributor and have to remove the entire distributor just to retrieve it.

6. Remove the points by lifting them straight up off the locating dowel on the plate. Wipe off the cam and apply new cam lubricant. Discard the old set of points.

7. Slip the new set of points onto the locating dowel and install the screws that

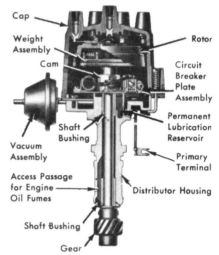

Cutaway view of a distributor for the American Motors 304 cu in. V8

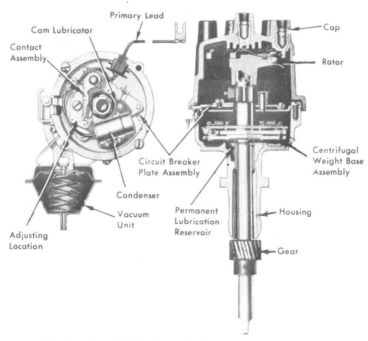

Cutaway view of a distributor for the American Motors sixes

The distributor for the F-head 4 cylinder engine

1. Condenser
2. Lubricating wick
3. Breaker arm pivot
4. Distributor camshaft
5. Contacts of the point assembly
6. Oiler
7. Adjustment lockscrew
8. Adjusting screw

hold the assembly onto the plate. Do not tighten them all the way.

8. Attach the new condenser to the plate with the ground screw.

9. Attach the condenser lead to the points at the proper place. On American Motors engines, and the V6, the primary wire from the coil must now be attached to the points also. Make sure that the connectors for these two wires do not touch the body of the distributor; they will short out the primary circuit of the ignition if they do.

10. Apply a small amount of cam lubricant to the shaft where the rubbing block of the points touches.

Adjustment of the Breaker Points with a Feeler Gauge

1. If the contact points of the assembly are not parallel, bend the stationary contact so they make contact across the entire surface of the contacts. Bend only the bracket part of the point assembly—not the contact surface.

2. Turn the engine until the rubbing block of the points is on one of the high points of the distributor cam. You can do this by either turning the ignition switch to the start position and releasing it quickly or by using a wrench on the bolt that holds the crankshaft pulley to the crankshaft.

3. Place the correct size feeler gauge between the contacts. Make sure it is parallel with the contact surfaces.

4. With your free hand, insert a screwdriver into the notch provided for adjustment or into the eccentric adjusting screw,

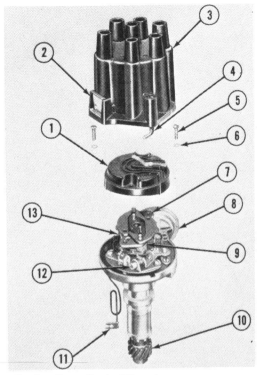

The distributor for the V6 engine

1. Rotor
2. Point dwell adjustment window
3. Distributor cap
4. Cap latch
5. Rotor mounting screw
6. Lockwasher
7. Advance mechanism
8. Vacuum advance unit
9. Distributor camshaft
10. Drive gear
11. Primary lead
12. Points assembly
13. Condenser

and then twist the screwdriver to either increase or decrease the gap to the proper setting. This procedure is for the F-head only. All others have to be adjusted at the adjusting screw with an allen wrench.

5. Tighten the adjustment lockscrew and recheck the contact gap to make sure that it didn't change when the lockscrew was tightened.

6. Replace the rotor, distributor cap, and the high-tension wire that connects the top of the distributor and the coil. Make sure that the rotor is firmly seated all the way onto the distributor shaft and that the tab of the rotor is aligned with the notch in the shaft. Align the tab in the base of the distributor cap with the notch in the distributor body. Make sure that the cap is firmly seated on the distributor and that the retainer springs are in place. Make sure that the end of the high-tension wire is firmly placed in the top of the distributor and the coil.

NOTE: *On American Motors engines and the V6, the distributor cap retaining clips are replaced by spring-loaded screws with L-shaped tips that clamp under the distributor housing when the screw is depressed and turned.*

Adjustment of the Breaker Points with a Dwell Meter

1. Adjust the points with a feeler gauge as described above.

2. Connect the dwell meter to the ignition circuit as according to the manufacturer's instructions. One lead of the meter is to be connected to a ground and the other lead is to be connected to the distributor post on the coil. An adapter is usually provided for this purpose.

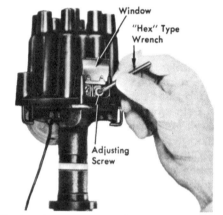

Adjusting the point gap or dwell of the 304 cu in. V8

There is a little window in the side of the distributor that can be raised so that the points can be adjusted with an allen wrench.

Adjusting the point gap or dwell of the V6 engine

3. If the dwell meter has a set line on it, adjust the meter to zero the indicator.

4. Start the engine.

NOTE: *Be careful when working on any vehicle while the engine is running. Make sure that the transmission is in neutral and that the parking brake is on. Keep hands, clothing, tools, and the wires of the test instruments clear of the rotating fan blades.*

5. Observe the reading on the dwell meter. If the meter does not have a scale for four-cylinder engines, multiply the eight-cylinder reading by two. If the reading is within the specified range, turn off the engine and remove the dwell meter.

6. If the reading is above the specified range, the breaker point gap is too small. If the reading is below the specified range, the gap is too large. In either case, the engine must be stopped and the gap adjusted in the manner previously covered.

NOTE: *On the V6 engine and American Motors engines, it is possible to adjust the dwell while the engine is running.* Start the engine and check the reading on the dwell meter. When the correct reading is obtained, disconnect the dwell meter.

7. Check the adjustment of the ignition timing.

IGNITION TIMING

Ignition timing is the measurement, in degrees of crankshaft rotation, of the point at which the spark plugs fire in each of the cylinders. It is measured in degrees before or after Top Dead Center (TDC) of the compression stroke. Ignition timing is controlled by turning the distributor in the engine.

Ideally, the air-fuel mixture in the cylinder will be ignited by the spark plug just as the piston passes TDC of the compression stroke. If this happens, the piston will be beginning the power stroke just as the compressed and ignited air-fuel mixture starts to expand. The expansion of the air-fuel mixture then forces the piston down on the power stroke and turns the crankshaft.

Because it takes a fraction of a second for the spark plug to ignite the gases in the cylinder, the spark plug must fire a little before the piston reaches TDC. Otherwise, the mixture will not be completely ignited as the piston passes TDC and the full benefit of the explosion will not be used by the engine. The timing measurement is given in degrees of crankshaft rotation before the piston reaches TDC (BTDC). If the setting for the ignition timing is 5° BTDC, the spark plug must fire 5° before that piston reaches TDC. This only holds true, however, when the engine is at idle speed.

As the engine speed increases, the pistons go faster. The spark plugs have to ignite the fuel even sooner if it is to be completely ignited when the piston reaches TDC. To do this, the distributor has a means to advance the timing of the spark as the engine speed increases. In some Jeeps that were made before 1972, the advancing of the spark in the distributor was accomplished by weights alone. Others have a vacuum diaphragm to assist the weights. It is necessary to disconnect the vacuum line to the distributor when the engine is being timed.

If the ignition is set too far advanced (BTDC), the ignition and expansion of the fuel in the cylinder will occur too soon and tend to force the piston down while it is still traveling up. This causes engine ping. If the engine is too far retarded after TDC (ATDC), the piston will have already passed TDC and started on its way down when the fuel is ignited. This will cause the piston to be forced down for only a portion of its travel. This will result in poor engine performance and lack of power.

The timing is best checked with a timing light. This device is connected in series with the no. 1 spark plug. The current that fires the spark plug also causes the light to flash.

There is a notch on the front of the crankshaft pulley on F head engines.

There are also marks to indicate TDC and 5° BTDC on the timing gear cover that can assist you in setting your timing. When the engine is running, the timing light is aimed at the crankshaft pulley, and the marks on the timing gear cover the flashes of the timing light so you can read the timing setting. On American Motors engines, the timing marks on the pulley are the same as on the F head engine, but the marks on the engine block are different. There are scales divided into degrees

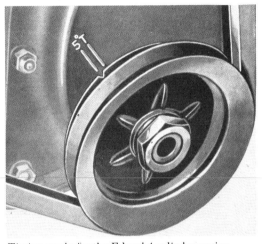

Timing marks for the F-head 4 cylinder engine

Notch

Timing marks for the American Motors Sixes—1972–74

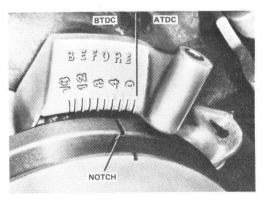

Timing marks on 1975–76 American Motors Sixes

Timing marks for the American Motors 304 cu in. V8

Timing marks for the V6 engine

to mark timing differences between different engines which may, in fact, share the same block.

Ignition Timing Adjustment

1. Locate the timing marks on the pulley and on the front of the engine.

2. Clean off the timing marks so you can see them.

3. Mark the timing marks with a piece of chalk or white paint. Mark the one on the engine that will indicate correct timing when it is aligned with the mark on the pulley.

4. Attach a tachometer to the engine.

5. Attach a timing light according to the manufacturer's instructions. If the timing light has three wires, one (usually green or blue) is attached to the no. 1 spark plug with an adapter. The other two are connected to the battery. The red one goes to the positive side of the battery and the black one is connected to the negative terminal of the battery.

6. Disconnect the vacuum line to the distributor at the distributor on Jeeps that were made prior to 1972. Screw a plug into the end of the hose where the vacuum line was disconnected from the distributor. You can also disconnect only the distributor end of the hose and plug it.

7. Check to make sure that all of the wires clear the fan and then start the engine.

8. Adjust the idle to the correct setting.

9. Aim the timing light at the timing

marks. If the marks that you put on the pulley and the engine are aligned, the timing is correct. Turn off the engine and remove the tachometer and the timing light. If the marks are not in alignment, proceed to the following steps.

10. Turn off the engine.

11. Loosen the distributor lockbolt just enough so that the distributor can be turned with a little effort.

12. Start the engine. Keep the cords of the timing light clear of the fan.

13. With the timing light aimed at the pulley and the marks on the engine, turn the distributor in the direction of rotor rotation to retard the spark, and in the opposite direction of rotor rotation to advance the spark. Line up the marks on the pulley and the engine.

14. When the marks are aligned, tighten the distributor lockbolt and recheck the timing with the timing light to make sure that the distributor did not move when you tightened the distributor lockbolt.

15. Turn off the engine and remove the timing light.

TROUBLESHOOTING
BID IGNITION SYSTEM

1. Check all of the BID ignition system electrical connections.

2. Disconnect the coil-to-distributor high tension lead at the distributor.

3. Hold the end of the lead $\frac{1}{2}$ in. away from a ground. Crank the engine. If there is a spark, the trouble is not in the ignition system.

4. If there was no spark in Step 3, connect a test light with a No. 57 bulb between the positive coil terminal $(+)$ and a good ground. Have an assistant turn the ignition switch to "ON" and "START" (Do not start the engine). The bulb should light in both positions; if it doesn't, the fault lies in the battery-to-coil circuit. Check the ignition switch and related wiring.

5. If the test light lit in Step 4, disconnect the coil-to-distributor leads at the connector and connect the test light between the positive $(+)$ and negative $(-)$ coil terminals.

6. Turn the ignition switch On. If the test light doesn't come on, check the control unit's ground lead. If the ground lead is in good condition, replace the control unit.

7. If the bulb lights in Step 6, leave the test light in place and short the terminals on the coil-to-distributor connector together with a jumper lead, (connector separated) at the coil side of the connector. If the light stays on, replace the control unit.

8. If the test light goes out, remove it. Check for a spark, as in Steps 2 and 3, each time that the coil-to-distributor connector terminals are shorted together with the jumper lead. If there is a spark, replace the control unit; if there is no spark, replace the coil.

VALVE ADJUSTMENT

Valve adjustment determines how far the valves enter into the cylinder and how long they stay open and closed.

If the valve clearance is too large, part of the lift of the camshaft will be used in removing the excessive clearance. The valve will, consequently, not be opening as far as it should. This condition has two effects; the valve train components will emit a tapping sound as they take up the excessive clearance and the engine will perform poorly.

If the valve clearance is too small, the intake valves and the exhaust valves will open too far and they will not fully seat on the cylinder head when they close. When a valve seats itself on the cylinder head, it does two things; it seals the combustion chamber so that none of the gases in the cylinder escape and it cools itself by transferring some of the heat it absorbs from the combustion in the cylinder to the cylinder head and to the engine's cooling system. If the valve clearance is too small, the engine will run poorly because of the gases escaping from the combustion chamber. The valves will also become overheated and will warp, since they cannot transfer heat unless they are touching the valve seat in the cylinder head.

NOTE: *While all valve adjustments must be made as accurately as possible, it is better to have the valve adjustment slightly loose than slightly tight, as burned valves may result from overly tight adjustments.*

The only Jeep engine on which the valves can be adjusted is the F-head four-cylinder. The V6, 232 cu in. six, 258 cu in. six, and the 304 cu in. V8 all have nonadjustable rocker arms.

F-HEAD ENGINE

NOTE: *The engine must be cold when the valves are adjusted on the F-head engine.*

1. Start the engine and let it run until it has reached operating temperature. Remove the valve cover and check all the cylinder head bolts to make sure they are tightened to the correct torque specifications.

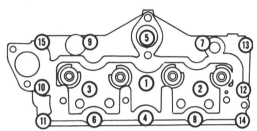

The cylinder head tightening sequence for the F-head engine

2. While the engine is cooling, remove the side valve spring cover. Be careful not to burn yourself on the exhaust pipe; it may still be hot.

3. After the engine has cooled to ambient temperature, turn the engine until the lifter for the front intake valve is down as far as it will go. The lifter should be resting on the center of the heel (back) of the cam lobe for that valve. You can observe the position of the lifter by looking through the side valve spring cover opening. Put the correct size feeler gauge between the rocker arm and the valve stem for that particular intake valve. There should be a very slight drag on the feeler gauge when it is pulled through the gap. If there is a slight drag, you can assume that the valves are at the correct setting. If the feeler gauge cannot pass between the rocker arm and the valve stem, the gap between them is too small and must be increased. If the gauge can be passed through the gap without any drag, the gap is too large and must be decreased. Loosen the locknut on the top of the rocker arm (pushrod side) by turning it counterclockwise.

Turn the adjusting screw clockwise to lessen the gap and counterclockwise to increase the gap. When the gap is correct, turn the locknut clockwise to lock the adjusting screw. Follow this procedure for all of the intake valves, making sure that the

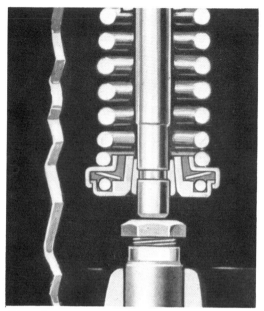

The adjustment screw for the exhaust valves on the F-head engine

lifter is all the way down for each adjustment.

4. Turn the engine so that the first exhaust valve is completely closed and the lifter that operates that particular valve is all of the way down and on the heel of the cam lobe that operates it.

5. Insert the correct size feeler gauge between the valve stem of the exhaust valve and the adjusting screw. This is

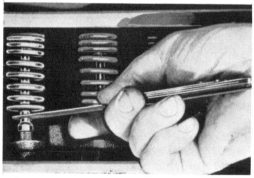

Adjusting the exhaust valves on the F-head engine

done through the side of the engine in the space that is exposed when the side valve spring cover is removed. If there is a slight drag on the feeler gauge, you can assume that the gap is correct. If there is too much drag or not enough, turn the adjusting screw clockwise to increase the gap and counterclockwise to decrease the gap.

6. When all of the valves have been adjusted to the proper clearance, replace the valve covers. If the gaskets are in good shape then they can be used again. If they are cracked, torn, or squashed out of shape, they must be replaced because they will surely leak.

CARBURETOR

This section contains only tune-up adjustment procedures for carburetors. Descriptions, adjustments, and overhaul procedures for carburetors can be found in the "Fuel System" section of this book.

When the engine in your Jeep is running, the air-fuel mixture from the carburetor is being drawn into the engine by a partial vacuum which is created by the movement of the pistons downward on the intake stroke. The amount of air-fuel mixture that enters into the engine is controlled by the throttle plate(s) in the bottom of the carburetor. When the engine is not running the throttle plate(s) is closed, completely blocking off the bottom of the carburetor from the inside of the engine. The throttle plates are connected by the throttle linkage to the accelerator pedal in the passenger compartment of the Jeep. When you depress the pedal, you open the throttle plates in the carburetor to admit more air-fuel mixture to the engine.

When the engine is not running, the throttle plates are closed. When the engine is idling, it is necessary to have the throttle plates open slightly. To prevent having to hold your foot on the pedal when the engine is idling, an idle speed adjusting screw was added to the carburetor linkage.

The idle adjusting screw contacts a lever (throttle lever) on the outside of the carburetor. When the screw is turned, it either opens or closes the throttle plates of the carburetor, raising or lowering the idle speed of the engine. This screw is called the curb idle adjusting screw.

Idle Speed Adjustment—Pre-1972

1. Start the engine and run it until it reaches operating temperature.

2. If it hasn't already been done, check and adjust the ignition timing. After you have set the timing, turn off the engine.

3. Attach a tachometer to the engine.

4. Remove the air cleaner, except on American Motors engines. Leave the air

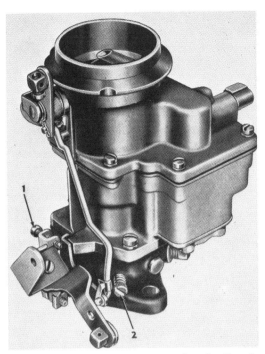

Idle mixture adjustment screw and curb idle adjustment screw on the Model YF 938 S Carter carburetor which was used on the early CJ-3B. Variations of this carburetor were used on all of the F-head engines in the CJ-3B, CJ-5, and CJ-6

1. Curb idle speed adjusting screw
2. Idle mixture adjusting screw

cleaner on these models. Turn on the headlights to high beam.

5. Start the engine and check the idle speed on the tachometer. If the reading on the tachometer is correct, turn off the en-

The Rochester Model 2G carburetor used on the V6 engine

1. Fuel inlet
2. Choke
3. Choke cable bracket
4. Curb idle speed adjusting screw
5. Idle mixture adjusting screws

gine and remove the tachometer. If it is not correct, proceed to the following steps.

6. Turn the idle adjusting screw at the bottom of the carburetor with a screwdriver—clockwise to increase the idle speed and counterclockwise to decrease it.

Mixture Adjustment—Pre-1972

The idle mixture screw is located at the very bottom of the carburetor.

1. Turn the screw until it is all the way in. Do not force the screw in any further because it is very easy to damage the needle valve and its seat by screwing the adjusting screw in too tightly.

2. Turn the screw out $3/4$–$1 3/4$ turns. This should be the normal adjustment setting. For a richer mixture, turn the screw in. The ideal setting for the mixture adjustment screw results in the maximum engine rpm.

The Model YF carburetor that is used on the American Motors sixes

Idle Speed and Mixture Adjustment—1972

Use the "lean best idle" procedure to adjust the idle speed and mixture on 1972 American Motors engines.

1. Start engine and allow it to reach normal operating temperature. If engine is equipped with air pump, disconnect bypass valve air inlet hose.

2. Adjust the idle speed to specified rpm by turning either the idle adjustment screw or throttle stop solenoid.

NOTE: *If idle adjustment procedure is not completed within 3 minutes, run engine at 2,000 rpm for 1 minute to stabilize engine temperature.*

3. Turn mixture screw(s) counterclockwise (richer) until loss of rpm is noticed, the turn mixture screw(s) clockwise (leaner), past original starting point, counting the number of turns of the screw(s).

4. Continue turning mixture screw(s) clockwise until engine loses rpm due to an overly lean mixture.

5. Return the screw(s) to the midpoint between the two extremes and the highest rpm reading.

6. Turn the mixture adjusting screw(s) clockwise (leaner) to the point where engine rpm just begins to drop, then counterclockwise the minimum amount to obtain the previously established highest rpm. This is the "lean best idle."

NOTE: *This procedure should first be attempted with limiter caps installed on the mixture adjustment screw(s). If a satisfactory idle cannot be obtained with the caps in place, then carefully remove them by threading a sheet metal screw into the center of the cap and make the adjustment as outlined above. Once the "lean best idle" has been established, install service limiter caps with the tabs positioned against the full rich stops.*

Idle Speed and Mixture Adjustment—1973–76

The procedure for adjusting the idle speed and mixture on 1973–76 Jeep CJs is called the lean drop procedure and is made with the engine operating at normal operating temperature and the air cleaner in place as follows:

1. Turn the mixture screws to the full rich position with the tabs on limiters against stops. Note position of screw head slot inside limiter cap slots.

2. Remove idle limiter caps.

3. Remove limiter caps by threading a sheet metal screw in center of cap and turning clockwise. Discard limiter caps.

4. Reset adjustment screws to same position noted before limiter caps were removed.

5. Start engine and allow it to reach normal operating temperature.

6. Adjust idle speed to 30 rpm above the specified rpm. See "Tune-Up Specifications" chart.

a. On 6 cylinder engines with throttle stop solenoid, turn nut on solenoid plunger in or out to obtain specified rpm. This is done with solenoid wire connected;

b. On V8 engines with throttle stop solenoid, turn hex screw on throttle stop solenoid carriage to obtain specified rpm. This is done with solenoid wire connected;

c. Tighten solenoid locknut, if so equipped;

d. Disconnect solenoid wire and adjust curb idle speed screw to obtain idle speed of 500 rpm;

e. Reconnect solenoid wire.

7. Starting from full rich stop position, as was determined before limiter caps were removed, turn mixture adjusting screws clockwise (leaner) until a loss of engine speed is noticed.

8. Turn screws counterclockwise (richer) until the highest rpm reading is obtained at lean best idle setting. The lean best idle setting is on the lean side of the highest rpm setting without changing rpm.

9. If the idle speed changed more than 30 rpm during the mixture adjustment procedure, reset the idle speed to 30 rpm above the specified rpm with idle speed adjusting screw or the throttle stop solenoid and repeat the mixture adjustment.

10. The final adjustment is to turn the mixture adjusting screws clockwise until engine rpm drops as follows:

1973–74	
6 Cylinder	35 rpm
V8	40 rpm
1975	
6 Cylinder	35 rpm
6 Cylinder with EGR	50 rpm
V8	40 rpm
1976	
6 Cylinder Automatic	25 rpm
6 Cylinder Manual	50 rpm
V8 Automatic	20 rpm
V8 Manual	100 rpm

11. Install new limiter caps over mixture adjusting screws with tabs positioned against full rich stops. Be careful not to disturb idle mixture setting while installing caps.

Engine Tune-Up

Engine tune-up is a procedure performed to restore engine performance, deteriorated due to normal wear and loss of adjustment. The three major areas considered in a routine tune-up are compression, ignition, and carburetion, although valve adjustment may be included.

A tune-up is performed in three steps: *analysis*, in which it is determined whether normal wear is responsible for performance loss, and which parts require replacement or service; *parts replacement or service*; and *adjustment*, in which engine adjustments are returned to original specifications. Since the advent of emission control equipment, precision adjustment has become increasingly critical, in order to maintain pollutant emission levels.

Analysis

The procedures below are used to indicate where adjustments, parts service or replacement are necessary within the realm of a normal tune-up. If, following these tests, all systems appear to be functioning properly, proceed to the Troubleshooting Section for further diagnosis.

—Remove all spark plugs, noting the cylinder in which they were installed. Remove the air cleaner, and position the throttle and choke in the full open position. Disconnect the coil high tension lead from the coil and the distributor cap. Insert a compression gauge into the spark plug port of each cylinder, in succession, and crank the engine with

Maxi. Press. Lbs. Sq. In.	Min. Press. Lbs. Sq. In.	Max. Press. Lbs. Sq. In.	Min. Press. Lbs. Sq. In.
134	101	188	141
136	102	190	142
138	104	192	144
140	105	194	145
142	107	196	147
146	110	198	148
148	111	200	150
150	113	202	151
152	114	204	153
154	115	206	154
156	117	208	156
158	118	210	157
160	120	212	158
162	121	214	160
164	123	216	162
166	124	218	163
168	126	220	165
170	127	222	166
172	129	224	168
174	131	226	169
176	132	228	171
178	133	230	172
180	135	232	174
182	136	234	175
184	138	236	177
186	140	238	178

Compression pressure limits
© Buick Div. G.M. Corp.)

the starter to obtain the highest possible reading. Record the readings, and compare the highest to the lowest on the compression pressure limit chart. If the difference exceeds the limits on the chart, or if all readings are excessively low, proceed to a wet compression check (see Troubleshooting Section).

—Evaluate the spark plugs according to the spark plug chart in the Troubleshooting Section, and proceed as indicated in the chart.

—Remove the distributor cap, and inspect it inside and out for cracks and/or carbon tracks, and inside for excessive wear or burning of the rotor contacts. If any of these faults are evident, the cap must be replaced.

—Check the breaker points for burning, pitting or wear, and the contact heel resting on the distributor cam for excessive wear. If defects are noted, replace the entire breaker point set.

—Remove and inspect the rotor. If the contacts are burned or worn, or if the rotor is excessively loose on the distributor shaft (where applicable), the rotor must be replaced.

—Inspect the spark plug leads and the coil high tension lead for cracks or brittleness. If any of the wires appear defective, the entire set should be replaced.

—Check the air filter to ensure that it is functioning properly.

Parts Replacement and Service

The determination of whether to replace or service parts is at the mechanic's discretion; however, it is suggested that any parts in questionable condition be replaced rather than reused.

—Clean and regap, or replace, the spark plugs as needed. Lightly coat the threads with engine oil and install the plugs. CAUTION: *Do not over-torque taper-seat spark plugs, or plugs being installed in aluminum cylinder heads.*

—If the distributor cap is to be reused, clean the inside with a dry rag, and remove corrosion from the rotor contact points with fine emery cloth. Remove the spark plug wires one by one, and clean the wire ends and the inside of the towers. If the boots are loose, they should be replaced.

If the cap is to be replaced, transfer the wires one by one, cleaning the wire ends and replacing the boots if necessary.

—If the original points are to remain in service, clean them lightly with emery cloth, lubricate the contact heel with grease specifically designed for this purpose. Rotate the crankshaft until the heel rests on a high point of the distributor cam, and adjust the point gap to specifications.

When replacing the points, remove the original points and condenser, and wipe out the inside of the distributor housing with a clean, dry rag. Lightly lubricate the contact heel and pivot point, and install the points and condenser. Rotate the crankshaft until the heel rests on a high point of the distributor cam, and adjust the point gap to specifications. NOTE: *Always replace the condenser when changing the points.*

—If the rotor is to be reused, clean the contacts with solvent. Do not alter the spring tension of the rotor center contact. Install the rotor and the distributor cap.

—Replace the coil high tension lead and/or the spark plug leads as necessary.

—Clean the carburetor using a spray solvent (e.g., Gumout Spray). Remove the varnish from the throttle bores, and clean the linkage. Disconnect and plug the fuel line, and run the engine until it runs out of fuel. Partially fill the float chamber with solvent, and reconnect the fuel line. In extreme cases, the jets can be pressure flushed by inserting a rubber plug into the float vent, running the spray nozzle through it, and spraying the solvent until it squirts out of the venturi fuel dump.

—Clean and tighten all wiring connections in the primary electrical circuit.

Additional Services

The following services *should* be performed in conjunction with a routine tune-up to ensure efficient performance.

—Inspect the battery and fill to the proper level with distilled water. Remove the cable clamps, clean clamps and posts thoroughly, coat the posts lightly with petroleum jelly, reinstall and tighten.

—Inspect all belts, replace and/or adjust as necessary.

—Test the PCV valve (if so equipped), and clean or replace as indicated. Clean all crankcase ventilation hoses, or replace if cracked or hardened.

—Adjust the valves (if necessary) to manufacturer's specifications.

Adjustments

—Connect a dwell-tachometer between the distributor primary lead and ground. Remove the distributor cap and rotor (unless equipped with Delco externally adjustable distributor). With the ignition off, crank the engine with a remote starter switch and measure the point dwell angle. Adjust the dwell angle to specifications. NOTE: *Increasing the gap decreases the dwell angle and* *vice-versa.* Install the rotor and distributor cap.

—Connect a timing light according to the manufacturer's specifications. Identify the proper timing marks with chalk or paint. NOTE: *Luminescent (day-glo) paint is excellent for this purpose.* Start the engine, and run it until it reaches operating temperature. Disconnect and plug any distributor vacuum lines, and adjust idle to the speed required to adjust timing, according to specifications. Loosen the distributor clamp and adjust timing to specifications by rotating the distributor in the engine. NOTE: *To advance timing, rotate distributor opposite normal direction of rotor rotation, and vice-versa.*

—Synchronize the throttles and mixture of multiple carburetors (if so equipped) according to procedures given in the individual car sections.

—Adjust the idle speed, mixture, and idle quality, as specified in the car sections. Final idle adjustments should be made with the air cleaner installed. CAUTION: *Due to strict emission control requirements on 1969 and later models, special test equipment (CO meter, SUN Tester) may be necessary to properly adjust idle mixture to specifications.*

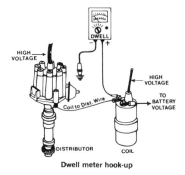

Dwell meter hook-up

Trouble-shooting

The following section is designed to aid in the rapid diagnosis of engine problems. The systematic format is used to diagnose problems ranging from engine starting difficulties to the need for engine overhaul. It is assumed that the user is equipped with basic hand tools and test equipment (tach-dwell meter, timing light, voltmeter, and ohmmeter).

Troubleshooting is divided into two sections. The first, *General Diagnosis*, is used to locate the problem area. In the second, *Specific Diagnosis*, the problem is systematically evaluated.

General Diagnosis

PROBLEM: *Symptom*	Begin diagnosis at Section Two, Number ———
Engine won't start:	
Starter doesn't turn	1.1, 2.1
Starter turns, engine doesn't	2.1
Starter turns engine very slowly	1.1, 2.4
Starter turns engine normally	3.1, 4.1
Starter turns engine very quickly	6.1
Engine fires intermittently	4.1
Engine fires consistently	5.1, 6.1
Engine runs poorly:	
Hard starting	3.1, 4.1, 5.1, 8.1
Rough idle	4.1, 5.1, 8.1
Stalling	3.1, 4.1, 5.1, 8.1
Engine dies at high speeds	4.1, 5.1
Hesitation (on acceleration from standing stop)	5.1, 8.1
Poor pickup	4.1, 5.1, 8.1
Lack of power	3.1, 4.1, 5.1, 8.1
Backfire through the carburetor	4.1, 8.1, 9.1
Backfire through the exhaust	4.1, 8.1, 9.1
Blue exhaust gases	6.1, 7.1
Black exhaust gases	5.1
Running on (after the ignition is shut off)	3.1, 8.1
Susceptible to moisture	4.1
Engine misfires under load	4.1, 7.1, 8.4, 9.1
Engine misfires at speed	4.1, 8.4
Engine misfires at idle	3.1, 4.1, 5.1, 7.1, 8.4

PROBLEM: *Symptom*	Probable Cause
Engine noises: ①	
Metallic grind while starting	Starter drive not engaging completely
Constant grind or rumble	*Starter drive not releasing, worn main bearings
Constant knock	Worn connecting rod bearings
Knock under load	Fuel octane too low, worn connecting rod bearings
Double knock	Loose piston pin
Metallic tap	*Collapsed or sticky valve lifter, excessive valve clearance, excessive end play in a rotating shaft
Scrape	*Fan belt contacting a stationary surface
Tick while starting	S.U. electric fuel pump (normal), starter brushes
Constant tick	*Generator brushes, shreaded fan belt
Squeal	*Improperly tensioned fan belt
Hiss or roar	*Steam escaping through a leak in the cooling system or the radiator overflow vent
Whistle	*Vacuum leak
Wheeze	Loose or cracked spark plug

①—It is extremely difficult to evaluate vehicle noises. While the above are general definitions of engine noises, those starred (*) should be considered as possibly originating elsewhere in the car. To aid diagnosis, the following list considers other potential sources of these sounds.

Metallic grind:
Throwout bearing; transmission gears, bearings, or synchronizers; differential bearings, gears; something metallic in contact with brake drum or disc.

Metallic tap:
U-joints; fan-to-radiator (or shroud) contact.

Scrape:
Brake shoe or pad dragging; tire to body contact; suspension contacting undercarriage or exhaust; something non-metallic contacting brake shoe or drum.

Tick:
Transmission gears; differential gears; lack of radio suppression; resonant vibration of body panels; windshield wiper motor or transmission; heater motor and blower.

Squeal:
Brake shoe or pad not fully releasing; tires (excessive wear, uneven wear, improper inflation); front or rear wheel alignment (most commonly due to improper toe-in).

Hiss or whistle:
Wind leaks (body or window); heater motor and blower fan.

Roar:
Wheel bearings; wind leaks (body and window).

Specific Diagnosis

This section is arranged so that following each test, instructions are given to proceed to another, until a problem is diagnosed.

INDEX

Group		Topic
1	*	Battery
2	*	Cranking system
3	*	Primary electrical system
4	*	Secondary electrical system
5	*	Fuel system
6	*	Engine compression
7	**	Engine vacuum
8	**	Secondary electrical system
9	**	Valve train
10	**	Exhaust system
11	**	Cooling system
12	**	Engine lubrication

*—The engine need not be running.
**—The engine must be running.

SAMPLE SECTION

Test and Procedure	Results and Indications	Proceed to
4.1—Check for spark: Hold each spark plug wire approximately ¼" from ground with gloves or a heavy, dry rag. Crank the engine and observe the spark.	→ If no spark is evident:	4.2
	→ If spark is good in some cases:	4.3
	→ If spark is good in all cases:	4.6

DIAGNOSIS

1.1—Inspect the battery visually for case condition (corrosion, cracks) and water level.	If case is cracked, replace battery:	1.4
	If the case is intact, remove corrosion with a solution of baking soda and water (CAUTION: *do not get the solution into the battery*), and fill with water:	1.2

1.2—Check the battery cable connections: Insert a screwdriver between the battery post and the cable clamp. Turn the headlights on high beam, and observe them as the screwdriver is gently twisted to ensure good metal to metal contact.

Testing battery cable connections using a screwdriver

If the lights brighten, remove and clean the clamp and post; coat the post with petroleum jelly, install and tighten the clamp: 1.4

If no improvement is noted: 1.3

1.3—Test the state of charge of the battery using an individual cell tester or hydrometer.

Spec. Grav. Reading	Charged Condition
1.260-1.280	Fully Charged
1.230-1.250	Three Quarter Charged
1.200-1.220	One Half Charged
1.170-1.190	One Quarter Charged
1.140-1.160	Just About Flat
1.110-1.130	All The Way Down

State of battery charge

Electrolyte temperature (°F)	Specific gravity correction
+ 120	+.016
+ 100	+.012
	+.008 } ADD to reading
+ 80	+.004
	no correction
+ 60	—.004
	—.008
+ 40	—.012
	—.016
+ 20	—.020
	—.024
0	—.028 } SUBTRACT from reading
	—.032
— 20	—.036
	—.040

The effect of temperature on the specific gravity of battery electrolyte

If indicated, charge the battery. NOTE: *If no obvious reason exists for the low state of charge (i.e., battery age, prolonged storage), the charging system should be tested:* 1.4

Test and Procedure	Results and Indications	Proceed to
1.4—Visually inspect battery cables for cracking, bad connection to ground, or bad connection to starter.	If necessary, tighten connections or replace the cables:	2.1

Tests in Group 2 are performed with coil high tension lead disconnected to prevent accidental starting.

Test and Procedure	Results and Indications	Proceed to
2.1—Test the starter motor and solenoid: Connect a jumper from the battery post of the solenoid (or relay) to the starter post of the solenoid (or relay).	If starter turns the engine normally:	2.2
	If the starter buzzes, or turns the engine very slowly:	2.4
	If no response, replace the solenoid (or relay).	3.1
	If the starter turns, but the engine doesn't, ensure that the flywheel ring gear is intact. If the gear is undamaged, replace the starter drive.	3.1
2.2—Determine whether ignition override switches are functioning properly (clutch start switch, neutral safety switch), by connecting a jumper across the switch(es), and turning the ignition switch to "start".	If starter operates, adjust or replace switch:	3.1
	If the starter doesn't operate:	2.3
2.3—Check the ignition switch "start" position: Connect a 12V test lamp between the starter post of the solenoid (or relay) and ground. Turn the ignition switch to the "start" position, and jiggle the key.	If the lamp doesn't light when the switch is turned, check the ignition switch for loose connections, cracked insulation, or broken wires. Repair or replace as necessary:	3.1
	If the lamp flickers when the key is jiggled, replace the ignition switch.	3.3

Checking the ignition switch "start" position

Test and Procedure	Results and Indications	Proceed to
2.4—Remove and bench test the starter, according to specifications in the car section.	If the starter does not meet specifications, repair or replace as needed:	3.1
	If the starter is operating properly:	2.5
2.5—Determine whether the engine can turn freely: Remove the spark plugs, and check for water in the cylinders. Check for water on the dipstick, or oil in the radiator. Attempt to turn the engine using an 18″ flex drive and socket on the crankshaft pulley nut or bolt.	If the engine will turn freely only with the spark plugs out, and hydrostatic lock (water in the cylinders) is ruled out, check valve timing:	9.2
	If engine will not turn freely, and it is known that the clutch and transmission are free, the engine must be disassembled for further evaluation:	Next Chapter

Tests and Procedures	*Results and Indications*	*Proceed to*
3.1—Check the ignition switch "on" position: Connect a jumper wire between the distributor side of the coil and ground, and a 12V test lamp between the switch side of the coil and ground. Remove the high tension lead from the coil. Turn the ignition switch on and jiggle the key.	If the lamp lights:	3.2
	If the lamp flickers when the key is jiggled, replace the ignition switch:	3.3
	If the lamp doesn't light, check for loose or open connections. If none are found, remove the ignition switch and check for continuity. If the switch is faulty, replace it:	3.3

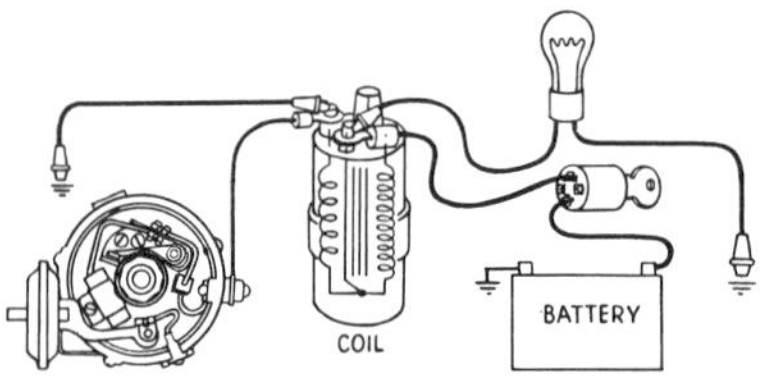

Checking the ignition switch "on" position

| 3.2—Check the ballast resistor or resistance wire for an open circuit, using an ohmmeter. | Replace the resistor or the resistance wire if the resistance is zero. | 3.3 |

| 3.3—Visually inspect the breaker points for burning, pitting, or excessive wear. Gray coloring of the point contact surfaces is normal. Rotate the crankshaft until the contact heel rests on a high point of the distributor cam, and adjust the point gap to specifications. | If the breaker points are intact, clean the contact surfaces with fine emery cloth, and adjust the point gap to specifications. If pitted or worn, replace the points and condenser, and adjust the gap to specifications: | 3.4 |
| | NOTE: *Always lubricate the distributor cam according to manufacturer's recommendations when servicing the breaker points.* | |

| 3.4—Connect a dwell meter between the distributor primary lead and ground. Crank the engine and observe the point dwell angle. | If necessary, adjust the point dwell angle: NOTE: *Increasing the point gap decreases the dwell angle, and vice-versa.* | 3.6 |
| | If dwell meter shows little or no reading: | 3.5 |

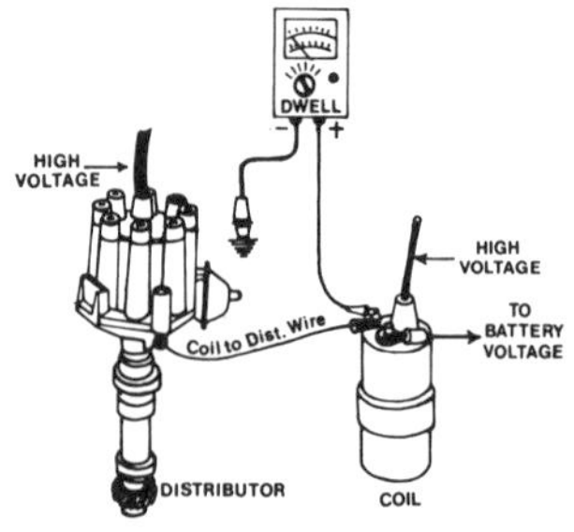

Dwell meter hook-up

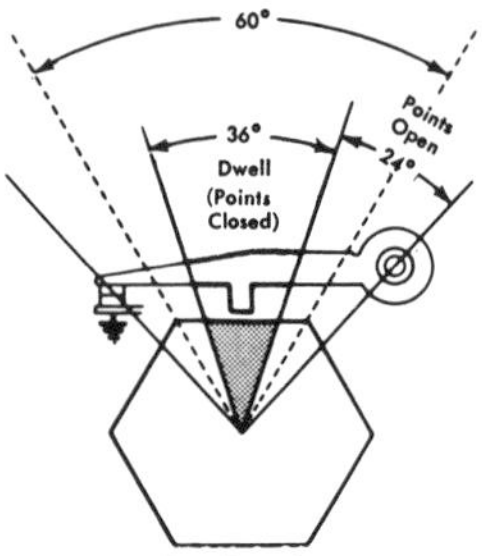

Dwell angle

| 3.5—Check the condenser for short: Connect an ohmmeter across the condenser body and the pigtail lead. | If any reading other than infinite resistance is noted, replace the condenser: | 3.6 |

Checking the condenser for short

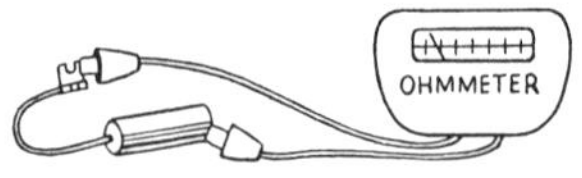

Test and Procedure	*Results and Indications*	*Proceed to*
3.6—Test the coil primary resistance: Connect an ohmmeter across the coil primary terminals, and read the resistance on the low scale. Note whether an external ballast resistor or resistance wire is utilized. **Testing the coil primary resistance**	Coils utilizing ballast resistors or resistance wires should have approximately 1.0Ω resistance; coils with internal resistors should have approximately 4.0Ω resistance. If values far from the above are noted, replace the coil:	4.1
4.1—Check for spark: Hold each spark plug wire approximately ¼″ from ground with gloves or a heavy, dry rag. Crank the engine, and observe the spark.	If no spark is evident: If spark is good in some cylinders: If spark is good in all cylinders:	4.2 4.3 4.6
4.2—Check for spark at the coil high tension lead: Remove the coil high tension lead from the distributor and position it approximately ¼″ from ground. Crank the engine and observe spark. CAUTION: *This test should not be performed on cars equipped with transistorized ignition.*	If the spark is good and consistent: If the spark is good but intermittent, test the primary electrical system starting at 3.3: If the spark is weak or non-existent, replace the coil high tension lead, clean and tighten all connections and retest. If no improvement is noted:	4.3 3.3 4.4
4.3—Visually inspect the distributor cap and rotor for burned or corroded contacts, cracks, carbon tracks, or moisture. Also check the fit of the rotor on the distributor shaft (where applicable).	If moisture is present, dry thoroughly, and retest per 4.1: If burned or excessively corroded contacts, cracks, or carbon tracks are noted, replace the defective part(s) and retest per 4.1: If the rotor and cap appear intact, or are only slightly corroded, clean the contacts thoroughly (including the cap towers and spark plug wire ends) and retest per 4.1: If the spark is good in all cases: If the spark is poor in all cases:	4.1 4.1 4.6 4.5
4.4—Check the coil secondary resistance: Connect an ohmmeter across the distributor side of the coil and the coil tower. Read the resistance on the high scale of the ohmmeter. **Testing the coil secondary resistance**	The resistance of a satisfactory coil should be between 4KΩ and 10KΩ. If the resistance is considerably higher (i.e., 40KΩ) replace the coil, and retest per 4.1: NOTE: *This does not apply to high performance coils.*	4.1

Test and Procedure	Results and Indications	Proceed to
4.5—Visually inspect the spark plug wires for cracking or brittleness. Ensure that no two wires are positioned so as to cause induction firing (adjacent and parallel). Remove each wire, one by one, and check resistance with an ohmmeter.	Replace any cracked or brittle wires. If any of the wires are defective, replace the entire set. Replace any wires with excessive resistance (over 8000Ω per foot for suppression wire), and separate any wires that might cause induction firing.	4.6
4.6—Remove the spark plugs, noting the cylinders from which they were removed, and evaluate according to the chart below.	See below.	See below.

	Condition	Cause	Remedy	Proceed to
	Electrodes eroded, light brown deposits.	Normal wear. Normal wear is indicated by approximately .001″ wear per 1000 miles.	Clean and regap the spark plug if wear is not excessive: Replace the spark plug if excessively worn:	4.7
	Carbon fouling (black, dry, fluffy deposits).	If present on one or two plugs:		
		Faulty high tension lead(s).	Test the high tension leads:	4.5
		Burnt or sticking valve(s).	Check the valve train: (Clean and regap the plugs in either case.)	9.1
		If present on most or all plugs: Overly rich fuel mixture, due to restricted air filter, improper carburetor adjustment, improper choke or heat riser adjustment or operation.	Check the fuel system:	5.1
	Oil fouling (wet black deposits)	Worn engine components. NOTE: *Oil fouling may occur in new or recently rebuilt engines until broken in.*	Check engine vacuum and compression: Replace with new spark plug	6.1
	Lead fouling (gray, black, tan, or yellow deposits, which appear glazed or cinder-like).	Combustion by-products.	Clean and regap the plugs: (Use plugs of a different heat range if the problem recurs.)	4.7

	Condition	Cause	Remedy	Proceed to
	Gap bridging (deposits lodged between the electrodes).	Incomplete combustion, or transfer of deposits from the combustion chamber.	Replace the spark plugs:	4.7
	Overheating (burnt electrodes, and extremely white insulator with small black spots).	Ignition timing advanced too far.	Adjust timing to specifications:	8.2
		Overly lean fuel mixture.	Check the fuel system:	5.1
		Spark plugs not seated properly.	Clean spark plug seat and install a new gasket washer: (Replace the spark plugs in all cases.)	4.7
	Fused spot deposits on the insulator.	Combustion chamber blow-by.	Clean and regap the spark plugs:	4.7
	Pre-ignition (melted or severely burned electrodes, blistered or cracked insulators, or metallic deposits on the insulator).	Incorrect spark plug heat range.	Replace with plugs of the proper heat range:	4.7
		Ignition timing advanced too far.	Adjust timing to specifications:	8.2
		Spark plugs not being cooled efficiently.	Clean the spark plug seat, and check the cooling system:	11.1
		Fuel mixture too lean.	Check the fuel system:	5.1
		Poor compression.	Check compression:	6.1
		Fuel grade too low.	Use higher octane fuel:	4.7

Test and Procedure	Results and Indications	Proceed to
4.7—Determine the static ignition timing: Using the flywheel or crankshaft pulley timing marks as a guide, locate top dead center on the *compression* stroke of the No. 1 cylinder. Remove the distributor cap.	Adjust the distributor so that the rotor points toward the No. 1 tower in the distributor cap, and the points are just opening:	4.8
4.8—Check coil polarity: Connect a voltmeter negative lead to the coil high tension lead, and the positive lead to ground (NOTE: *reverse the hook-up for positive ground cars*). Crank the engine momentarily. **Checking coil polarity**	If the voltmeter reads up-scale, the polarity is correct:	5.1
	If the voltmeter reads down-scale, reverse the coil polarity (switch the primary leads):	5.1

Test and Procedure	*Results and Indications*	*Proceed to*
5.1—Determine that the air filter is functioning efficiently: Hold paper elements up to a strong light, and attempt to see light through the filter.	Clean permanent air filters in gasoline (or manufacturer's recommendation), and allow to dry. Replace paper elements through which light cannot be seen:	5.2
5.2—Determine whether a flooding condition exists: Flooding is identified by a strong gasoline odor, and excessive gasoline present in the throttle bore(s) of the carburetor.	If flooding is not evident:	5.3
	If flooding is evident, permit the gasoline to dry for a few moments and restart. If flooding doesn't recur:	5.6
	If flooding is persistant:	5.5
5.3—Check that fuel is reaching the carburetor: Detach the fuel line at the carburetor inlet. Hold the end of the line in a cup (not styrofoam), and crank the engine.	If fuel flows smoothly:	5.6
	If fuel doesn't flow (NOTE: *Make sure that there is fuel in the tank*), or flows erratically:	5.4
5.4—Test the fuel pump: Disconnect all fuel lines from the fuel pump. Hold a finger over the input fitting, crank the engine (with electric pump, turn the ignition or pump on); and feel for suction.	If suction is evident, blow out the fuel line to the tank with low pressure compressed air until bubbling is heard from the fuel filler neck. Also blow out the carburetor fuel line (both ends disconnected):	5.6
	If no suction is evident, replace or repair the fuel pump: NOTE: *Repeated oil fouling of the spark plugs, or a no-start condition, could be the result of a ruptured vacuum booster pump diaphragm, through which oil or gasoline is being drawn into the intake manifold (where applicable).*	5.6
5.5—Check the needle and seat: Tap the carburetor in the area of the needle and seat.	If flooding stops, a gasoline additive (e.g., Gumout) will often cure the problem:	5.6
	If flooding continues, check the fuel pump for excessive pressure at the carburetor (according to specifications). If the pressure is normal, the needle and seat must be removed and checked, and/or the float level adjusted:	5.6
5.6—Test the accelerator pump by looking into the throttle bores while operating the throttle.	If the accelerator pump appears to be operating normally:	5.7
	If the accelerator pump is not operating, the pump must be reconditioned. Where possible, service the pump with the carburetor(s) installed on the engine. If necessary, remove the carburetor. Prior to removal:	5.7
5.7—Determine whether the carburetor main fuel system is functioning: Spray a commercial starting fluid into the carburetor while attempting to start the engine.	If the engine starts, runs for a few seconds, and dies:	5.8
	If the engine doesn't start:	6.1

Test and Procedures	Results and Indications	Proceed to
5.8—Uncommon fuel system malfunctions: See below:	If the problem is solved:	6.1
	If the problem remains, remove and recondition the carburetor.	

Condition	Indication	Test	Usual Weather Conditions	Remedy
Vapor lock	Car will not re-start shortly after running.	Cool the components of the fuel system until the engine starts.	Hot to very hot	Ensure that the exhaust manifold heat control valve is operating. Check with the vehicle manufacturer for the recommended solution to vapor lock on the model in question.
Carburetor icing	Car will not idle, stalls at low speeds.	Visually inspect the throttle plate area of the throttle bores for frost.	High humidity, 32-40° F.	Ensure that the exhaust manifold heat control valve is operating, and that the intake manifold heat riser is not blocked.
Water in the fuel	Engine sputters and stalls; may not start.	Pump a small amount of fuel into a glass jar. Allow to stand, and inspect for droplets or a layer of water.	High humidity, extreme temperature changes.	For droplets, use one or two cans of commercial gas dryer (Dry Gas) For a layer of water, the tank must be drained, and the fuel lines blown out with compressed air.

Test and Procedure	Results and Indications	Proceed to
6.1—Test engine compression: Remove all spark plugs. Insert a compression gauge into a spark plug port, crank the engine to obtain the maximum reading, and record.	If compression is within limits on all cylinders:	7.1
	If gauge reading is extremely low on all cylinders:	6.2
	If gauge reading is low on one or two cylinders: (If gauge readings are identical and low on two or more adjacent cylinders, the head gasket must be replaced.)	6.2

Testing compression
(© Chevrolet Div. G.M. Corp.)

Compression pressure limits
(© Buick Div. G.M. Corp.)

Maxi. Press. Lbs. Sq. In.	Min. Press. Lbs. Sq. In.	Maxi. Press. Lbs. Sq. In.	Min. Press. Lbs. Sq. In.	Max. Press. Lbs. Sq. In.	Min. Press. Lbs. Sq. In.	Max. Press. Lbs. Sq. In.	Min. Press. Lbs. Sq. In.
134	101	162	121	188	141	214	160
136	102	164	123	190	142	216	162
138	104	166	124	192	144	218	163
140	105	168	126	194	145	220	165
142	107	170	127	196	147	222	166
146	110	172	129	198	148	224	168
148	111	174	131	200	150	226	169
150	113	176	132	202	151	228	171
152	114	178	133	204	153	230	172
154	115	180	135	206	154	232	174
156	117	182	136	208	156	234	175
158	118	184	138	210	157	236	177
160	120	186	140	212	158	238	178

Test and Procedure	Results and Indications	Proceed to
6.2—Test engine compression (wet): Squirt approximately 30 cc. of engine oil into each cylinder, and retest per 6.1.	If the readings improve, worn or cracked rings or broken pistons are indicated:	Next Chapter
	If the readings do not improve, burned or excessively carboned valves or a jumped timing chain are indicated:	7.1
	NOTE: *A jumped timing chain is often indicated by difficult cranking.*	
7.1—Perform a vacuum check of the engine: Attach a vacuum gauge to the intake manifold beyond the throttle plate. Start the engine, and observe the action of the needle over the range of engine speeds.	See below.	See below

	Reading	Indications	Proceed to
	Steady, from 17-22 in. Hg.	Normal.	8.1
	Low and steady.	Late ignition or valve timing, or low compression:	6.1
	Very low	Vacuum leak:	7.2
	Needle fluctuates as engine speed increases.	Ignition miss, blown cylinder head gasket, leaking valve or weak valve spring:	6.1, 8.3
	Gradual drop in reading at idle.	Excessive back pressure in the exhaust system:	10.1
	Intermittent fluctuation at idle.	Ignition miss, sticking valve:	8.3, 9.1
	Drifting needle.	Improper idle mixture adjustment, carburetors not synchronized (where applicable), or minor intake leak. Synchronize the carburetors, adjust the idle, and retest. If the condition persists:	7.2
	High and steady.	Early ignition timing:	8.2

Test and Procedure	Results and Indications	Proceed to
7.2—Attach a vacuum gauge per 7.1, and test for an intake manifold leak. Squirt a small amount of oil around the intake manifold gaskets, carburetor gaskets, plugs and fittings. Observe the action of the vacuum gauge.	If the reading improves, replace the indicated gasket, or seal the indicated fitting or plug:	8.1
	If the reading remains low:	7.3
7.3—Test all vacuum hoses and accessories for leaks as described in 7.2. Also check the carburetor body (dashpots, automatic choke mechanism, throttle shafts) for leaks in the same manner.	If the reading improves, service or replace the offending part(s):	8.1
	If the reading remains low:	6.1
8.1—Check the point dwell angle: Connect a dwell meter between the distributor primary wire and ground. Start the engine, and observe the dwell angle from idle to 3000 rpm.	If necessary, adjust the dwell angle. NOTE: *Increasing the point gap reduces the dwell angle and vice-versa.* If the dwell angle moves outside specifications as engine speed increases, the distributor should be removed and checked for cam accuracy, shaft end-play and concentricity, bushing wear, and adequate point arm tension (NOTE: *Most of these items may be checked with the distributor installed in the engine, using an oscilloscope*):	8.2
8.2—Connect a timing light (per manufacturer's recommendation) and check the dynamic ignition timing. Disconnect and plug the vacuum hose(s) to the distributor if specified, start the engine, and observe the timing marks at the specified engine speed.	If the timing is not correct, adjust to specifications by rotating the distributor in the engine: (Advance timing by rotating distributor opposite normal direction of rotor rotation, retard timing by rotating distributor in same direction as rotor rotation.)	8.3
8.3—Check the operation of the distributor advance mechanism(s): To test the mechanical advance, disconnect all but the mechanical advance, and observe the timing marks with a timing light as the engine speed is increased from idle. If the mark moves smoothly, without hesitation, it may be assumed that the mechanical advance is functioning properly. To test vacuum advance and/or retard systems, alternately crimp and release the vacuum line, and observe the timing mark for movement. If movement is noted, the system is operating.	If the systems are functioning:	8.4
	If the systems are not functioning, remove the distributor, and test on a distributor tester:	8.4
8.4—Locate an ignition miss: With the engine running, remove each spark plug wire, one by one, until one is found that doesn't cause the engine to roughen and slow down.	When the missing cylinder is identified:	4.1

Test and Procedure	Results and Indications	Proceed to
9.1—Evaluate the valve train: Remove the valve cover, and ensure that the valves are adjusted to specifications. A mechanic's stethoscope may be used to aid in the diagnosis of the valve train. By pushing the probe on or near push rods or rockers, valve noise often can be isolated. A timing light also may be used to diagnose valve problems. Connect the light according to manufacturer's recommendations, and start the engine. Vary the firing moment of the light by increasing the engine speed (and therefore the ignition advance), and moving the trigger from cylinder to cylinder. Observe the movement of each valve.	See below	See below

Observation	Probable Cause	Remedy	Proceed to
Metallic tap heard through the stethoscope.	Sticking hydraulic lifter or excessive valve clearance.	Adjust valve. If tap persists, remove and replace the lifter:	10.1
Metallic tap through the stethoscope, able to push the rocker arm (lifter side) down by hand.	Collapsed valve lifter.	Remove and replace the lifter:	10.1
Erratic, irregular motion of the valve stem.*	Sticking valve, burned valve.	Recondition the valve and/or valve guide:	Next Chapter
Eccentric motion of the pushrod at the rocker arm.*	Bent pushrod.	Replace the pushrod:	10.1
Valve retainer bounces as the valve closes.*	Weak valve spring or damper.	Remove and test the spring and damper. Replace if necessary:	10.1

*—When observed with a timing light.

Test and Procedure	Results and Indications	Proceed to
9.2—Check the valve timing: Locate top dead center of the No. 1 piston, and install a degree wheel or tape on the crankshaft pulley or damper with zero corresponding to an index mark on the engine. Rotate the crankshaft in its direction of rotation, and observe the opening of the No. 1 cylinder intake valve. The opening should correspond with the correct mark on the degree wheel according to specifications.	If the timing is not correct, the timing cover must be removed for further investigation:	

Test and Procedure	*Results and Indications*	*Proceed to*
10.1—Determine whether the exhaust manifold heat control valve is operating: Operate the valve by hand to determine whether it is free to move. If the valve is free, run the engine to operating temperature and observe the action of the valve, to ensure that it is opening.	If the valve sticks, spray it with a suitable solvent, open and close the valve to free it, and retest. If the valve functions properly:	10.2
	If the valve does not free, or does not operate, replace the valve:	10.2
10.2—Ensure that there are no exhaust restrictions: Visually inspect the exhaust system for kinks, dents, or crushing. Also note that gasses are flowing freely from the tailpipe at all engine speeds, indicating no restriction in the muffler or resonator.	Replace any damaged portion of the system:	11.1
11.1—Visually inspect the fan belt for glazing, cracks, and fraying, and replace if necessary. Tighten the belt so that the longest span has approximately ½″ play at its mid-point under thumb pressure.	Replace or tighten the fan belt as necessary:	11.2

Checking the fan belt tension
(© Nissan Motor Co. Ltd.)

Test and Procedure	*Results and Indications*	*Proceed to*
11.2—Check the fluid level of the cooling system.	If full or slightly low, fill as necessary:	11.5
	If extremely low:	11.3
11.3—Visually inspect the external portions of the cooling system (radiator, radiator hoses, thermostat elbow, water pump seals, heater hoses, etc.) for leaks. If none are found, pressurize the cooling system to 14-15 psi.	If cooling system holds the pressure:	11.5
	If cooling system loses pressure rapidly, re-inspect external parts of the system for leaks under pressure. If none are found, check dipstick for coolant in crankcase. If no coolant is present, but pressure loss continues:	11.4
	If coolant is evident in crankcase, remove cylinder head(s), and check gasket(s). If gaskets are intact, block and cylinder head(s) should be checked for cracks or holes. If the gasket(s) is blown, replace, and purge the crankcase of coolant:	12.6
	NOTE: *Occasionally, due to atmospheric and driving conditions, condensation of water can occur in the crankcase. This causes the oil to appear milky white. To remedy, run the engine until hot, and change the oil and oil filter.*	

Test and Procedure	_Results and Indication_	_Proceed to_
11.4—Check for combustion leaks into the cooling system: Pressurize the cooling system as above. Start the engine, and observe the pressure gauge. If the needle fluctuates, remove each spark plug wire, one by one, noting which cylinder(s) reduce or eliminate the fluctuation. **Radiator pressure tester** (© American Motors Corp.)	Cylinders which reduce or eliminate the fluctuation, when the spark plug wire is removed, are leaking into the cooling system. Replace the head gasket on the affected cylinder bank(s).	
11.5—Check the radiator pressure cap: Attach a radiator pressure tester to the radiator cap (wet the seal prior to installation). Quickly pump up the pressure, noting the point at which the cap releases. **Testing the radiator pressure cap** (© American Motors Corp.)	If the cap releases within ± 1 psi of the specified rating, it is operating properly: If the cap releases at more than ± 1 psi of the specified rating, it should be replaced:	11.6 11.6
11.6—Test the thermostat: Start the engine cold, remove the radiator cap, and insert a thermometer into the radiator. Allow the engine to idle. After a short while, there will be a sudden, rapid increase in coolant temperature. The temperature at which this sharp rise stops is the thermostat opening temperature.	If the thermostat opens at or about the specified temperature: If the temperature doesn't increase: (If the temperature increases slowly and gradually, replace the thermostat.)	11.7 11.7
11.7—Check the water pump: Remove the thermostat elbow and the thermostat, disconnect the coil high tension lead (to prevent starting), and crank the engine momentarily.	If coolant flows, replace the thermostat and retest per 11.6: If coolant doesn't flow, reverse flush the cooling system to alleviate any blockage that might exist. If system is not blocked, and coolant will not flow, recondition the water pump.	11.6 —
12.1—Check the oil pressure gauge or warning light: If the gauge shows low pressure, or the light is on, for no obvious reason, remove the oil pressure sender. Install an accurate oil pressure gauge and run the engine momentarily.	If oil pressure builds normally, run engine for a few moments to determine that it is functioning normally, and replace the sender. If the pressure remains low: If the pressure surges: If the oil pressure is zero:	— 12.2 12.3 12.3

Test and Procedure	*Results and Indications*	*Proceed to*
12.2—Visually inspect the oil: If the oil is watery or very thin, milky, or foamy, replace the oil and oil filter.	If the oil is normal:	12.3
	If after replacing oil the pressure remains low:	12.3
	If after replacing oil the pressure becomes normal:	—
12.3—Inspect the oil pressure relief valve and spring, to ensure that it is not sticking or stuck. Remove and thoroughly clean the valve, spring, and the valve body.	If the oil pressure improves:	—
	If no improvement is noted:	12.4

Oil pressure relief valve
(© British Leyland Motors)

Test and Procedure	*Results and Indications*	*Proceed to*
12.4—Check to ensure that the oil pump is not cavitating (sucking air instead of oil): See that the crankcase is neither over nor underfull, and that the pickup in the sump is in the proper position and free from sludge.	Fill or drain the crankcase to the proper capacity, and clean the pickup screen in solvent if necessary. If no improvement is noted:	12.5
12.5—Inspect the oil pump drive and the oil pump:	If the pump drive or the oil pump appear to be defective, service as necessary and retest per 12.1:	12.1
	If the pump drive and pump appear to be operating normally, the engine should be disassembled to determine where blockage exists:	Next Chapter
12.6—Purge the engine of ethylene glycol coolant: Completely drain the crankcase and the oil filter. Obtain a commercial butyl cellosolve base solvent, designated for this purpose, and follow the instructions precisely. Following this, install a new oil filter and refill the crankcase with the proper weight oil. The next oil and filter change should follow shortly thereafter (1000 miles).		

3 · Engine and Engine Rebuilding

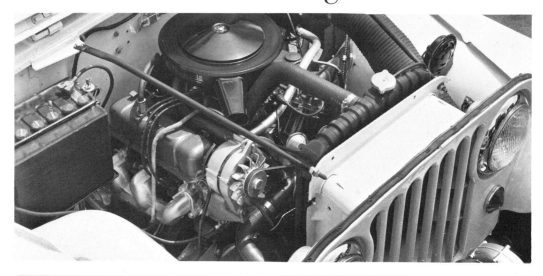

Engine Electrical

DISTRIBUTOR

Removal

To remove the distributor assembly, follow the procedure below.

1. Remove the high-tension wires from the distributor cap terminal towers, noting their positions to assure correct reassembly. For diagrams of firing orders and distributor wiring, refer to the tune-up and troubleshooting section.

2. Remove the primary lead from the terminal post at the side of the distributor.

3. Disconnect the vacuum tube if there is one.

4. Unlatch the two distributor cap retaining hooks and remove the distributor cap.

5. Note the position of the rotor in relation to the base. Scribe a mark on the base of the distributor and on the engine block to facilitate reinstallation. Align the marks with the direction the metal tip of the rotor is pointing.

6. Remove the screw that holds the distributor to the engine.

7. Lift the distributor assembly from the engine.

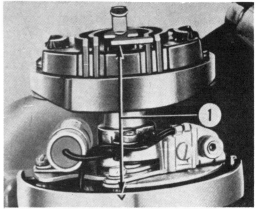

Scribe a mark on the base of the distributor below the metal tip of the rotor before removing the distributor from the engine

Installation

1. Insert the distributor shaft and assembly into the engine. Line up the mark on the distributor and the one on the engine with the metal tip of the rotor. Make sure that the vacuum advance diaphragm is pointed in the same direction as it was pointed originally. This will be done automatically if the marks on the engine and the distributor are lined up with the rotor.

NOTE: *On the F-Head, the distributor shaft fits into a slot in the end of the oil pump shaft.*

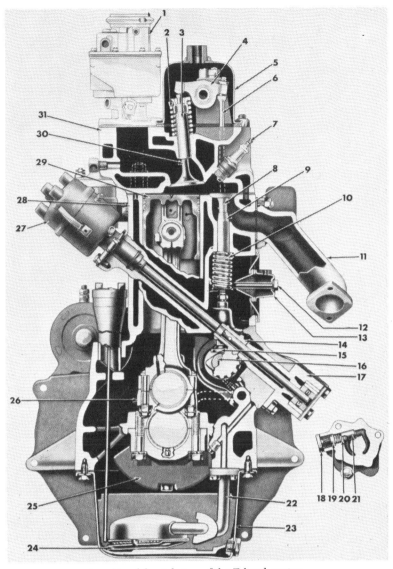

A sectional frontal view of the F-head engine

1. Carburetor
2. Intake valve spring
3. Intake valve stem guide
4. Rocker arm
5. Rocker arm cover
6. Intake valve pushrod
7. Spark plug
8. Exhaust valve
9. Exhaust valve stem guide
10. Exhaust valve spring
11. Exhaust manifold
12. Valve spring cover screw
13. Crankcase ventilator
14. Oil pump drive gear
15. Exhaust valve tappet
16. Camshaft
17. Oil pump
18. Oil pump relief spring retainer
19. Oil pump relief plunger gasket
20. Oil plunger relief spring
21. Oil pump relief plunger
22. Oil float support
23. Oil pan
24. Oil float
25. Crankshaft
26. Connecting rod
27. Distributor
28. Piston and pin
29. Cylinder block
30. Intake valve
31. Cylinder head

2. Install the distributor hold-down bolt and clamp. Leave the screw loose enough so that you can move the distributor with heavy hand pressure.

3. Connect the primary wire to the distributor side of the coil. Install the distributor cap on the distributor housing. Secure the distributor cap with the spring clips or the screw type retainers, whichever is used.

4. Install the spark plug wires. Make sure that the wires are pressed all of the way into the top of the distributor cap and firmly onto the spark plugs.

NOTE: *Design of the V6 engine requires a special form of distributor cam. The distributor may be serviced in the regular way and should cause no more problems than any other distributor, if the firing plan is thoroughly understood. The distributor cam is not ground to standard six cylinder indexing intervals. This particular form requires that the original pattern of spark plug wiring be used. The engine will not run in balance if number one spark plug wire is inserted into number six distributor cap tower, even though each wire in the firing sequence is advanced to the next distributor tower. There is a difference between the firing intervals of each succeeding cylinder through the 720° engine cycle.*

5. Adjust the point cam dwell and set the ignition timing. Refer to the tune-up section.

If the engine has been turned while the distributor has been removed, or if the marks were not drawn, it will be necessary to initially time the engine. Follow the procedure below.

Installation, Engine Disturbed

1. It is necessary to place the no. 1 cylinder in the firing position to correctly install the distributor. To locate this position, some engines have marks placed on the flywheel while other engines have marks placed on the timing gear covers and crankshaft pulleys. The flywheel marks may be viewed through a covered opening directly in back of the starting motor by loosening the hole cover and sliding it to one side.

2. Remove the no. 1 cylinder spark plug. Turn the engine until the piston in no. 1 cylinder is moving up on the compression stroke. This can be determined by placing your thumb over the spark plug hole and feeling the air being forced out of the cylinder. Stop turning F-head engines when either the 5° mark on the flywheel is in the middle of the flywheel inspection opening, or the marks on the crankshaft pulley and the timing gear cover are in alignment.

3. Oil the distributor housing lightly where the distributor bears on the cylinder block.

4. Install the distributor so that the rotor, which is mounted on the shaft, points toward the no. 1 spark plug terminal tower position when the cap is installed. Of course you won't be able to see the direction in which the rotor is pointing if the cap is on the distributor. Lay the cap on the top of the distributor and make a mark on the side of the distributor housing just below the no. 1 spark plug terminal. Make sure the rotor points toward that mark when you install the distributor.

5. When the distributor shaft has reached the bottom of the hole, move the rotor back and forth slightly until the driving lug on the end of the shaft enters the slot, which is cut in the end of the oil pump gear on the F-Head, or when the drive gears of the distributor and cam mesh on the other engines, and until the distributor assembly slides down into place.

On models that have a gear on the end of the distributor shaft and a gear on the end of the oil pump drive, these gears have to mesh with the same teeth as originally installed when the distributor is inserted into the engine. Once again, the marks that were placed on the engine and the base of the distributor housing come into play. If the distributor shaft gear and the oil pump drive gear are but one tooth off from what they are supposed to be, the engine will not run correctly.

6. When the distributor is correctly installed, the breaker points should be in such a position that they are just ready to break contact with each other. This is accomplished by rotating the distributor body after it has been installed in the engine. Once again, line up the marks that you made before the distributor was removed from the engine.

7. Install the distributor hold-down screw and the hold-down bracket. Be sure that the models that have vacuum advance

units are free to turn in the mounting socket. Note that the vacuum advance control of some distributors is connected directly to the plate on which the points are mounted. When this is the case, the plate must be free to turn rather than the distributor body.

8. Install the spark plug into the no. 1 spark plug hole and continue from step 3 of the distributor installation procedure.

NOTE: *A CJ-5 and CJ-6 F-head distributor (IAD 4041) is identical to the distributor of the CJ-3B (IAD 4008A) except for the hold-down arm. The CJ-5 and CJ-6 distributor was issued to replace the distributor originally installed in the CJ-3B. It is necessary to remove the oil pump in order to install the CJ-5 and CJ-6 distributor in the CJ-3B. Place the distributor in the correct timing position and install the hold-down screw. Engage the distributor drive and carefully mesh the gears without distributing the correct timing position of the distributor, and then replace the oil pump.*

ALTERNATOR AND GENERATOR

All Jeep Universals had DC generators before 1965. In 1965, alternators were installed on the Tuxedo Park versions of the CJ-5 and CJ-6. These models were known respectively as the CJ-5A and CJ-6A. After 1966, all Jeep Universals came equipped with alternators.

An alternator differs from a conventional DC shunt generator in that the ar-

The alternator used prior to 1972

1. Auxiliary terminal	4. Field terminal
2. Output terminal	5. Ground terminal
3. Auxiliary terminal	6. Ground terminal

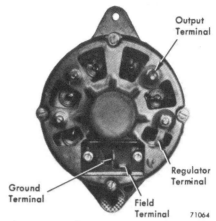

The alternator used on American Motors engines

mature is stationary, and is called the stator, while the field rotates and is called the rotor. The higher current values in the alternator's stator are conducted to the external circuit through fixed leads and connections, rather than through a rotating commutator and brushes as in a DC generator. This eliminates a major point of maintenance.

The alternator employs a three-phase stator winding. The rotor consists of a field coil encased between six-poled, interleaved sections, producing a twelve-pole magnetic field with alternating north and south poles. By rotating the rotor inside the stator, an alternating current is induced in the stator windings. This alternating current is changed to direct current by diodes and is routed out of the alternator through the output terminal. Diode rectifiers act as one-way electrical valves. Half of the diodes have a negative polarity and are grounded. The other half of the diodes have a positive polarity and are connected to the output terminal.

Since the diodes have a high resistance to the flow of current in one direction, and a low resistance in the opposite direction, they are connected in a manner which allows current to flow from the alternator to the battery in the low-resistance direction.

The high resistance in the other direction prevents the flow of current from the battery to the alternator. Because of this feature, there is no need for a circuit breaker between the alternator and the battery.

Residual magnetism in the rotor field poles is minimal. The starting field current must, therefore, be supplied by the battery. It is connected to the field winding through the ignition switch and the charge indicator lamp of the ammeter in the dash.

As in the DC shunt generator, the alternator voltage is regulated by varying the field current. This is accomplished electronically in the transistorized voltage regulator. No current regulator is required because all alternators have self-limiting current characteristics.

An alternator is better than a conventional, DC shunt generator because it is lighter and more compact, because it is designed to supply the battery and accessory circuits through a wide range of engine speeds, and because it eliminates the necessary maintenance of replacing brushes and servicing commutators.

The transistorized voltage regulator is an electronic switching device. It senses the voltage at the auxiliary terminal of the alternator and supplies the necessary field current for maintaining the system voltage at the output terminal. The output current is determined by the battery electrical load—such as operating the headlights or heater blower.

The transistorized voltage regulator is a sealed unit that has no adjustments and must be replaced as a complete unit when it ceases to operate.

Alternator Precautions

To prevent damage to the alternator and regulator, the following precautionary measures must be taken when working with the electrical system.

1. Never reverse battery connections. Always check the battery polarity visually. This is to be done before any connections are made to be sure that all of the connections correspond to the battery ground polarity of the Jeep.

2. Booster batteries for starting must be connected properly. Make sure that the positive cable of the booster battery is connected to the positive terminal of the battery that is getting the boost. This applies to both negative and ground cables.

3. Disconnect the battery cables before using a fast charger; the charger has a tendency to force current through the diodes in the opposite direction for which they were designed. This burns out the diodes.

4. Never use a fast charger as a booster for starting the vehicle.

5. Never disconnect the voltage regulator while the engine is running.

6. Do not ground the alternator output terminal.

7. Do not operate the alternator on an open circuit with the field energized.

8. Do not attempt to polarize an alternator.

Removal and Installation

1. Remove all of the electrical connections from the alternator or generator. Label all of the wires so that you can install them correctly.

2. Remove all of the attaching nuts, bolts and washers noting different sized threads or nuts and bolts that go in certain holes.

3. Remove the alternator carefully. It is expensive to replace.

4. To install, reverse the above procedure.

Belt Tension Adjustment

The fan belt drives the generator/alternator and the water pump. If it is too loose, it will slip and the generator/alternator will not be able to produce the rated current. If the belt is too loose, the water pump would not operate efficiently and the engine could overheat. Check the tension of the fan belt by pushing your thumb down on the longest span

Adjusting the alternator drive belt tension

of belt midway between the pulleys. If the belt flexes more than ½ in., it should be tightened. Loosen the bolt on the adjusting bracket and pivot bolt and move the alternator or generator away from the engine to tighten the belt. Do not apply pressure to the rear of the cast aluminum housing of an alternator; it might break. Tighten the adjusting bolts when the proper tension is reached.

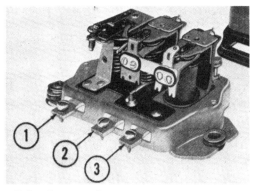

A Delco-Remy regulator

1. Battery terminal
2. Armature terminal
3. Field terminal

An Auto-Lite regulator

1. Armature terminal
2. Field terminal
3. Battery terminal

REGULATOR

The voltage regulators that are used with alternators are transistorized and cannot be serviced. If the voltage regulator is not operating properly, it must be replaced.

The voltage regulators that are used with shunt type generators are serviceable and can be adjusted. These regulators have three units: the circuit breaker, the voltage regulator and the current-limiting regulator. Each has a separate function.

Circuit Breaker

The circuit breaker consists of an electromagnet and a set of point contacts. One contact is mounted on a stationary bracket; the other is mounted on a movable armature which is controlled by the electromagnet. The movable contact is mounted on a spring arm so that a slight whipping action is produced as the contacts open and close.

The circuit breaker's electromagnet has two windings; the shunt coil and the series coil. The shunt coil is connected across the generator output like a voltmeter and the series coil is connected in series with the generator output like an ammeter. These two coils are wound in the same direction so that, when the generator is charging the battery, the magnetism of the series coil increases the total magnetism. When the battery discharges back through the generator, the magnetism of the series coil is reversed and the magnetism of the two coils is opposed. This results in a decreased pull on the armature and then spring action opens the contacts.

The sequence of operation of the circuit breaker is as follows:

When the generator is not running, the contacts are open. When the engine is started, the voltage builds at the armature terminal and in the shunt coil. As soon as it reaches the value for which the circuit breaker is calibrated, there is sufficient magnetism created by the shunt coil to pull down the armature, closing the contacts and automatically connecting the generator to the battery. With the contacts thus closed, the current in the series coil is flowing from the generator to the battery, or in the same direction as the current in the shunt coil, so that the pull on the armature is increased by the magnetism of the series coil.

When the engine is stopped and the generator loses speed, the voltage falls. As soon as the generator voltage drops below the battery terminal voltage, the current flows from the battery to the generator, reversing the direction of current in the series coil so that the magnetism created by the series coil opposes and reduces the magnetism of the shunt coil. This reduces the pull on the armature to a point where spring action opens the contacts.

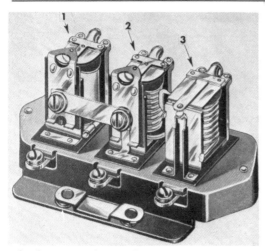

The three internal units of an Auto-Lite regulator

1. Voltage regulator
2. Current limiting regulator
3. Circuit breaker

Voltage Regulator

The function of the voltage regulator unit is to hold the generated voltage at a predetermined value as long as the circuit values allow the voltage to build to the operating load.

The electromagnet of the voltage regulator unit has a winding of many turns of fine wire and is connected across the charging circuit so that the system voltage controls the amount of magnetism.

The contacts of the voltage regulator unit are connected in the generator field circuit so that the field circuit is completed through the contacts when they are closed and through a resistor when the contacts are opened.

When the voltage rises to a predetermined amount, there is sufficient magnetism created by the regulator winding to pull the armature down. This opens the contacts and inserts resistance in the field circuit of the generator, thus reducing the field current. The generated voltage immediately drops, reducing the pull on the armature to the point where the spring closes the contacts. The output again rises and the cycle is repeated.

These cycles occur at sufficiently high frequencies to hold the generated voltage at a constant level and they will continue as long as the voltage of the circuit is high enough to keep the voltage regulator unit in operation. When there is a current load that is great enough to lower the battery voltage below the operating voltage of the voltage regulating unit, the contacts will remain closed and the generator will maintain a charging rate that is limited by its speed and capacity output.

Current-Limiting Regulator

The function of the current-limiting regulator is to limit the output of the generator to its maximum safe output.

The electromagnet of the current regulator unit consists of a winding of heavy wire connected in a series with the generator output. When the generator output reaches a predetermined level, the current in the winding produces enough magnetism to overcome spring tension and pull the armature down. This opens the contacts and inserts resistance in the field circuit of the generator. With the field current reduced by the resistance, the generator output falls and there is no longer sufficient magnetism to hold the contacts open. As soon as the spring closes the contacts, the output rises and the cycle is repeated. These cycles occur at a high enough frequency to limit the output to a minimum fluctuation.

Voltage Tests and Adjustments

Circuit Breaker

The circuit breaker is the unit with the heavy wire windings and is located on the end of the unit.

Connect an ammeter in series with the regulator B (battery) terminal and the lead that is removed from that terminal. Connect a voltmeter from the regulator A (armature) terminal to the regulator base.

Disconnect the field lead from the regulator F terminal and insert a variable resistance between the lead and the regulator terminal.

Run the generator at about 1,000 generator rpm. Insert all of the resistance in the field circuit. Slowly reduce the resistance, noting the voltage reading just before the change caused by the closing of the circuit breaker. Increase the charging rate to the figure specified for the regulator being tested, then reduce the charging rate by inserting resistance into the field circuit. Note the charging rate just before the circuit breaker opens and the ammeter reading drops to zero. The closing voltage and the opening voltage or current should be within the limits specified.

To adjust the closing voltage, change the armature spring tension by bending the hanger at the lower end of the spring. Increase the spring tension to raise the closing voltage or decrease the tension to lower the voltage. To adjust the opening voltage, raise or lower the stationary contact, keeping the contacts perfectly aligned. Increasing the contact gap lowers the opening voltage. Change the contact gap by expanding or contracting the stationary contact bracket, keeping the contacts aligned. Do not adjust the gap between the contacts to less than the specified minimum.

VOLTAGE REGULATOR

The voltage regulator unit is the one with the fine wire winding. Connect the ammeter as noted above and connect the voltmeter from the regulator B terminal to the regulator base. Remove the variable resistance from the field circuit.

Run the generator at one-half maximum output for 15 minutes to make sure the regulator is at normal temperature. Have the cover on the unit during this warm-up period and also when taking the readings.

Stop the engine, then bring it to approximately 2,500 generator rpm. Adjust the amperage to one-half of the maximum output by turning on lights or accessories and then note the voltmeter reading. This reading should be within the limits specified for the voltage regulator. To adjust the operating voltage, change the armature spring tension by bending the hanger at the lower end of the armature spring. After each adjustment, stop the engine and then restart it. Bring it up to speed and adjust the current before taking a reading. The clicks of the opening and closing of the contacts should be regular and clear without irregularities. If the tone is not clear and regular, remove the regulator cover and inspect the contacts. The contacts should be flat and not burned excessively, and should be aligned to make full face contact. Refer to the section on cleaning the contacts if necessary.

CURRENT REGULATOR

The current regulator is the unit in the middle of the unit with the heavy wire winding.

Connect the regulator and instruments as described above for the voltage regulator and run the generator at approximately 3,000 generator rpm. Turn on lights and accessories so the generator must charge at its maximum rate. The ammeter should show a reading within the specified limits. To adjust the opening amperage, change the armature spring tension by bending the hanger at the lower end of the armature spring. Stop the engine after each adjustment and then restart it. Bring the engine to speed and take an ammeter reading. Keep the cover on the unit when taking the readings.

The clicks of the points closing and opening should be clear in tone and regular in frequency without irregularities or misses. If this is not the case, the contacts will have to be serviced.

CONTACTS

The contacts should be inspected on all three of the units inside the cover of the voltage regulator. The contacts will become grayed and slightly worn during normal use. If the contacts are burned or dirty, or if they are not smooth or aligned properly, they should be adjusted and cleaned. File the contacts smooth. Just file enough so that there is a smooth surface presented to each contact. It is not necessary to file out every trace of pitting. After filing, dampen a clean cloth with carbon tetrachloride and pull the cloth between the contacts of each of the three units. Repeat with a clean dry cloth.

NOTE: *Keep in mind the fact that after filing the points, the gap might have been changed enough to affect the performance of the three units. Check the three units and perform the aforementioned procedures and adjustments. It might be a good idea to examine the contacts before making any adjustments. If the contacts need to be serviced, do it before adjusting spring tensions etc.*

Removal and Installation

If the voltage regulator still does not function properly, after all of the checks and adjustments, replace the entire unit. Follow the procedure below.

1. Remove all of the electrical connections. Label them as you remove them so you can replace them in the correct order on the replacement unit.

2. Remove all of the hold-down screws and then remove the unit from the vehicle.

3. Install the new voltage regulator using the hold-down screws from the old one, or new ones if they are provided with the replacement regulator. Tighten down the hold-down screws.

4. Connect the armature lead to the armature terminal of the voltage regulator.

5. Connect the battery lead to the battery terminal of the voltage regulator.

6. Momentarily touch the field lead to the battery terminal of the voltage regulator. This polarizes the generator and voltage regulator so they have the same polarization as the rest of the electrical system. This has to be done every time all of the leads are disconnected from the voltage regulator.

7. Connect the field lead to the field terminal of the voltage regulator.

STARTER MOTOR

The starter on the F-head four-cylinder engine can be removed from the top of the engine. The starter motor in the V6, straight sixes, and the 304 cu in. V8 have to be removed from beneath the vehicle.

Removal and Installation

1. Disconnect the battery and solenoid leads from the starter. Mark them so you can replace them in the correct position when the starter is to be installed.

2. Remove all of the attachment bolts that attach the starter to the bellhousing.

3. Lift the starter from the engine.

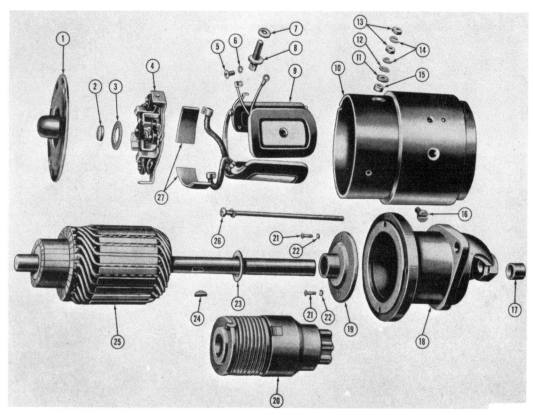

A typical starting motor for the F-head engine

1. End plate	10. Frame	19. Intermediate bearing
2. Plug	11. Insulating washer	20. Bendix drive
3. Thrust washer	12. Washer	21. Screw
4. Brush plate assembly	13. Nut	22. Lockwasher
5. Screw	14. Lockwasher	23. Thrust washer
6. Lockwasher	15. Insulating bushing	24. Key
7. Insulating washer	16. Pole shoe screw	25. Armature
8. Terminal	17. Sleeve bearing	26. Thru-bolt
9. Field coil and pole shoe set	18. Drive end frame	27. Insulator

4. Install the starter in the reverse order of the above.

Starter Drive Replacement

AUTOLITE

1. Remove the cover of the starter drive's actuating lever arm. Remove the thru-bolts, starter drive gear housing, and the return spring of the drive gear's actuating lever.

2. Remove the pivot pin which retains the starter gear actuating lever and remove the lever and armature.

3. Remove the stop-ring retainer. Remove and discard the stop-ring which holds the drive gear to the armature shaft and then remove the drive gear assembly.

To install the unit:

1. Lightly Lubriplate the armature shaft splines and install the starter drive gear assembly on the shaft. Install a new stop-ring and stop-ring retainer.

2. Position the starter drive gear actuating lever to the frame and starter drive assembly. Install the pivot pin.

3. Fill the starter drive gear housing one-quarter full of grease.

4. Position the drive actuating lever return spring and the drive gear housing to the frame, then install and tighten the thru-bolts. Be sure that the stop-ring retainer is properly seated in the drive housing.

DELCO-REMY

1. Remove the thru-bolts.

2. Remove the starter drive housing.

3. Slide the two-piece thrust collar off the end of the armature shaft.

4. Slide a standard ½ in. pipe coupling, or other spacer, onto the shaft so the end of the coupling butts against the edge of the retainer.

5. Tap the end of the coupling with a hammer, driving the retainer toward the armature end of the snap-ring.

6. Remove the snap-ring from its groove in the shaft with pliers. Slide the retainer and the starter drive from the armature.

To install the unit:

1. Lubricate the drive end of the shaft with silicone lubricant.

2. Slide the drive gear assembly onto the shaft, with the gear facing outward.

3. Slide the retainer onto the shaft with

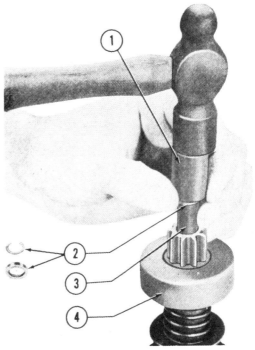

Removing the starter drive assembly from the armature shaft

1. ½ in. pipe coupling
2. Snap ring and retainer
3. Armature shaft
4. Drive assembly

the cupped surface facing away from the gear.

4. Stand the whole starter assembly on a block of wood with the snap-ring positioned on the upper end of the shaft. Drive the snap-ring down with a small block of wood and a hammer. Slide the snap-ring into its groove.

5. Install the thrust collar onto the shaft with the shoulder next to the snap-ring.

6. With the retainer on one side of the snap-ring and the thrust collar on the other side, squeeze them together with a pair of pliers until the ring seats in the retainer. On models without a thrust collar, use a washer. Remember to remove the washer before installing the starter in the engine.

PRESTOLITE

1. Slide the thrust collar off the armature shaft.

2. Using a standard ½ in. pipe connector, drive the snap-ring retainer off the shaft.

3. Remove the snap-ring from the groove, and then remove the drive assembly.

A cut-away view of a V6 starter motor

1. 'R' terminal contact	7. Shift lever	13. Bushing
2. Switch terminal	8. Bushing	14. Insulated brush holders
3. Grommet	9. Pinion stop	15. Brush spring
4. Plunger	10. Overrunning clutch	16. Grounded brush holder
5. Solenoid	11. Field coil	17. Brush
6. Return spring	12. Armature	

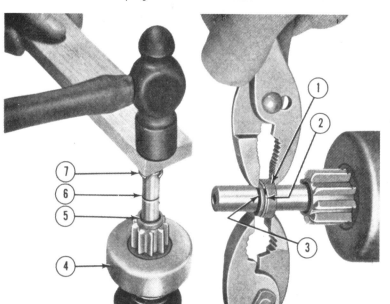

1. Retainer
2. Snap ring
3. Thrust collar
4. Drive assembly
5. Retainer
6. Groove in the armature shaft
7. Snap ring

Installing the pinion stop retainer and thrust collar on the armature shaft

To install the unit:

1. Lubricate the drive end and splines with Lubriplate.

2. Install the clutch assembly onto the shaft.

3. Install the snap-ring retainer with the cupped surface facing toward the end of the shaft.

4. Install the snap-ring into the groove. Use a new snap-ring if necessary.

5. Install the thrust collar onto the shaft with the shoulder against the snap-ring.

6. Force the retainer over the snap-ring in the same manner as was used for the Delco-Remy starters.

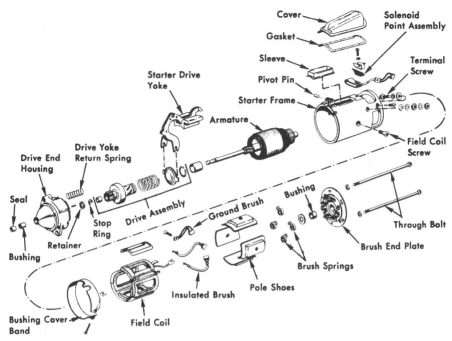

An exploded view of an American Motors starter

Solenoid or Relay Replacement

AUTOLITE

On the early CJ-3B, CJ-5, and CJ-6 with Autolite starters, there were no solenoids or relays to activate the starter drive. The starter drive activated itself by the centrifugal force of the starter motor and deactivated itself in the normal way (by the centrifugal force of the engine's flywheel).

Autolite starters were installed with solenoids mounted on the starter housing beginning in 1960.

To remove the solenoid from the starter, remove all of the leads to the solenoid, remove the connecting lever, and remove the attaching bolts that hold the solenoid assembly to the starter housing. Remove the solenoid assembly from the starter housing.

To install the solenoid assembly, reverse the above procedure.

DELCO-REMY

Remove the leads from the solenoid. Remove the drive housing of the starter motor. Remove the shift lever pin and bolt from the shift lever. Remove the attaching bolts that hold the solenoid assembly to the housing of the starter motor. Remove the starter solenoid from the starter housing. To install the solenoid, reverse the above procedure.

PRESTOLITE

Remove the leads to the solenoid assembly. Remove the attaching bolts that hold the solenoid to the starter housing. Remove the bolt from the shift lever. Remove the solenoid assembly from the starter housing. Reverse the procedure for installation.

BATTERY

Removal and Installation

Remove the hold-down screws from the battery box. Loosen the nuts that secure the cable ends to the battery terminals. Lift the battery cables from the terminals with a twisting motion.

If there is a battery cable puller available, make use of it. Lift the battery from the vehicle.

Before installing the battery in the vehicle, make sure that the battery terminals are clean and free from corrosion. Use a battery terminal cleaner on the terminals and on the inside of the battery cable ends. If cleaner is not available, use heavy sandpaper to remove the corrosion. A mixture of baking soda and water poured over the terminals and cable ends will neutralize any acid. Before installing the cables onto the terminals, cut a piece of felt cloth, or something similar, into a circle about 3 in. across. Cut a hole in the middle about the size of the battery terminals at their base. Push the cloth pieces over the ter-

minals so they lay flat on the top of the battery. Soak the pieces of cloth with oil. This will keep the formation of oxidized acid to a minimum. Place the battery in

Alternator and Regulator Specifications

| | ALTERNATOR | | | | REGULATOR | | | | | |
| | | | | | | Field Relay | | | Regulator | |
Manufacturer	Part No.	Field Current @ 12V	Output (amps)	Part No. or Manufacturer	Air Gap (in.)	Point Gap (in.)	Volts to Close	Air Gap (in.)	Point Gap (in.)	Volts @ 75°
Motorola	A12NW526	1.2–1.7	35	TVR12W14①	—	—	—	—	—	14.2–14.6
Motorola	A12NW528	1.2–1.7	35	R-2-K-1①	—	—	—	—	—	14.2–14.6
Motorola	——	1.8–2.5	37②	8RB-2005③①	—	—	—	—	—	13.7–14.2
Motorola	——	1.8–2.5	37②	8RH-2003①	—	—	—	—	—	13.7–14.8
Motorola④		2.5–3.0	40⑤	Motorcraft	—	—	—	—	—	14.5–13.7
Delco-Remy⑥		4.0–4.5	37⑦	1116387⑧	—	—	—	—	—	——

① Motorola transistorized regulator
② 55 amp alternator optional in '72, 51 amp alternator optional in 1973–'76
③ 8RD-2001 used in '73
④ V8 engines only 1976

⑤ 60 amp alternator optional
⑥ Six-Cylinder engines only 1976
⑦ 63 amp alternator optional
⑧ Delco-Remy

Generator and Regulator Specifications

| | GENERATORS—6 VOLT | | | | REGULATORS—6 VOLT | | | |
Make	Model No.	Output (amps)	Brush Spring Tension (oz)	Model No.	Regulated Voltage	Regulated Amperage	Cutout Relay Closing Voltage
Autolite	GGW 4801 GGW 7404	45	18–36	VBO-4601C	7.1–7.3	49	6.3–6.8
Delco-Remy	1102811	45	28	1972063	6.9–7.4	42–47	5.9–6.7

| | GENERATORS—12 VOLT | | | | REGULATORS—12 VOLT | | | |
Make	Model No.	Output (amps)	Brush Spring Tension (oz)	Model No.	Regulated Voltage	Regulated Amperage	Cutout Relay Closing Voltage
Autolite	GJP 7202 GJP 7402A	35	18–36	VBO4201E4A	14.3	36	12.6–13.6
Delco-Remy	1102096	35	28	1972029	13.8–14.8	30	11.8–13.5
Prestolite	GJP 7402A	35	18–36	R-2-K-1①	14.2–14.6	35	——

① Motorola transistorized regulator

Battery and Starter Specifications

| | BATTERY | | | | STARTERS | | | | | | | |
| | | | | | | Lock Test | | | No-Load Test | | | Brush Spring Tension (oz) |
Engine	Ampere Hour Capacity	Volts	Terminal Grounded	Make	Amps	Volts	Torque (ft lbs)	Amps	Volts	RPM	
F-head 134	100	6	Neg	Autolite	335	2	6	65	5	4300	42–53
F-head 134	50	12	Neg	Autolite	170①	4	1.5②	50	10	4400③	31–47
F-head 134	100	6	Neg	Delco-Remy	600	3	15	60	3	6000	24
F-head 134	50	12	Neg	Delco-Remy	435	5.8	10.5	75	10.3	6900	35
F-head 134	50	12	Neg	Prestolite	405	——	9	50	10	5300	32–40
V6	50	12	Neg	Delco-Remy	——	——	——	75	10.6	6200	32–40
232, 258, 304	50④	12	Neg	Autolite	600	3.4	13.0	65	12	9250	40

① 280 amps with model MDU 7004 starter
② 6.2 ft lbs with the model MDU 7004 starter

③ 5300 rpms with the model MDU 7004 starter
④ 60 and 70 amp battery optional

the vehicle. Install the cables onto the terminals. Tighten the nuts on the cable ends. Smear a light coating of grease on the cable ends and the tops of the terminals. This will further prevent buildup of oxidized acid on the terminals and the cable ends. Install and tighten the nuts of the battery box.

Engine Mechanical

DESIGN

F-HEAD 4 CYLINDER

The F-head, four-cylinder engine is of a combination valve-in-head and valve-in-block construction. The intake valves are mounted in the head and are operated by pushrods through rocker arms. The intake manifold is cast as an integral part of the cylinder head and is completely water-jacketed. This type of construction transfers heat from the cooling system to the intake passages and assists in vaporizing the fuel when the engine is cold. Therefore, there is no heat control valve (heat riser) needed in the exhaust manifold.

The exhaust valves are mounted in the block with thorough water jacketing to provide effective cooling of the valves.

The engine is pressure-lubricated. An oil pump which is driven by the camshaft forces the lubricant through oil channels and drilled passages in the crankshaft to efficiently lubricate the main and connecting rod bearings. Lubricant is also force-fed to the camshaft bearings, rocker arms, and timing gears. Cylinder walls and piston pins are lubricated from spurt holes in the 'follow' side of the connecting rods.

The circulation of the coolant is controlled by a thermostat in the water outlet elbow which is cast as part of the cylinder head.

The engine is equipped with a fully counterbalanced crankshaft that is supported by three main bearings. The counterweights of the crankshaft are independently forged and are permanently attached to the crankshaft with dowels and cap screws that are tack-welded. Crankshaft end-play is adjusted by placing shims between the crankshaft thrust washer and the shoulder on the crankshaft.

The pistons have an extra groove directly above the top ring which acts as a heat dam or insulator.

The engine has a compression ratio ranging from 6.3:1 to 7.8:1; this permits the use of regular octane gas. The displacement of the F-head engine is 134.2 cu in.

V6

The V6 engine has a displacement of 225 cu in. and a compression ratio of 9.0:1 which permits the use of regular octane gas.

It has two banks of three cylinders each which are opposed to one another at a 90° angle. The left bank of cylinders, as viewed from the driver's seat, is set forward of the right bank so that the connecting rods of opposite pairs of pistons and rods can be attached to the same crankpin.

The crankshaft counterbalance weights are cast as an integral part of the crankshaft. All of the crankshaft bearings are identical in diameter, except for no. 2 bearing which is the thrust bearing; it is larger than the rest.

The cast-iron heads are interchangeable although this is not recommended. They are exactly alike in every way, however.

The camshaft, which is located above the crankshaft—between the two banks, operates hydraulic valve lifters. The rocker arms are not adjustable.

232, 258 SIXES

The American Motors six-cylinder engines are inline sixes with overhead intake and exhaust valves. The valves are operated by separately mounted rocker arms in 1973, 1975–76 models. The rockers are mounted on a common shaft in 1972 and 1974 models. None of the rocker arms are adjustable.

304 V8

The 304 V8 has two banks of cylinders (four cylinders each) which are opposed to each other at a 90° angle. The camshaft is located above the crankshaft, between the two banks. It operates the valves through the use of hydraulic lifters, pushrods, and separately mounted rocker arms on 1972 models. The rocker arms are mounted in pairs on bridged pivots on 1973–76 models.

A two-barrel carburetor is used and the engine operates on regular gas.

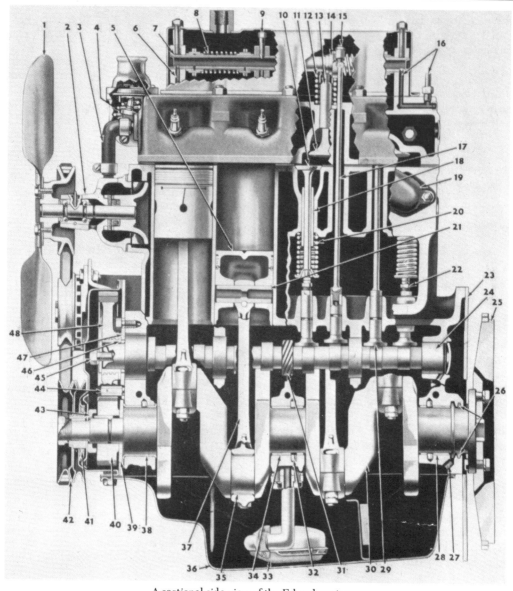

A sectional side view of the F-head engine

1. Fan assembly	17. Push rod	33. Oil float assembly
2. Water pump assembly	18. Exhaust valve guide	34. Center main bearing shell
3. Water bypass tube	19. Exhaust manifold	35. Connecting rod bearing
4. Thermostat	20. Exhaust valve spring	36. Oil pan
5. Piston	21. Piston pin	37. Connecting rod
6. Oil return tube	22. Valve tappet adjusting screw	38. Front main bearing shell
7. Rocker arm shaft	23. Engine rear support plate	38. Front engine plate
8. Rocker arm shaft spring	24. Camshaft	40. Crankshaft gear
9. Rocker arm shaft lock screw	25. Flywheel	41. Crankshaft front end seal
10. Exhaust valve	26. Rear bearing oil seal	42. Fan and generator pully
11. Intake valve	27. Oil return channel	43. Crankshaft gear spacer
12. Intake valve spring	28. Rear main bearing shell	44. Timing gear oil jet
13. Intake valve guide	29. Tappet	45. Camshaft gear screw
14. Rocker arm	30. Crankshaft	46. Camshaft thrust plate spacer
15. Adjusting screw	31. Oil pump drive gear	47. Camshaft thrust plate
16. Oil inlet tube	32. Main bearing dowel	48. Camshaft gear

Crankshaft and Connecting Rod Specifications

All measurements are given in in.

Engine Model	Engine Displacement (cu in.)	CRANKSHAFT				CONNECTING ROD		
		Main Brg. Journal Dia	Main Brg. Oil Clearance	Shaft End-Play	Thrust on No.	Journal Diameter	Oil Clearance	Side Clearance
4 cyl F-Head	134.2	2.333	0.0003–0.0029	0.005	1	1.9375	0.0010	0.004–0.010
6 cyl V6	225	2.4995	0.0004–0.0015	0.006	2	2.0000	0.0021	0.006–0.014
6 cyl OHV	232	2.4986–2.5001	0.001–0.003	0.0015–0.0065	3	2.0934–2.0955	0.001–0.002	0.005–0.014①
6 cyl OHV	258	2.4986–2.5001	0.001–0.003	0.0015–0.0065	3	2.0934–2.0955	0.001–0.002	0.005–0.014①
8 cyl V8	304	2.7489–2.7474②	0.001–0.003	0.003–0.008	3	2.0934–2.0955	0.001–0.002	0.006–0.018

① Connecting rod side clearance is 0.008–0.010 in 1973 only
② Rear main bearing journal diameter only—2.7479–2.7464

Valve Specifications

Engine Model	Engine Displacement (cu in.)	Seat Angle (deg)	Face Angle (deg)	Spring Test Pressure (lbs @ in.)	Spring Installed Height (in.)	STEM TO GUIDE CLEARANCE (in.)		STEM DIAMETER (in.)	
						Intake	Exhaust	Intake	Exhaust
4 cyl F-Head	134.2	45	46	①	②	0.0007–0.0022	0.0025–0.0045	0.3736	0.3710
6 cyl V6	225	45	45	59–69 @ 1 47/64	1 47/64	0.0012–0.0032	③	0.3410	0.3407
6 cyl OHV	232	30④	29⑤	100 @ 1 13/16	1 13/16	0.001–0.003	0.001–0.003	0.3720	0.3720
6 cyl OHV	258	30④	29⑤	100 @ 1 13/16	1 13/16	0.001–0.003	0.001–0.003	0.3720	0.3720
8 cyl V8	304	30④	29⑤	84 @ 1 13/16	1 13/16	0.001–0.003	0.001–0.003	0.3720	0.3720

① Intake 66 @ 1 21/32
　Exhaust 47 @ 2 7/64
② Intake 1 21/32
　Exhaust 2 7/64

③ 0.0015–0.0035 at the top of the guide and 0.002–0.004 at the bottom of the guide
④ Exhaust valve seat angle—44½°
⑤ Exhaust valve face angle—44°

Ring Gap

All measurements are given in in.

Engine Model	Engine Displacement (cu in.)	Top Compression	Bottom Compression	Oil Control
4 cyl F-Head	134.2	0.007–0.015①	0.007–0.015①	0.007–0.015①
6 cyl V6	225	0.010–0.020	0.010–0.020	0.015–0.035
6 cyl OHV	232	0.010–0.020	0.010–0.020	0.010–0.025②
6 cyl OHV	258	0.010–0.020	0.010–0.020	0.010–0.025②
8 cyl V8	304	0.010–0.020	0.010–0.020	0.010–0.025

① The maximum ring gap for the F-Head engine with the standard bore of 0.009 over nominal can be as high as 0.045 gap
② Ring gap for the oil control ring in 1973 only is 0.015–0.055

Ring Side Clearance

Model	Engine Displacement (cu in.)	Top Compression	Bottom Compression	Oil Control
4 cyl F-Head	134.2	0.002–0.004	0.0015–0.0035	0.001–0.0025
6 cyl V6	225	0.002–0.0035	0.003–0.005	0.0015–0.0085
6 cyl OHV	232	0.0015–0.003①	0.0015–0.003①	0.001–0.008②
6 cyl OHV	258	0.0015–0.003①	0.0015–0.003①	0.001–0.008②
8 cyl V8	304	0.0015–0.0035	0.0015–0.003	0.0011–0.008

① Ring side clearance is 0.0015–0.0035 for 1973 only
② Ring gap for the oil control ring in 1973 only is 0.015–0.055

Torque Specifications

Model	Engine Displacement (cu in.)	Cylinder Head Bolts (ft lbs)	Rod Bearing Bolts (ft lbs)	Main Bearing Bolts (ft lbs)	Crankshaft Balancer Bolt (ft lbs)	Flywheel to Crankshaft Bolts (ft lbs)	MANIFOLDS (ft lbs)	
							Intake	Exhaust
4 cyl F-Head	134.2	60–70	50–55①	65–75	60–70	35–41	20–35	29–35
6 cyl V6	225	65–80	30–40	95–120	140–160	50–65	25–35	15–20
6 cyl OHV	232	80–85②	26–30	75–85	50–64	100–110③	20–25④	20–25⑤
6 cyl OHV	258	80–85②	26–30	75–85	50–64	100–110③	20–25④	20–25⑤
8 cyl V8	304	105–115⑥	26–30⑫	95–100⑦	50–60⑧	100–110⑨	40–45⑩	30–35⑪

① 35–45 with ⅜ connecting rod cap bolt nuts
② 95–115 on 1973–76 models
③ 95–120 on 1973–76 models
④ 37–47 on 1973 models, 18–28 on 1974–76 models
⑤ 20–30 on 1973 models, 18–28 on 1974–76 models

⑥ 100–120 on 1973–76 models
⑦ 90–105 on 1973–76 models
⑧ 48–64 on 1973–76 models
⑨ 95–120 on 1973–76 models
⑩ 37–47 on 1973–76 models
⑪ 20–30 on 1973–76 models
⑫ 30–35 on 1976 models

General Engine Specifications

Year	Model	Engine Displacement (cu in.)	Carburetor Type (bbl)	Advertised Horsepower (@ rpm)	Advertised Torque @ rpm (ft lbs)	Bore and Stroke (in.)	Advertised Compression Ratio	Oil Pressure
1953--75	4 cyl F-Head	134.2	1	75 @ 4000①	114 @ 2000	3.125 x 3.375	6.7 : 1②	20③
	6 cyl V6	225	2	160 @ 4200	235 @ 2400	3.750 x 3.400	9.0 : 1	33④
	6 cyl OHV	232	1	100 @ 3600	185 @ 1800	3.750 x 3.500	8.0 : 1⑤	37⑥
	6 cyl OHV	258	1	110 @ 3500	195 @ 2000	3.750 x 3.895	8.0 : 1⑦	37⑥
	8 cyl V8	304	2	150 @ 4200	245 @ 2500	3.750 x 3.440	8.4 : 1	37⑥
1976	6 cyl OHV	232	1	90 @ 3050	170 @ 2000	3.750 x 3.500	8.0 : 1	24⑧
	6 cyl OHV	258	1	95 @ 3050	180 @ 2100	3.750 x 3.895	8.0 : 1	24⑧
	8 cyl V8	304	2	120 @ 3200	220 @ 2200	3.750 x 3.440	8.4 : 1	24⑧

① The first F-Head engine produced in 1953 for the CJ-3B was rated at 70 hp @ 4000 rpm. Later the engine was rated at 72 hp @ 4000 rpm. The later production engines were rated at 75 hp @ 4000 rpm.
② The figure above is the standard compression ratio for late-production engines. Optional compression ratios of 7.1 : 1 and 6.3 : 1 were available. The standard compression ratios for early-production engines was 7.4 : 1 and the options were 7.8 : 1 and 6.9 : 1. The compression pressures on all of the F-Head engines ranged from 120 to 130 psi.
③ At 2000 rpm
④ At 2400 rpm
⑤ 7.5 : 1 optional in 1972
⑥ At 1600 rpm. Oil pressure relief valve is set at 75 psi.
⑦ 7.6 : 1 optional in 1972
⑧ At 1100 rpm

ENGINE REMOVAL AND INSTALLATION

F-HEAD

1. Drain the cooling system by opening the draincocks at the bottom of the radiator and the lower right side of the cylinder block.

2. Disconnect the battery at the positive terminal to avoid the possibility of a short circuit.

3. Remove the air cleaner horn from the carburetor and disconnect the breather hose at the oil filler pipe.

4. Disconnect the carburetor choke and throttle controls by loosening the clamp bolts and setscrews.

5. Disconnect the fuel tank-to-fuel pump line at the fuel pump by unscrewing the connecting nut.

6. Plug the fuel line to prevent leakage. Disconnect the windshield wiper vacuum hose at the fuel pump.

7. Remove the radiator stay bar on the CJ-3B.

8. Remove the upper and lower radiator hoses. Remove the heater hoses, if so equipped, from the water pump and the rear of the cylinder head.

9. Remove the fan hub and fan blades.

10. Remove the four radiator attaching screws and remove the radiator and shroud as one unit.

11. Remove the starter motor cables and remove the starter motor.

12. Disconnect the wires from the alternator or the generator. Disconnect the ignition primary wire at the ignition coil.

13. Disconnect the oil pressure and temperature sending unit wires at the units.

14. Disconnect the exhaust pipe at the exhaust manifold by removing the stud nuts.

15. Remove the spark plug wires from the cable bracket that is mounted to the rocker arm cover. Remove the cable bracket by removing the stud nuts.

16. Remove the rocker arm cover by removing the attaching stud nuts.

17. Attach a lifting bracket to the engine using the head bolts. Be sure that the bolts selected will hold the engine with the weight balanced. Attach the lifting bracket to a boom hoist, or other lifting device, and take up all of the slack.

18. Remove the two nuts and bolts from each front engine support. Disconnect the engine ground strap. Remove the engine supports. Lower the engine slightly to permit access to the two top bolts on the flywheel housing.

19. Remove the bolts that attach the flywheel housing to the engine.

20. Pull the engine forward, or roll the vehicle backward, until the clutch clears the flywheel housing. Lift the engine from the vehicle.

21. To install the engine, reverse the above procedure.

V6

1. Remove the hood.

2. Disconnect the battery ground cable from the engine and the battery.

3. Remove the air cleaner.

4. Drain the coolant from the radiator and engine.

5. Disconnect the alternator wiring harness from the connector at the regulator.

6. Disconnect the upper and lower radiator hoses from the engine.

7. Remove the right and left radiator support bars.

8. Remove the radiator from the vehicle.

9. Disconnect the engine wiring harnesses from the connectors which are located on the firewall.

10. Disconnect the battery cable and wiring from the engine starter assembly.

11. Remove the starter assembly from the engine.

12. Disconnect the engine fuel hoses from the fuel lines at the right frame rails.

13. Plug the fuel lines.

14. Disconnect the throttle linkage and the choke cable from the carburetor and remove the cable support bracket that is mounted on the engine.

15. Disconnect the exhaust pipes from the right and left sides of the engine.

16. Place a jack under the transmission and support the weight of the transmission.

17. Remove the bolts that secure the engine to the front motor mounts.

18. Attach a suitable sling to the engine lifting eyes and, using a hoist, lift the engine just enough to support its weight.

19. Remove the bolts that secure the engine to the flywheel housing.

20. Raise the engine slightly and slide the engine forward to remove the trans-

mission main shaft from the clutch plate splines.

NOTE: *The engine and the transmission must be raised slightly to release the spline from the clutch plate while sliding the engine forward.*

21. When the engine is free of the transmission shaft, raise the engine and remove it from the vehicle.

22. To install the engine, reverse the procedure given above.

232 AND 258 SIXES, AND 304 V8

1. Remove the air cleaner.
2. Drain the cooling system.
3. Disconnect the upper and lower radiator hoses.
4. If equipped with an automatic transmission, disconnect the cooler lines from the radiator.
5. Remove the radiator and the fan.
6. If so equipped, remove the power steering pump and the drive belt, and place the unit aside. Do not remove the power steering hoses. Remove the battery and tray if equipped with the V8 (1972–75).
7. Disconnect all wires, lines, linkage, and hoses that are connected to the engine. Remove the oil filter on the Sixes.
8. Remove both of the engine front support cushion-to-frame retaining nuts.
9. Disconnect the exhaust pipe, or pipes if equipped with the V8, at the support bracket and exhaust manifold.
10. Support the weight of the engine with a lifting device.
11. Remove the front support cushion and bracket assemblies from the engine.
12. Remove the transfer case shift lever boot and the transmission access cover.
13. If equipped with an automatic transmission, remove the upper bolts securing the transmission bellhousing to the engine. If equipped with a manual transmission, remove the upper bolts that secure the clutch housing to the engine.
14. Remove the starter motor.
15. If the vehicle is equipped with an automatic transmission:
   a. Remove the engine adapter plate inspection covers;
   b. Mark the assembled position of the converter and flex plate and remove the converter-to-flex plate retaining screws;
   c. Remove the remaining bolts secur-

ing the transmission bellhousing to the engine.

16. If equipped with a manual transmission, remove the lower cover of the clutch housing and the remaining bolts that secure the clutch housing to the engine.

17. Support the transmission with a floor jack.

18. Attach a suitable sling to the engine and using a hoist, lift the engine upward and forward at the same time, removing it from the vehicle.

19. Install the engine by reversing the above procedure.

ROCKER SHAFTS AND ROCKER STUDS

Removal and Installation

F-HEAD

Remove the rocker arm cover attaching bolts and remove the rocker arm cover. Remove the nuts from the rocker arm shaft support studs. Remove the intake valve pushrods from the engine. Install in the reverse order. Tighten the rocker arm retaining bolts to 30–36 ft lbs.

V6

Remove the crankcase ventilator valve from the right side valve cover. Remove the four attaching bolts from the right and left side valve covers and remove both of the valve covers.

Unscrew, but do not remove, the bolts that attach the rocker arm assemblies to the cylinder heads. Remove the rocker arm assemblies, with the bolts in place, from the cylinder heads. Mark each of the pushrods so that they can be installed in their original positions. Remove the pushrods. Install in the reverse order. Tighten the bolts to 30 ft lbs, a little a a time.

1972 AND 1974 232, 258 SIXES

Remove the valve cover by removing the six valve cover attaching screws. Loosen, but do not remove, the six bolts that attach the rocker arm assembly to the cylinder head. Lift the whole rocker arm assembly off the head with the bolts in place. Identify each of the pushrods so that they can be replaced in their original positions. Remove the pushrods. Install in reverse order. Tighten the bolts, working evenly, from the center outward. Tighten to 22 ft lbs.

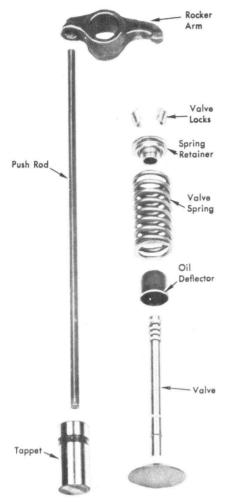

An exploded view of the valve train of the V6 and 1972 and 1974 232 and 258 Sixes

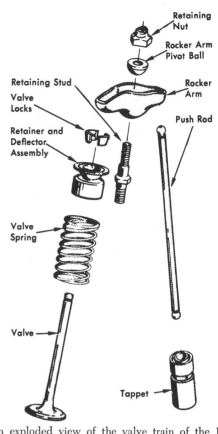

An exploded view of the valve train of the 1972 304 V8

1973, 1975–76 232, 258 Sixes and 1973–76 304 V8

On these engines the rocker arms pivot on a bridged pivot that is secured with two capscrews. The bridged pivots maintain proper rocker arm-to-valve tip alignment.

1. Remove the rocker cover and gasket.

2. Remove the two capscrews at each bridged pivot, backing off each capscrew one turn at a time to avoid breaking the bridge.

3. Remove each bridged pivot and corresponding pair of rocker arms and place them on a clean surface in the same order as they are removed.

NOTE: *Bridged pivots, capscrews, rockers, and pushrods must all be reinstalled in their original positions.*

4. Clean all the parts in a suitable sol-

vent and use compressed air to blow out the oil passages in the pushrods and the rocker arms. Replace any excessively worn parts.

5. Install rocker arms, pushrods and bridged pivots in the same positions from which they were removed.

NOTE: *Be sure that the bottom end of*

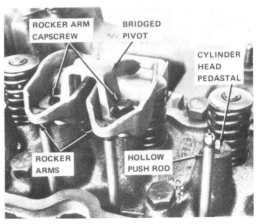

The upper valve train on 1973, 1975–76 American Motors Sixes and 1973–76 304 V8

each pushrod is centered in the plunger cap of each hydraulic valve tappet.

6. Install the capscrews and tighten them one turn at a time, alternating between the two screws on each bridge. Tighten the capscrews to 21 ft lbs on the Sixes and 10 ft lbs on the 304 V8.

7. Install the rocker cover(s) with new gasket(s).

1972 304 V8

The 304 V8 has each rocker arm individually mounted on a separate stud. Each rocker assembly consists of the following: a rocker arm retaining stud, a rocker arm pivot ball, a rocker arm, and a retaining nut which screws onto the rocker arm retaining stud. Each assembly is removed and installed separately. To remove, unscrew the rocker retaining nut from the stud and lift off the rocker arm and its pivot ball. To remove the stud from the block use a wrench. Label the push rods so that they can be installed in their original positions and remove them from the block.

When installing the rocker arm retaining studs, use caution not to cross thread them. They are designed to cause an interference fit. Lubricate the studs with high pressure grease before installing them in the head. Install the rocker arm assemblies in the reverse order of removal. Tighten the rocker arm retaining nuts to 23 ft lbs.

CYLINDER HEAD

Removal and Installation

NOTE: *It is important to note that each engine has its own head bolt tightening sequence and torque. Incorrect tightening procedure may cause head warpage and compression loss. Correct sequence and torque for each engine model is shown in this chapter.*

F-Head

1. Drain the coolant.
2. Remove the upper radiator hose.
3. Remove the carburetor.
4. On early engines remove the by-pass hose on the front of the cylinder head.
5. Remove the rocker arm cover.
6. Remove the rocker arm attaching stud nuts and rocker arm shaft assembly.
7. Remove the cylinder head bolts. One of the bolts is located below the car-

buretor mounting, inside the intake manifold.

8. Lift off the cylinder head.

9. Remove the push rods and the valve lifters.

10. Reverse the above procedure to install the cylinder head. Tighten the head bolts first to 40 ft lbs then to the specified torque in the correct sequence.

F-head cylinder head torque sequence

V6

1. Remove the intake manifold.
2. Remove the rocker cover.
3. Remove the exhaust pipes at the flanges.
4. Remove the alternator in order to remove the right head.
5. Remove the dipstick and power steering pump, if so equipped, in order to remove the left head.
6. Remove the valve cover and the rocker assemblies. Mark these parts so that they can be re-installed in exactly the same positions.

V6 cylinder head torque sequence

7. Unbolt the head bolts and lift off the cylinder head(s). It is very important that the inside of the engine be protected from dirt. The hydraulic lifters are particularly susceptible to being damaged by dirt.

8. To install, use the reverse procedure.

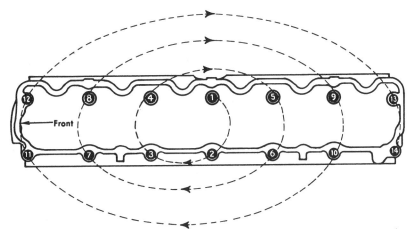

232, 258 Six cylinder head torque sequence

232, 258 SIXES

1. Drain the cooling system and disconnect the hoses at the thermostat housing.

2. Remove the cylinder head cover (valve cover), the gasket, the rocker arm assembly, and the pushrods.

NOTE: *The push rods* must *be replaced in their original positions.*

3. Remove the intake and exhaust manifold from the cylinder head.

4. Disconnect the spark plug wires and remove the spark plugs to avoid damaging them.

5. Disconnect the temperature sending unit wire, ignition coil and bracket assembly and battery ground cable from the engine.

6. Remove the cylinder head bolts, the cylinder head and gasket from the block.

7. To install reverse the above procedure. Tighten the headbolts to the specified torque, in the proper sequence.

304 V8

1. Drain the cooling system and cylinder block.

2. When removing the right cylinder head, it may be necessary to remove the heater core housing from the firewall.

3. Remove the valve cover(s) and gasket(s).

4. Remove the rocker arm assemblies and the push rods.

NOTE: *The valve train components must be replaced in their original positions.*

5. Remove the spark plugs to avoid damaging them.

6. Remove the intake manifold with the carburetor still attached.

7. Remove the exhaust pipes at the flange of the exhaust manifold. When replacing the exhaust pipes it is advisable to install new gaskets at the flange.

8. Loosen all of the drive belts.

9. Disconnect the battery ground cable and alternator bracket from the right cylinder head.

10. Disconnect the air pump and power steering pump brackets from the left cylinder head.

11. Remove the cylinder head bolts and lift the head(s) from the cylinder block.

12. Remove the cylinder head gasket from the head or the block.

13. To install, reverse the above procedure.

NOTE: *Apply an even coat of sealing compound to both sides of the new head gasket only. Wire brush the cylinder head bolts, then lightly oil them prior to installation. First, tighten all bolts to 80 ft lbs then tighten to the specified torque. Follow the correct sequence.*

Overhaul

V6, 232, 258, AND 304 V8

See the engine rebuilding section.

F-HEAD

After removing the head from the cylinder block, remove the valves from the cylinder head. These valves are the intake valves, and are removed in the following manner:

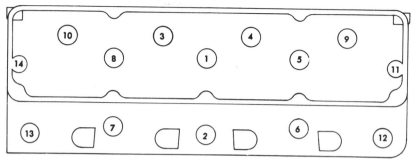

304 V8 cylinder head torque sequence

1. Depress the valve spring with a valve spring tool.

2. Remove the valve spring retainer locks.

3. Remove the rubber O-ring from the top of the valve.

4. Remove the valve spring retainer and the valve spring from the head.

5. Remove the valve from the head.

6. Replace the valves by reversing the above procedure.

NOTE: *All of the valves must be replaced in their original positions. Even though the exhaust valves are located in the block of the engine and not the head the procedure for removing them will be given here.*

1. Remove the attaching bolts from the side valve spring cover. Remove the side valve spring cover and gasket.

2. Use rags to block off the three holes in the exhaust chamber to prevent the valve retaining locks from falling into the crankcase, should they be accidentally dropped.

3. Using a valve spring compressor, compress the valve springs only on those valves which are in the closed position (valve seated against the head). Remove the exhaust valve spring retainer locks, the retainer, and the exhaust valve spring. Close the other valves by rotating the camshaft and repeat the above operation for the remaining valves.

4. Lift all of the valves from the cylinder block. If the valve cannot be removed from the block, pull the valve upward as far as possible and remove the spring. Lower the valve and remove any carbon deposits from the valve stem. This will permit removal of the valve.

5. Install by reversing the above procedure.

NOTE: *All of the valves must be re-*

placed in their original positions. Do not get the exhaust and intake valve springs mixed. They are not interchangeable.

Refer to the engine rebuilding section for further servicing of the cylinder head and its components.

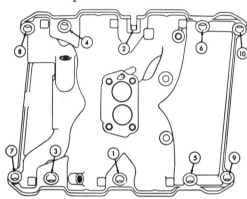

Intake manifold tightening sequence for the V6

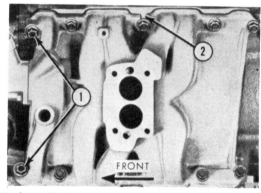

Replace all of the cap bolts in their original location in the intake manifold of the V6

1. Long bolt   2. Open bot hole

INTAKE MANIFOLD

Removal and Installation

F-Head

On the F-head engine the intake manifold is cast as an integral part of the head.

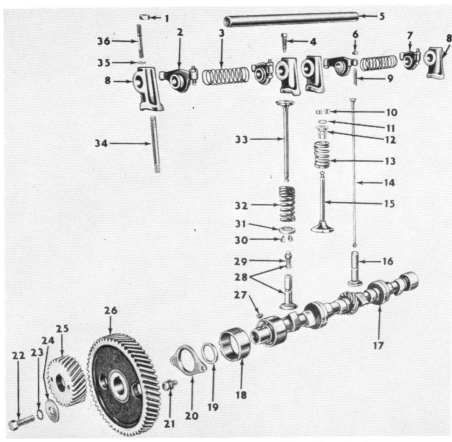

An exploded view of the valve train assembly of the F-head

1. Nut
2. Left rocker arm
3. Rocker arm shaft spring
4. Rocker shaft lock screw
5. Rocker shaft
6. Nut
7. Right rocker arm
8. Rocker arm shaft bracket
9. Intake valve tappet adjusting screw
10. Intake valve upper retainer lock
11. Oil seal
12. Intake valve spring upper retainer
13. Intake valve spring
14. Intake valve push rod
15. Intake valve
16. Intake valve tappet
17. Camshaft
18. Camshaft front bearing
19. Camshaft thrust plate spacer
20. Camshaft thrust plate
21. Bolt and lock washer
22. Bolt
23. Lockwasher
24. Camshaft gear washer
25. Crankshaft gear
26. Camshaft gear
27. Woodruff key No. 9
28. Exhaust valve tappet
29. Tappet adjusting screw
30. Spring retainer lock
31. Roto cap assembly
32. Exhaust valve spring
33. Exhaust valve
34. Rocker shaft support stud
35. Washer
36. Rocker arm cover stud

V6

1. Drain the cooling system.

2. Disconnect the crankcase vent hose, distributor vacuum hose, and the fuel line from the carburetor.

3. Disconnect the two distributor leads from the coil.

4. Disconnect the wire from the temperature sending unit.

5. Remove the ten cap bolts that hold the intake manifold to the cylinder head. They *must* be replaced in their original location.

6. Remove the intake manifold assembly and gasket from the engine.

7. Reverse the above procedure for installation. Tighten the bolts to the correct torque, and in the proper sequence.

232, 258 Sixes

The intake manifold and exhaust manifold are mounted externally on the left side of the engine and are attached to the cylinder head. The intake and exhaust manifolds are removed as a unit. On some engines, an exhaust gas recirculation valve

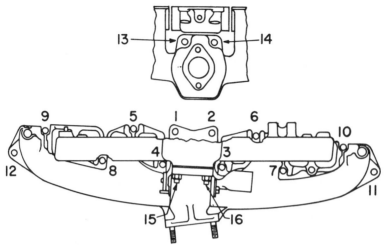

Intake manifold tightening sequence for the 232 and 258 Sixes

is mounted on the side of the intake manifold.

1. Remove the air cleaner and carburetor.

2. Disconnect the accelerator cable from the accelerator bellcrank.

3. Disconnect the PCV vacuum hose from the intake manifold.

4. Disconnect the distributor vacuum hose and electrical wires at the TCS solenoid vacuum valve.

5. Remove the TCS solenoid vacuum valve and bracket from the intake manifold. In some cases it might not be necessary to remove the TCS unit.

6. If so equipped, disconnect the EGR valve and backpressure sensor vacuum hoses.

7. Remove the power steering mounting bracket and pump and set it aside without disconnecting the hoses.

8. Remove the EGR valve and backpressure sensor, if so equipped.

9. Disconnect the exhaust pipe from the manifold flange.

10. Remove the manifold attaching bolts, nuts and clamps.

11. Separate the intake manifold and exhaust manifold from the engine as an assembly. Discard the gasket.

12. If either manifold is to be replaced, they should be separated at the heat riser area.

13. Clean the mating surfaces of the manifolds and the cylinder head before replacing the manifolds. Replace them in reverse order of the above procedure with a new gasket. Tighten the bolts and nuts to the specified torque in the proper sequence.

304 V8

1. Drain the coolant from the radiator.

2. Remove the air cleaner assembly.

3. Disconnect the spark plug wires. Remove the spark plug wire brackets from the valve covers, and the bypass valve bracket.

4. Disconnect the upper radiator hose and the by-pass hose from the intake manifold. Disconnect the heater hose from the rear of the manifold.

5. Disconnect the ignition coil bracket and lay the coil aside.

6. Disconnect the TCS solenoid vacuum valve from the right side valve cover.

7. Disconnect all lines, hoses, linkages and wires from the carburetor and intake manifold and TCS components as required.

8. Disconnect the air delivery hoses at the air distribution manifolds.

9. Disconnect the air pump diverter valve and lay the valve and the bracket assembly, including the hoses, forward of the engine.

10. Remove the intake manifold after removing the cap bolts that hold it in place. Remove and discard the side gaskets and the end seals.

11. Clean the mating surfaces of the intake manifold and the cylinder head before replacing the intake manifold. Use new gaskets and tighten the cap bolts to the correct torque. Install in reverse order of the above procedure.

EXHAUST MANIFOLD
Removal and Installation
F-Head

1. Remove the air delivery hose from the air injection tube assembly if the engine is so equipped. If not proceed to step two.
2. Remove the five nuts from the manifold studs.
3. Pull the manifold from the mounting studs. Be careful not to damage the air injection tubes if the engine is equipped with the emission control air pump.
4. Remove the gaskets from the cylinder block.
5. If the exhaust manifold is to be replaced it will be necessary to remove the air injection tubes from the exhaust manifold. The application of heat may be necessary to aid removal.
6. Use new gaskets when replacing the exhaust manifold. Make sure that the mating surfaces of both the exhaust manifold and the cylinder head are clean. Tighten the attaching nuts to the correct torque specification. Replace in reverse order of the above procedure.

V6

1. Remove the five attaching screws, one nut, and exhaust manifold(s) from the side of the cylinder head(s).
2. Use a new gasket when replacing the exhaust manifolds. Make sure that the mating surfaces of the manifold and the cylinder head are clean. Tighten the manifold nuts and bolts to the correct torque.

232, 258 Sixes

The intake and exhaust manifolds of the 232 and 258 cu in. Sixes must be removed together. See the procedure for removing and installing the intake manifold.

304 V8

1. Disconnect the spark plug wires.
2. Disconnect the air delivery hose at the distribution manifold.
3. Remove the air distribution manifold and the injection tubes.
4. Disconnect the exhaust pipe at the manifold.
5. Remove the exhaust manifold attaching bolts and washers along with the spark plug shields.

6. Separate the exhaust manifold from the cylinder head.
7. Install in reverse order of the above procedure. Clean the mating surfaces and tighten the attaching bolts to the correct torque.

TIMING GEAR COVER
Timing Gear Cover Oil Seal Replacement
F-Head

1. Remove the drive belts and crankshaft pulley.
2. Remove the attaching bolts, nuts and lock washers that hold the timing gear cover to the engine.
3. Remove the timing gear cover.
4. Remove the timing pointer.
5. Remove the timing gear cover gasket.
6. Remove and discard the crankshaft oil seal from the timing gear cover.
7. Replace in reverse order of the above procedure. Replace the crankshaft oil seal. Use a new timing gear cover gasket.

V6

1. Remove the water pump and crankshaft pulley.
2. Remove the two bolts that attach the oil pan to the timing chain cover.
3. Remove the five bolts that attach the timing chain cover to the engine block.
4. Remove the cover and gasket.
5. Remove the crankshaft front oil seal.
6. From the rear of the timing chain cover, coil new packing around the crankshaft hole in the cover so that the ends of the packing are at the top. Drive in the new packing with a punch. It will be necessary to ream out the hole to obtain clearance for the crankshaft vibration damper hub.

232, 258 Sixes

1. Remove the drive belts, engine fan and hub assembly, the accessory pulley and vibration damper.
2. Remove the oil pan to timing chain cover screws and the screws that attach the cover to the block.
3. Raise the timing chain cover just high enough to detach the retaining nibs of the oil pan neoprene seal from the bottom side of the cover. This must be done to prevent pulling the seal end tabs away from the

tongues of the oil pan gaskets which would cause a leak.

4 Remove the timing chain cover and gasket from the engine.

5. Use a razor blade to cut off the oil pan seal end tabs flush with the front face of the cylinder block and remove the seal. Clean the timing chain cover, oil pan, and cylinder block surfaces.

Trim the timing gear cover gasket as indicated before installation—232, 258 Sixes

6. Remove the crankshaft oil seal from the timing chain cover.

7. Install in reverse order of the above procedure. It will be necessary to cut the same amount from the end tabs of a new oil pan seal as was cut from the original seal, before installing the new gasket.

304 V8

1. Remove the negative battery cable.

2. Drain the cooling system and disconnect the radiator hoses and by-pass hose.

3. Remove all of the drive belts and the fan and spacer assembly.

4. Remove the alternator and the front portion of the alternator bracket as an assembly.

5. Disconnect the heater hose.

6. Remove the power steering pump, and/or the air pump, and the mounting bracket as an assembly. Do not disconnect the power steering hoses.

7. Remove the distributor cap and note the position of the rotor. Remove the distributor. (See the Engine Electrical Section.)

8. Remove the fuel pump.

9. Remove the vibration damper and pulley.

10. Remove the two front oil pan bolts and the bolts which secure the timing chain cover to the engine block.

NOTE: *The timing gear cover retaining bolts vary in length and must be installed in the same locations from which they were removed.*

11. Remove the cover by pulling forward until it is free of the locating dowel pins.

12. Clean the gasket surface of the cover and the engine block.

13. Pry out the original seal from inside the timing chain cover and clean the seal bore.

14. Drive the new seal into place from the inside with a block of wood until it contacts the outer flange of the cover.

15. Apply a light film of motor oil to the lips of the new seal.

16. Before reinstalling the timing gear cover, remove the lower locating dowel pin from the engine block. The pin is required for correct alignment of the cover and must either be reused or a replacement dowel pin installed after the cover is in position.

17. Cut both sides of the oil pan gasket flush with the engine block with a razor blade.

18. Trim a new gasket to correspond to the amount cut off at the oil pan.

19. Apply seal to both sides of the new gasket and install the gasket on the timing case cover.

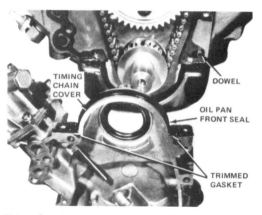

Trim the timing gear cover gasket as indicated before installation—304 V8

20. Install the new front oil pan seal.

21. Align the tongues of the new oil pan gasket pieces with the oil pan seal and cement them into place on the cover.

22. Apply a bead of sealer to the cutoff edges of the original oil pan gaskets.

23. Place the timing case cover into position and install the front oil pan bolts. Tighten the bolts slowly and evenly until the cover aligns with the upper locating dowel.

24. Install the lower dowel through the cover and drive it into the corresponding hole in the engine block.

25. Install the cover retaining bolts in the same locations from which they were removed. Tighten to 25 ft lbs.

26. Assemble the remaining components in the reverse order of removal.

Removing the timing gears with a puller—F-Head

1. Puller   2. Camshaft gear

TIMING CHAIN OR GEARS AND TENSIONER

Removal and Installation

F-HEAD

1. Remove the timing gear cover.

2. Use a puller to remove both the crankshaft and the camshaft gear from the engine after removing all attaching nuts and bolts.

3. Remove the Woodruff Keys.

Installation is as follows:

1. Install the Woodruff Key in the longer of the two keyways on the front end of the crankshaft.

2. Install the crankshaft timing gear on the front end of the crankshaft with the timing mark facing away from the cylinder block.

3. Align the keyway in the gear with the Woodruff Key and then drive or press the gear onto the crankshaft firmly against the thrust washer.

4. Turn the camshaft or the crankshaft as necessary so that the timing marks on the two gears will be together after the camshaft gear is installed.

5. Install the Woodruff Key in the keyway on the front of the camshaft.

6. Start the large timing gear on the camshaft with the timing mark facing out.

Alignment of the timing gear marks on the F-head

NOTE: *Do not drive the gear onto the camshaft as the camshaft may drive the plug out of the rear of the engine and cause an oil leak.*

7. Install the camshaft retaining screw and torque it to 30–40 ft lbs. This will draw the gear onto the camshaft as the screw is tightened. Standard running tolerance between the timing gears is 0.000 to 0.002 in.

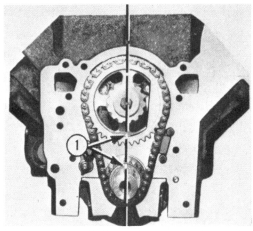

Number (1) shows alignment of the timing sprocket marks on the V6

V6

1. Remove the timing chain cover.

2. Make sure that the timing marks on the crankshaft and the camshaft sprockets are aligned. This will make installing the parts easier.

NOTE: *It is not necessary to remove the timing chain dampers (tensioners) unless they are worn or damaged and require replacement.*

3. Remove the front crankshaft oil slinger.

4. Remove the bolt and the special washer that hold the camshaft distributor drive gear and fuel pump eccentric at the forward end of the camshaft. Remove the eccentric and the gear from the camshaft.

5. Alternately pry forward the camshaft sprocket and then the crankshaft sprocket until the camshaft sprocket is pried from the camshaft.

6. Remove the camshaft sprocket, sprocket key, and timing chain from the engine.

7. Pry the crankshaft sprocket from the crankshaft.

Install as follows:

1. If the engine has not been disturbed proceed to step Number 4 for installation procedures.

2. If the engine has been disturbed turn the crankshaft so that number one piston is at top dead center.

3. Temporarily install the sprocket key and the camshaft sprocket on the camshaft. Turn the camshaft so that the index mark of the sprocket is downward. Remove the key and sprocket from the camshaft.

4. Assemble the timing chain and sprockets. Install the keys, sprockets, and chain assembly on the camshaft and crankshaft so that the index marks of both the sprockets are aligned.

NOTE: *It will be necessary to hold the spring loaded timing chain damper out of the way while installing the timing chain and sprocket assembly.*

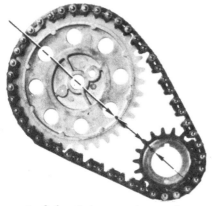

Alignment of the timing sprocket marks on the 232 and 258 Sixes

5. Install the front oil slinger on the crankshaft with the inside diameter against the sprocket (concave side toward the front of the engine).

6. Install the fuel pump eccentric on the camshaft and the key, with the oil groove of the eccentric forward.

7. Install the distributor drive gear on the camshaft. Secure the gear and eccentric to the camshaft with the retaining washer and bolt.

8. Torque the bolt to 40–55 ft lbs.

232, 258 SIXES

1. Remove the drive belts, engine fan and hub assembly, accessory pulley, vibration damper and timing chain cover.

2. Remove the oil seal from the timing chain cover.

3. Remove the camshaft sprocket retaining bolt and washer.

4. Rotate the crankshaft until the timing mark on the crankshaft sprocket is closest to and in a center line with the timing pointer of the camshaft sprocket.

5. Remove the crankshaft sprocket, camshaft sprocket and timing chain as an assembly. Disassemble the chain and sprockets.

Installation is as follows:

1. Assemble the timing chain, crankshaft sprocket and camshaft sprocket with the timing marks aligned.

2. Install the assembly to the crankshaft and the camshaft.

3. Install the camshaft sprocket retaining bolt and washer and tighten to 45–55 ft lbs.

4. Install the timing chain cover and a new oil seal.

5. Install the vibration damper, accessory pulley, engine fan and hub assembly and drive belts. Tighten the belts to the proper tension.

304 V8

1. Remove the timing chain cover and gasket.

2. Remove the crankshaft oil slinger.

3. Remove the camshaft sprocket retaining bolt and washer, distributor drive gear and fuel pump eccentric.

4. Rotate the crankshaft until the timing mark on the crankshaft sprocket is adjacent to, and on a center line with, the timing mark on the camshaft sprocket.

5. Remove the crankshaft sprocket,

Alignment of the timing sprocket marks on the 304 V8

camshaft sprocket and timing chain as an assembly.

6. Clean all of the gasket surfaces.

Installation is as follows:

1. Assemble the timing chain, crankshaft sprocket and camshaft sprocket with the timing marks on both sprockets aligned.

2. Install the assembly to the crankshaft and the camshaft.

3. Install the fuel pump eccentric, distributor drive gear, washer and retaining bolt. Tighten the bolt to 25–35 ft lbs.

4. Install the crankshaft oil slinger.

5. Install the timing chain cover using a new gasket and oil seal.

CAMSHAFT

Removal and Installation

F-HEAD

1. Remove the engine.

2. Remove the exhaust manifold.

3. Remove the oil pump and the distributor.

4. Remove the crankshaft pulley.

5. Remove the cylinder head.

6. Remove the exhaust valves.

7. Remove the timing gear cover and the crankshaft and camshaft timing gears.

8. Remove the front end plate.

9. Push the intake and exhaust valve lifters into the cylinder block as far as possible so that the ends of the lifters are not in contact with the camshaft.

10. Secure each tappet in the raised position by installing a clip-type clothes pin on the shank of each tappet or tie them up in the valve chamber.

11. Remove the camshaft thrust plate attaching screws. Remove the camshaft thrust plate and spacer.

12. Pull the camshaft forward out of the cylinder block being careful to prevent damage to the camshaft bearing surfaces.

13. Install in the reverse order of the above procedure.

V6

1. Remove the engine.

2. Remove the intake manifold and carburetor assembly.

3. Remove the distributor.

4. Remove the fuel pump.

5. Remove the alternator, drive belts, cooling fan, fan pulley, and water pump.

6. Remove the crankshaft pulley and the vibration damper.

7. Remove the oil pump.

8. Remove the timing chain cover.

9. Remove the timing chain and the camshaft sprocket, along with the distributor drive gear and the fuel pump eccentric.

10. Remove the rocker arm assemblies.

NOTE: *The push rods need not be removed. But if they are, be sure that they are replaced in their original positions.*

11. Lift the tappets up so that they are not in contact with the camshaft. Use wire clips or clip-type clothes pins to hold the tappets up.

12. Carefully guide the camshaft forward out of the engine. Avoid marring the bearing surfaces.

13. Install in reverse order of the above procedure.

232, 258 SIXES

1. Drain the cooling system and remove the radiator.

2. Remove the valve cover and gasket, the rocker assemblies, push rods, cylinder head and gasket and the lifters.

NOTE: *The valve train components must be replaced in their original locations.*

3. Remove the drive belts, cooling fan, fan hub assembly, vibration damper and the timing chain cover.

4. Remove the fuel pump and distribu-

tor assembly, including the spark plug wires.

5. Rotate the crankshaft until the timing mark of the crankshaft sprocket is adjacent to, and on a center line with, the timing mark of the camshaft sprocket.

6. Remove the crankshaft sprocket, camshaft sprocket, and the timing chain as an assembly.

7. Remove the front bumper or grille as required and carefully slide out the camshaft.

8. Install in reverse order of the above procedure.

304 V8

1. Disconnect the battery cables.

2. Drain the radiator and both banks of the block. Remove the lower hose at the radiator, the by-pass hose at the pump, the thermostat housing and the radiator.

3. Remove the distributor, all wires, and the coil from the manifold.

4. Remove the intake manifold as an assembly.

5. Remove the valve covers, rocker arms and push rods.

6. Remove the lifters.

NOTE: *The valve train components must be replaced in their original locations.*

7. Remove the cooling fan and hub assembly, fuel pump, and heater hose at the water pump.

8. Remove the alternator and bracket as an assembly. Just move it aside, do not disconnect the wiring.

9. Remove the crankshaft pulley and the damper. Remove the lower radiator hose at the water pump.

10. Remove the timing chain cover.

11. Remove the distributor-oil pump drive gear, fuel pump eccentric, sprockets and the timing chain.

12. Remove the hood catch support.

13. Remove the camshaft carefully by sliding it forward out of the engine.

14. Install by reversing the above procedure.

PISTONS AND CONNECTING RODS

Removal and Installation

F-HEAD

The pistons and connecting rods can be removed from the engine with the engine

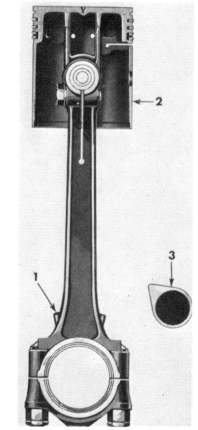

F-head piston and rod assembly

1. Oil spray hole
2. Piston skirt T-slot
3. Relative position of camshaft

in the vehicle. Refer to the engine rebuilding section for the proper procedure. The connecting rod identifying number must be toward the camshaft side of the block.

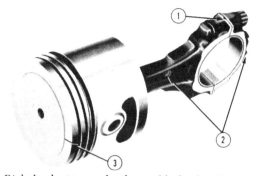

Right bank piston and rod assembly for the V6

1. Oil spurt up
2. Boss on cap and rod forward
3. Notch on piston forward

Mark all pistons and rods so that they can be replaced in their original positions.

V6

Use connecting rod bolt guides on the bolts to hold the upper half of the bearing shell in place when removing the bearing caps and bearings from the lower half of the connecting rods.

Place the notch on the pistons forward and the oil spurt hole in the bottom of the connecting rod facing up.

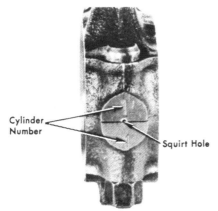

Connecting rod numbering and squirt hole location for the 232 and 258 Sixes

232, 258 Sixes and 304 V8

The connecting rods and caps are stamped with the number of the cylinder to which they belong. Replace them in their original positions.

The numbered sides and squirt hole must face the camshaft when assembled in the Sixes. The numbered sides must face out on the 304 V8.

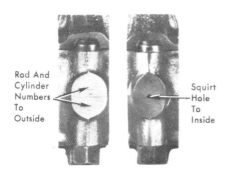

Connecting rod numbering and squirt hole location for the 304 V8

Engine Lubrication

OIL PAN

Removal and Installation

F-Head, V6

To remove the oil pan on the F-head and the V6, remove the oil pan attaching bolts and remove the oil pan. Clean all of the attaching surfaces and install new gaskets.

232, 258 Sixes and 304 V8

1. Raise the vehicle and drain the engine oil.

2. Remove the starter motor.

3. Place a jack under the transmission bell housing. Disconnect the engine right support cushion bracket from the block and raise the engine to allow sufficient clearance for oil pan removal.

4. Remove the oil pan attaching bolts and remove the oil pan.

5. Remove the oil pan front and rear neoprene oil seals and the side gaskets. Thoroughly clean the gasket surfaces of the oil pan and the engine block. Remove all of the sludge and dirt from the oil pan sump.

6. Apply a generous amount of RTV silicone to the end tabs of a new oil pan front seal and install the seal to the timing case cover.

7. Cement new oil pan side gaskets into position on the engine block and apply a generous amount of RTV silicone to the side gasket contacting surface of the seal end tabs.

8. Install the seal in the recess of the rear main bearing cap, making sure that it is fully seated.

9. Coat the oil pan contacting surface of the front and rear oil pan seals with engine oil.

10. Install the oil pan and assemble the engine mount in the reverse order of removal. Make sure that the crankcase drain plug is installed and tightened.

REAR MAIN OIL SEAL

Replacement

F-Head, V6, 232 and 258 Sixes and 304 V8

1. Remove the engine from the vehicle.

2. Remove the timing chain cover and the crankshaft timing gear.

3. Remove the oil pan, oil float support and the oil float.

4. Slide the crankshaft thrust washer and all of the end-play adjusting shims off the front end of the crankshaft.

5. Move the two pieces of the rear main bearing cap packing away from the side of the bearing cap and the cylinder block.

6. You will now be able to see the marks on the bearing caps and the cylinder block for bearing number and position.

7. Remove the screws and lockwashers that attach the main bearing caps to the cylinder block. Use a lifting bar beneath the ends of each bearing cap. Be careful not to exert too much pressure which could damage the cap or the dowels they fit onto. Lift each cap evenly on both sides until free of the dowels. If there is any reason to believe that any of the dowels have become bent during bearing cap removal, remove them and install new dowels.

8. Remove the crankshaft.

9. Remove the upper half of the rear main bearing oil seal from the cylinder block and the lower half from the oil seal groove in the rear main bearing cap.

10. Install the main bearing caps and bearings on the cylinder block in their original positions.

11. Reassemble the engine in reverse order of the above procedure.

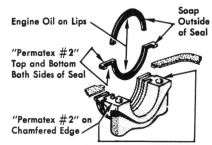

Rear main oil seal and cap assembly for the American Motors engines

NOTE: *It is possible to replace the rear main rubber seal without removing the crankshaft. The procedure is as follows:*

1. Loosen the crankshaft cap bolts and lower the crankshaft not more than $\frac{1}{32}$ in. Remove the rear main bearing cap. Do not turn the crankshaft while it is loosened.

2. Push the seal around the groove until it can be gripped and removed with a pair of pliers.

3. Coat the new seal with clean motor oil and slide it into the groove until $\frac{3}{8}$ in. protrudes from the groove. On American Motors engines push the seal around until its ends are flush with the block.

4. Install the other half of the seal in the bearing cap with $\frac{3}{8}$ in. protruding from the opposite side. This is so that the juncture of the two halves of the seal is not at the same point as the juncture of the bearing cap and the cylinder block.

5. Install the rear main bearing cap and tighten all the caps to the proper torque. Be sure that the caps have not fallen out of place and that they are tightened in a straight manner.

OIL PUMP

Removal and Installation

F-HEAD

1. Set number one piston at TDC in order to reinstall the oil pump without disturbing the ignition timing.

2. Remove the distributor cover and note the position of the rotor. Keep the rotor in that position when the oil pump is installed.

3. Remove the cap screws and lockwashers that attach the oil pump to the cylinder block. Carefully slide the oil pump and its drive shaft out of the cylinder block.

The oil pump is driven by the camshaft by means of a spiral gear. The distributor in turn is driven by the oil pump by means of a tongue on the end of the distributor shaft which engages a slot in the end of the oil pump shaft. Because the tongue and the slot are both machined off center, the two shafts can be meshed in only one position. Since the position of the distributor shaft determines the timing of the engine, and is controlled by the oil pump shaft, the position of the oil pump shaft with respect to the camshaft is important.

If only the oil pump has been removed, install it so that the slot in the end of the shaft lines up with the tip of the distributor shaft and allows that shaft to slip into it without disturbing the original position of the distributor. If the engine has been disturbed or both the distributor and the oil pump have been removed, follow the procedure given below.

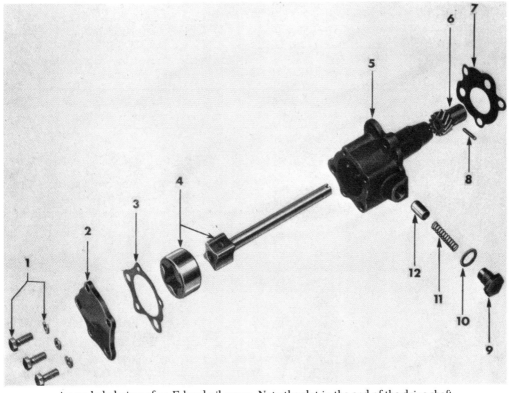

An exploded view of an F-head oil pump. Note the slot in the end of the drive shaft

1. Cover screw	5. Body assembly	9. Relief valve retainer
2. Cover	6. Driven gear	10. Relief valve retainer gasket
3. Cover gasket	7. Pump gasket	11. Relief valve spring
4. Shaft and rotors	8. Gear retaining pin	12. Relief valve plunger

1. Turn the crankshaft to align the timing marks on the crankshaft and camshaft timing gears.

2. Install the oil pump gasket on the pump.

3. With the wider side of the shaft on top, start the oil pump drive shaft into the opening in the cylinder keeping the mounting holes in the body of the pump in alignment with the holes in the cylinder block.

4. Insert a long blade screwdriver into the distributor shaft opening in the side of the cylinder block and engage the slot in the oil pump shaft. Turn the shaft so that the slot is positioned at what would be roughly the nine-thirty position on a clock face.

5. Remove the screw driver and observe the position of the slot in the end of the oil pump shaft to make certain it is properly positioned.

6. Replace the screwdriver and, while turning the screwdriver clockwise to guide the oil pump drive shaft gear into engagement with the camshaft gear, press against the oil pump to force it into position.

7. Remove the screwdriver and again observe the position of the slot. If the installation was properly made, the slot will be in a position roughly equivalent to the eleven o'clock position on the face of a clock, with the wider side of the shaft still on the top. If the slot is improperly positioned, remove the oil pump and repeat the operation.

8. Coat the threads of the capscrews with gasket cement and secure the oil pump in place.

V6

1. Remove the oil filter.

2. Disconnect the wire from the oil pressure indicator switch in the filter by-pass valve cap.

3. Remove the screws that attach the oil pump cover assembly to the timing chain cover.

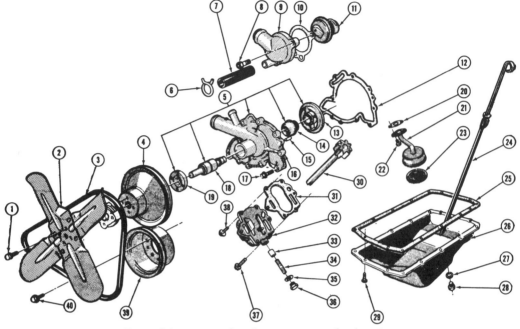

Engine lubrication and cooling components for the V6

1. Bolt and lock washer
2. Fan assembly
3. Fan and alternator belt
4. Fan driven pulley
5. Water pump assembly
6. Hose clamp
7. Thermostat by-pass hose
8. Hex head bolt
9. Water outlet elbow
10. Water outlet elbow gasket
11. Thermostat
12. Water pump gasket
13. Impeller and insert, water pump
14. Water pump seal

15. Dowel pin
16. Water pump cover
17. Bolt
18. Water pump shaft and bearing
19. Fan hub
20. Oil suction pipe gasket
21. Oil suction housing, pipe and flange
22. Bolt
23. Oil pump screen
24. Oil dipstick
25. Oil pan gasket
26. Oil pan assembly
27. Drain plug gasket

28. Drain plug
29. Screw and lockwasher
30. Oil pump shaft and gear
31. Oil pump cover gasket
32. Valve by-pass and cover assembly
33. Oil pressure valve
34. Valve by-pass spring
35. Oil pressure valve cap gasket
36. Oil pressure valve cap
37. Screw
38. Screw
39. Fan driving pulley
40. Hex head bolt

4. Remove the cover assembly and slide out the oil pump.

5. Install in reverse order of the above procedure.

232, 258 Sixes

1. Drain the oil and remove the oil pan.

2. Remove the oil pump retaining screws and separate the oil pump and gasket from the engine block.

NOTE: *Do not disturb the position of the oil pick-up tube and screen assembly in the pump body. If the tube is moved within the pump body, a new assembly must be installed to assure an airtight seal.*

3. Install in reverse order of the above procedure.

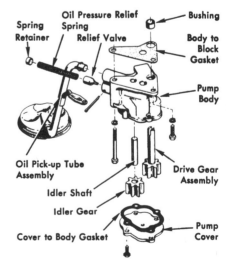

Oil pump assembly for the 232 and 258 Sixes

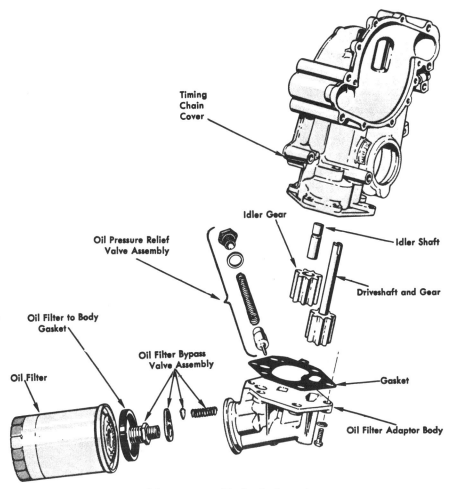

Timing Chain Cover

Idler Gear

Idler Shaft

Oil Pressure Relief Valve Assembly

Driveshaft and Gear

Oil Filter to Body Gasket

Oil Filter Bypass Valve Assembly

Oil Filter

Gasket

Oil Filter Adaptor Body

Oil pump assembly for the 304 V8

304 V8

Remove the retaining screws and separate the oil pump cover, gasket and oil filter (as an assembly) from the pump body in the timing chain cover. Install in reverse order with a new filter and gasket.

Engine Cooling

The satisfactory performance of any water cooled engine is controlled to a great extent by the proper operation of the cooling system. The engine block is fully water jacketed to prevent distortion of the cylinder walls. Directed cooling and water holes in the cylinder head causes water to flow past the valve seats, which are one of the hottest parts of any engine, and carry the heat away from the valves and seats.

The minimum temperature of the coolant is controlled by a thermostat mounted in the outlet passage of the engine. When the coolant temperature is below the temperature rating of the thermostat, the thermostat remains closed and the coolant is directed through the radiator-by-pass hose to the water pump. If the coolant temperature is too high, the thermostat opens and coolant flow is directed to the top of the radiator. The radiator dissipates the excess engine heat before the coolant is recirculated through the engine.

The cooling system is pressurized and the operating pressure is regulated by the rating of the radiator cap which contains a relief valve.

RADIATOR

Removal and Installation

1. Drain the radiator by opening the drain cock and removing the radiator pressure cap.

2. Remove the upper and lower hose clamps and hoses at the radiator.

3. Disconnect the automatic transmission oil cooler lines at the radiator, if so equipped. Remove the radiator shroud from the radiator, if so equipped.

4. Remove all attaching screws that secure the radiator to the radiator body support.

5. Remove the radiator.

6. Replace in reverse order of the above procedure.

THERMOSTAT

Removal and Installation

The thermostat is located in the water outlet housing at the front of the engine. On the V6 and the 304 V8 the water outlet housing is located in the front of the intake manifold.

The early F-heads have a 165° thermostat. Later F-heads and the V6 have 190° thermostats. The 232 and 258 Sixes have 205° thermostats. The 304 V8 has a 195° thermostat.

To remove the thermostats from all of these engines, first drain the cooling system. It is not necessary to disconnect or remove any of the hoses. Remove the two attaching screws and lift the housing from the engine. Remove the thermostat and the gasket. To install, place the thermostat in the housing with the spring inside the engine. Install a new gasket with a small amount of sealing compound applied to both sides. Install the water outlet and tighten the attaching bolts to 30 ft lbs. Refill the cooling system.

Engine Rebuilding

This section describes, in detail, the procedures involved in rebuilding a typical engine. The procedures specifically refer to an inline engine, however, they are basically identical to those used in rebuilding engines of nearly all design and configurations. Procedures for servicing atypical engines (i.e., horizontally opposed) are described in the appropriate section, although in most cases, cylinder head reconditioning procedures described in this chapter will apply.

The section is divided into two sections. The first, Cylinder Head Reconditioning, assumes that the cylinder head is removed from the engine, all manifolds are removed, and the cylinder head is on a workbench. The camshaft should be removed from overhead cam cylinder heads. The second section, Cylinder Block Reconditioning, covers the block, pistons, connecting rods and crankshaft. It is assumed that the engine is mounted on a work stand, and the cylinder head and all accessories are removed.

Procedures are identified as follows:

Unmarked—Basic procedures that must be performed in order to successfully complete the rebuilding process.

Starred (*)—Procedures that should be performed to ensure maximum performance and engine life.

Double starred (**)—Procedures that may be performed to increase engine performance and reliability. These procedures are usually reserved for extremely heavy-duty or competition usage.

In many cases, a choice of methods is also provided. Methods are identified in the same manner as procedures. The choice of method for a procedure is at the discretion of the user.

The tools required for the basic rebuilding procedure should, with minor exceptions, be those

TORQUE (ft. lbs.)*

U.S.

Bolt Diameter (inches)	Bolt Grade (SAE)				Wrench Size (inches)	
	1 and 2	5	6	8	Bolt	Nut
1/4	5	7	10	10.5	3/8	7/16
5/16	9	14	19	22	1/2	9/16
3/8	15	25	34	37	9/16	5/8
7/16	24	40	55	60	5/8	3/4
1/2	37	60	85	92	3/4	13/16
9/16	53	88	120	132	7/8	7/8
5/8	74	120	167	180	15/16	1
3/4	120	200	280	296	1-1/8	1-1/8
7/8	190	302	440	473	1-5/16	1-5/16
1	282	466	660	714	1-1/2	1-1/2

Metric

Bolt Diameter (mm)	Bolt Grade				Wrench Size (mm) Bolt and Nut
	5D	8G	10K	12K	
6	5	6	8	10	10
8	10	16	22	27	14
10	19	31	40	49	17
12	34	54	70	86	19
14	55	89	117	137	22
16	83	132	175	208	24
18	111	182	236	283	27
22	182	284	394	464	32
24	261	419	570	689	36

*—Torque values are for lightly oiled bolts. CAUTION: Bolts threaded into aluminum require much less torque.

General Torque Specifications

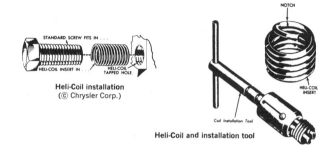

Heli-Coil installation
(© Chrysler Corp.)

Heli-Coil and installation tool

Heli-Coil Insert			Drill	Tap	Insert. Tool	Extract- ing Tool
Thread Size	Part No.	Insert Length (In.)	Size	Part No.	Part No.	Part No.
1/2 -20	1185-4	3/8	17/64 (.266)	4 CPB	528-4N	1227-6
5/16-18	1185-5	15/32	Q (.332)	5 CPB	528-5N	1227-6
3/8 -16	1185-6	9/16	X (.397)	6 CPB	528-6N	1227-6
7/16-14	1185-7	21/32	29/64 (.453)	7 CPB	528-7N	1227-16
1/2 -13	1185-8	3/4	33/64 (.516)	8 CPB	528-8N	1227-16

Heli-Coil Specifications

included in a mechanic's tool kit. An accurate torque wrench, and a dial indicator (reading in thousandths) mounted on a universal base should be available. Bolts and nuts with no torque specification should be tightened according to size (see chart). Special tools, where required, all are readily available from the major tool suppliers (i.e., Craftsman, Snap-On, K-D). The services of a competent automotive machine shop must also be readily available.

When assembling the engine, any parts that will be in frictional contact must be pre-lubricated, to provide protection on initial start-up. Vortex Pre-Lube, STP, or any product specifically formulated for this purpose may be used. NOTE: *Do not use engine oil.* Where semi-permanent (locked but removable) installation of bolts or nuts is desired, threads should be cleaned and coated with Loctite. Studs may be permanently installed using Loctite Stud and Bearing Mount.

Aluminum has become increasingly popular for use in engines, due to its low weight and excellent heat transfer characteristics. The following precautions must be observed when handling aluminum engine parts:

—Never hot-tank aluminum parts.

—Remove all aluminum parts (identification tags, etc.) from engine parts before hot-tanking (otherwise they will be removed during the process).

—Always coat threads lightly with engine oil or anti-seize compounds before installation, to prevent seizure.

—Never over-torque bolts or spark plugs in aluminum threads. Should stripping occur, threads can be restored according to the following procedure, using Heli-Coil thread inserts:

Tap drill the hole with the stripped threads to the specified size (see chart). Using the specified tap (NOTE: *Heli-Coil tap sizes refer to the size thread being replaced, rather than the actual tap size*), tap the hole for the Heli-Coil. Place the insert on the proper installation tool (see chart). Apply pressure on the insert while winding it clockwise into the hole, until the top of the insert is one turn below the surface. Remove the installation tool, and break the installation tang from the bottom of the in-

sert by moving it up and down. If the Heli-Coil must be removed, tap the removal tool firmly into the hole, so that it engages the top thread, and turn the tool counter-clockwise to extract the insert.

Snapped bolts or studs may be removed, using a stud extractor (unthreaded) or Vise-Grip pliers (threaded). Penetrating oil (e.g., Liquid Wrench) will often aid in breaking frozen threads. In cases where the stud or bolt is flush with, or below the surface, proceed as follows:

Drill a hole in the broken stud or bolt, approximately ½ its diameter. Select a screw extractor (e.g., Easy-Out) of the proper size, and tap it into the stud or bolt. Turn the extractor counterclockwise to remove the stud or bolt.

Magnaflux and Zyglo are inspection techniques used to locate material flaws, such as stress cracks. Magnafluxing coats the part with fine magnetic particles, and subjects the part to a magnetic field. Cracks cause breaks

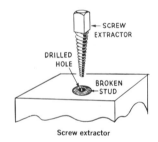

Screw extractor

in the magnetic field, which are outlined by the particles. Since Magnaflux is a magnetic process, it is applicable only to ferrous materials. The Zyglo process coats the material with a fluorescent dye penetrant, and then subjects it to blacklight inspection, under which cracks glow bright-

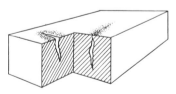

Magnaflux indication of cracks

ly. Parts made of any material may be tested using Zyglo. While Magnaflux and Zyglo are excellent for general inspection, and locating hidden defects, specific checks of suspected cracks may be made at lower cost and more readily using spot check dye. The dye is sprayed onto the suspected area, wiped off, and the area is then sprayed with a developer. Cracks then will show up bright-ly. Spot check dyes will only indicate surface cracks; therefore, structural cracks below the surface may escape detection. When questionable, the part should be tested using Magnaflux or Zyglo.

CYLINDER HEAD RECONDITIONING

Procedure	*Method*
Identify the valves:  **Valve identification** (© SAAB)	Invert the cylinder head, and number the valve faces front to rear, using a permanent felt-tip marker.
Remove the rocker arms:	Remove the rocker arms with shaft(s) or balls and nuts. Wire the sets of rockers, balls and nuts together, and identify according to the corresponding valve.
Remove the valves and springs:	Using an appropriate valve spring compressor (depending on the configuration of the cylinder head), compress the valve springs. Lift out the keepers with needlenose pliers, release the compressor, and remove the valve, spring, and spring retainer.
Check the valve stem-to-guide clearance:  **Checking the valve stem-to-guide clearance** (© American Motors Corp.)	Clean the valve stem with lacquer thinner or a similar solvent to remove all gum and varnish. Clean the valve guides using solvent and an expanding wire-type valve guide cleaner. Mount a dial indicator so that the stem is at 90° to the valve stem, as close to the valve guide as possible. Move the valve off its seat, and measure the valve guide-to-stem clearance by moving the stem back and forth to actuate the dial indicator. Measure the valve stems using a micrometer, and compare to specifications, to determine whether stem or guide wear is responsible for excessive clearance.
De-carbon the cylinder head and valves: 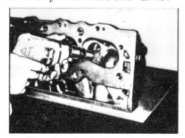 **Removing carbon from the cylinder head** (© Chevrolet Div. G.M. Corp.)	Chip carbon away from the valve heads, combustion chambers, and ports, using a chisel made of hardwood. Remove the remaining deposits with a stiff wire brush. NOTE: *Ensure that the deposits are actually removed, rather than burnished.*

Procedure	Method
Hot-tank the cylinder head:	Have the cylinder head hot-tanked to remove grease, corrosion, and scale from the water passages. NOTE: *In the case of overhead cam cylinder heads, consult the operator to determine whether the camshaft bearings will be damaged by the caustic solution.*
Degrease the remaining cylinder head parts:	Using solvent (i.e., Gunk), clean the rockers, rocker shaft(s) (where applicable), rocker balls and nuts, springs, spring retainers, and keepers. Do not remove the protective coating from the springs.
Check the cylinder head for warpage:  ①③ CHECK DIAGONALLY ② CHECK ACROSS CENTER A 2895-A **Checking the cylinder head for warpage** (© Ford Motor Co.)	Place a straight-edge across the gasket surface of the cylinder head. Using feeler gauges, determine the clearance at the center of the straight-edge. Measure across both diagonals, along the longitudinal centerline, and across the cylinder head at several points. If warpage exceeds .003″ in a 6″ span, or .006″ over the total length, the cylinder head must be resurfaced. NOTE: *If warpage exceeds the manufacturers maximum tolerance for material removal, the cylinder head must be replaced.* When milling the cylinder heads of V-type engines, the intake manifold mounting position is altered, and must be corrected by milling the manifold flange a proportionate amount.
** Porting and gasket matching:  **Marking the cylinder head for gasket matching** (© Petersen Publishing Co.)  **Port configuration before and after gasket matching** (© Petersen Publishing Co.)	** Coat the manifold flanges of the cylinder head with Prussian blue dye. Glue intake and exhaust gaskets to the cylinder head in their installed position using rubber cement and scribe the outline of the ports on the manifold flanges. Remove the gaskets. Using a small cutter in a hand-held power tool (i.e., Dremel Moto-Tool), gradually taper the walls of the port out to the scribed outline of the gasket. Further enlargement of the ports should include the removal of sharp edges and radiusing of sharp corners. Do not alter the valve guides. NOTE: *The most efficient port configuration is determined only by extensive testing. Therefore, it is best to consult someone experienced with the head in question to determine the optimum alterations.*

Procedure	Method
** Polish the ports:	** Using a grinding stone with the above mentioned tool, polish the walls of the intake and exhaust ports, and combustion chamber. Use progressively finer stones until all surface imperfections are removed. NOTE: *Through testing, it has been determined that a smooth surface is more effective than a mirror polished surface in intake ports, and vice-versa in exhaust ports.*

Relieved and polished ports
(© Petersen Publishing Co.)

Polished combustion chamber
(© Petersen Publishing Co.)

Procedure	Method
* Knurling the valve guides:	* Valve guides which are not excessively worn or distorted may, in some cases, be knurled rather than replaced. Knurling is a process in which metal is displaced and raised, thereby reducing clearance. Knurling also provides excellent oil control. The possibility of knurling rather than replacing valve guides should be discussed with a machinist.

Cut-away view of a knurled valve guide
(© Petersen Publishing Co.)

Procedure	Method
Replacing the valve guides: NOTE: *Valve guides should only be replaced if damaged or if an oversize valve stem is not available.*	Depending on the type of cylinder head, valve guides may be pressed, hammered, or shrunk in. In cases where the guides are shrunk into the head, replacement should be left to an equipped machine shop. In other cases, the guides are replaced as follows: Press or tap the valve guides out of the head using a stepped drift (see illustration). Determine the height above the boss that the guide must extend, and obtain a stack of washers, their I.D. similar to the guide's O.D., of that height. Place the stack of washers on the guide, and insert the guide into the boss. NOTE: *Valve guides are often tapered or beveled for installation.* Using the stepped installation tool (see illustration), press or tap the guides into position. Ream the guides according to the size of the valve stem.

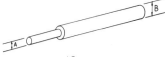

A-VALVE GUIDE I.D.
B-SLIGHTLY SMALLER THAN VALVE GUIDE O.D.

Valve guide removal tool

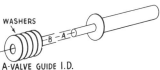

WASHERS

A-VALVE GUIDE I.D.
B-LARGER THAN THE VALVE GUIDE O.D.

Valve guide installation tool (with washers used during installation)

Procedure	*Method*
Replacing valve seat inserts:	Replacement of valve seat inserts which are worn beyond resurfacing or broken, if feasible, must be done by a machine shop.
Resurfacing (grinding) the valve face:  Grinding a valve (ⓒ Subaru) 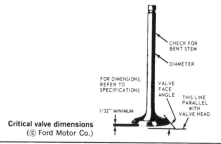 Critical valve dimensions (ⓒ Ford Motor Co.)	Using a valve grinder, resurface the valves according to specifications. CAUTION: *Valve face angle is not always identical to valve seat angle.* A minimum margin of 1/32″ should remain after grinding the valve. The valve stem tip should also be squared and resurfaced, by placing the stem in the V-block of the grinder, and turning it while pressing lightly against the grinding wheel.
Resurfacing the valve seats using reamers:  Reaming the valve seat (ⓒ S.p.A. Fiat) Valve seat width and centering (ⓒ Ford Motor Co.)	Select a reamer of the correct seat angle, slightly larger than the diameter of the valve seat, and assemble it with a pilot of the correct size. Install the pilot into the valve guide, and using steady pressure, turn the reamer clockwise. CAUTION: *Do not turn the reamer counter-clockwise.* Remove only as much material as necessary to clean the seat. Check the concentricity of the seat (see below). If the dye method is not used, coat the valve face with Prussian blue dye, install and rotate it on the valve seat. Using the dye marked area as a centering guide, center and narrow the valve seat to specifications with correction cutters. NOTE: *When no specifications are available, minimum seat width for exhaust valves should be 5/64″, intake valves 1/16″.* After making correction cuts, check the position of the valve seat on the valve face using Prussian blue dye.
* Resurfacing the valve seats using a grinder:  Grinding a valve seat (ⓒ Subaru)	Select a pilot of the correct size, and a coarse stone of the correct seat angle. Lubricate the pilot if necessary, and install the tool in the valve guide. Move the stone on and off the seat at approximately two cycles per second, until all flaws are removed from the seat. Install a fine stone, and finish the seat. Center and narrow the seat using correction stones, as described above.

Procedure	Method
Checking the valve seat concentricity: 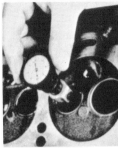 Checking the valve seat concentricity using a dial gauge (© American Motors Corp.)	Coat the valve face with Prussian blue dye, install the valve, and rotate it on the valve seat. If the entire seat becomes coated, and the valve is known to be concentric, the seat is concentric. * Install the dial gauge pilot into the guide, and rest the arm on the valve seat. Zero the gauge, and rotate the arm around the seat. Run-out should not exceed .002″.
* Lapping the valves: NOTE: *Valve lapping is done to ensure efficient sealing of resurfaced valves and seats. Valve lapping alone is not recommended for use as a resurfacing procedure.* 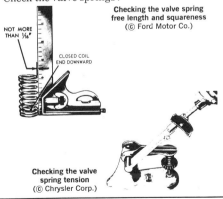 Hand lapping the valves 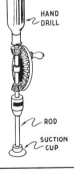 HAND DRILL ROD SUCTION CUP Home made mechanical valve lapping tool	* Invert the cylinder head, lightly lubricate the valve stems, and install the valves in the head as numbered. Coat valve seats with fine grinding compound, and attach the lapping tool suction cup to a valve head (NOTE: *Moisten the suction cup*). Rotate the tool between the palms, changing position and lifting the tool often to prevent grooving. Lap the valve until a smooth, polished seat is evident. Remove the valve and tool, and rinse away all traces of grinding compound. ** Fasten a suction cup to a piece of drill rod, and mount the rod in a hand drill. Proceed as above, using the hand drill as a lapping tool. CAUTION: *Due to the higher speeds involved when using the hand drill, care must be exercised to avoid grooving the seat.* Lift the tool and change direction of rotation often.
Check the valve springs: Checking the valve spring free length and squareness (© Ford Motor Co.) NOT MORE THAN 1/16″ CLOSED COIL END DOWNWARD Checking the valve spring tension (© Chrysler Corp.)	Place the spring on a flat surface next to a square. Measure the height of the spring, and rotate it against the edge of the square to measure distortion. If spring height varies (by comparison) by more than 1/16″ or if distortion exceeds 1/16″, replace the spring. ** In addition to evaluating the spring as above, test the spring pressure at the installed and compressed (installed height minus valve lift) height using a valve spring tester. Springs used on small displacement engines (up to 3 liters) should be ± 1 lb. of all other springs in either position. A tolerance of ± 5 lbs. is permissible on larger engines.

Procedure	*Method*
* Install valve stem seals:  **Valve stem seal installation** (© Ford Motor Co.) SEAL	* Due to the pressure differential that exists at the ends of the intake valve guides (atmospheric pressure above, manifold vacuum below), oil is drawn through the valve guides into the intake port. This has been alleviated somewhat since the addition of positive crankcase ventilation, which lowers the pressure above the guides. Several types of valve stem seals are available to reduce blow-by. Certain seals simply slip over the stem and guide boss, while others require that the boss be machined. Recently, Teflon guide seals have become popular. Consult a parts supplier or machinist concerning availability and suggested usages. NOTE: *When installing seals, ensure that a small amount of oil is able to pass the seal to lubricate the valve guides; otherwise, excessive wear may result.*
Install the valves:	Lubricate the valve stems, and install the valves in the cylinder head as numbered. Lubricate and position the seals (if used, see above) and the valve springs. Install the spring retainers, compress the springs, and insert the keys using needlenose pliers or a tool designed for this purpose. NOTE: *Retain the keys with wheel bearing grease during installation.*
Checking valve spring installed height: 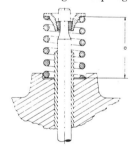  **Valve spring installed height dimension** (© Porsche) **Measuring valve spring installed height** (© Petersen Publishing Co.)	Measure the distance between the spring pad and the lower edge of the spring retainer, and compare to specifications. If the installed height is incorrect, add shim washers between the spring pad and the spring. CAUTION: *Use only washers designed for this purpose.*
** CC'ing the combustion chambers:	** Invert the cylinder head and place a bead of sealer around a combustion chamber. Install an apparatus designed for this purpose (burette mounted on a clear plate; see illustration) over the combustion chamber, and fill with the specified fluid to an even mark on the burette. Record the burette reading, and fill the combustion chamber with fluid. (NOTE: *A hole drilled in the plate will permit air to escape*). Subtract the burette reading, with the combustion chamber filled, from the previous reading, to determine combustion chamber volume in cc's. Duplicate this procedure in all combustion

Procedure	*Method*

CC'ing the combustion chamber
(© Petersen Publishing Co.)

chambers on the cylinder head, and compare the readings. The volume of all combustion chambers should be made equal to that of the largest. Combustion chamber volume may be increased in two ways. When only a small change is required (usually), a small cutter or coarse stone may be used to remove material from the combustion chamber. NOTE: *Check volume frequently.* Remove material over a wide area, so as not to change the configuration of the combustion chamber. When a larger change is required, the valve seat may be sunk (lowered into the head). NOTE: *When altering valve seat, remember to compensate for the change in spring installed height.*

Inspect the rocker arms, balls, studs, and nuts (where applicable):

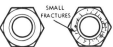

Stress cracks in rocker nuts
(© Ford Motor Co.)

Visually inspect the rocker arms, balls, studs, and nuts for cracks, galling, burning, scoring, or wear. If all parts are intact, liberally lubricate the rocker arms and balls, and install them on the cylinder head. If wear is noted on a rocker arm at the point of valve contact, grind it smooth and square, removing as little material as possible. Replace the rocker arm if excessively worn. If a rocker stud shows signs of wear, it must be replaced (see below). If a rocker nut shows stress cracks, replace it. If an exhaust ball is galled or burned, substitute the intake ball from the same cylinder (if it is intact), and install a new intake ball. NOTE: *Avoid using new rocker balls on exhaust valves.*

Replacing rocker studs:

Reaming the stud bore for oversize rocker studs
(© Buick Div. G.M. Corp.)

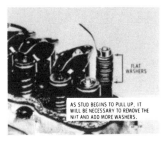

Extracting a pressed in rocker stud
(© Buick Div. G.M. Corp.)

FLAT WASHERS

AS STUD BEGINS TO PULL UP, IT WILL BE NECESSARY TO REMOVE THE NUT AND ADD MORE WASHERS.

In order to remove a threaded stud, lock two nuts on the stud, and unscrew the stud using the lower nut. Coat the lower threads of the new stud with Loctite, and install.

Two alternative methods are available for replacing pressed in studs. Remove the damaged stud using a stack of washers and a nut (see illustration). In the first, the boss is reamed .005-.006″ oversize, and an oversize stud pressed in. Control the stud extension over the boss using washers, in the same manner as valve guides. Before installing the stud, coat it with white lead and grease. To retain the stud more positively, drill a hole through the stud and boss, and install a roll pin. In the second method, the boss is tapped, and a threaded stud installed. Retain the stud using Loctite Stud and Bearing Mount.

Procedure	*Method*
Inspect the rocker shaft(s) and rocker arms (where applicable):  **Disassembled rocker shaft parts arranged for inspection** (ⓒ American Motors Corp.) 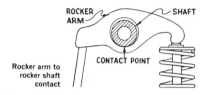 ROCKER ARM — SHAFT — CONTACT POINT — **Rocker arm to rocker shaft contact**	Remove rocker arms, springs and washers from rocker shaft. NOTE: *Lay out parts in the order they are removed.* Inspect rocker arms for pitting or wear on the valve contact point, or excessive bushing wear. Bushings need only be replaced if wear is excessive, because the rocker arm normally contacts the shaft at one point only. Grind the valve contact point of rocker arm smooth if necessary, removing as little material as possible. If excessive material must be removed to smooth and square the arm, it should be replaced. Clean out all oil holes and passages in rocker shaft. If shaft is grooved or worn, replace it. Lubricate and assemble the rocker shaft.
Inspect the camshaft bushings and the camshaft (overhead cam engines):	See next section.
Inspect the pushrods:	Remove the pushrods, and, if hollow, clean out the oil passages using fine wire. Roll each pushrod over a piece of clean glass. If a distinct clicking sound is heard as the pushrod rolls, the rod is bent, and must be replaced.
	* The length of all pushrods must be equal. Measure the length of the pushrods, compare to specifications, and replace as necessary.
Inspect the valve lifters:  Check for Concave Wear on Face of Tappet Using Tappet for Straight Edge **Checking the lifter face** (ⓒ American Motors Corp.)	Remove lifters from their bores, and remove gum and varnish, using solvent. Clean walls of lifter bores. Check lifters for concave wear as illustrated. If face is worn concave, replace lifter, and carefully inspect the camshaft. Lightly lubricate lifter and insert it into its bore. If play is excessive, an oversize lifter must be installed (where possible). Consult a machinist concerning feasibility. If play is satisfactory, remove, lubricate, and reinstall the lifter.
* Testing hydraulic lifter leak down: 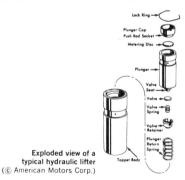 Lock Ring — Plunger Cap — Push Rod Socket — Metering Disc — Plunger — Valve Seat — Valve — Valve Spring — Valve Retainer — Plunger Return Spring — Tappet Body **Exploded view of a typical hydraulic lifter** (ⓒ American Motors Corp.)	Submerge lifter in a container of kerosene. Chuck a used pushrod or its equivalent into a drill press. Position container of kerosene so pushrod acts on the lifter plunger. Pump lifter with the drill press, until resistance increases. Pump several more times to bleed any air out of lifter. Apply very firm, constant pressure to the lifter, and observe rate at which fluid bleeds out of lifter. If the fluid bleeds very quickly (less than 15 seconds), lifter is defective. If the time exceeds 60 seconds, lifter is sticking. In either case, recondition or replace lifter. If lifter is operating properly (leak down time 15-60 seconds), lubricate and install it.

CYLINDER BLOCK RECONDITIONING

Procedure	*Method*

Checking the main bearing clearance:

Plastigage installed on main bearing journal
(© Chevrolet Div. G.M. Corp.)

**Measuring Plastigage to determine
main bearing clearance**
(© Chevrolet Div. G.M. Corp.)

SCRATCHES — SCRATCHED BY DIRT / DIRT IMBEDDED INTO BEARING MATERIAL / OVERLAY WIPED OUT — LACK OF OIL / BRIGHT (POLISHED) SECTIONS — IMPROPER SEATING / OVERLAY GONE FROM ENTIRE SURFACE — TAPERED JOURNAL / RADIUS RIDE / CRATERS OR POCKETS — FATIGUE FAILURE

Causes of bearing failure
(© Ford Motor Co.)

Invert engine, and remove cap from the bearing to be checked. Using a clean, dry rag, thoroughly clean all oil from crankshaft journal and bearing insert. NOTE: *Plastigage is soluble in oil; therefore, oil on the journal or bearing could result in erroneous readings.* Place a piece of Plastigage along the full length of journal, reinstall cap, and torque to specifications. Remove bearing cap, and determine bearing clearance by comparing width of Plastigage to the scale on Plastigage envelope. Journal taper is determined by comparing width of the Plastigage strip near its ends. Rotate crankshaft 90° and retest, to determine journal eccentricity. NOTE: *Do not rotate crankshaft with Plastigage installed.* If bearing insert and journal appear intact, and are within tolerances, no further main bearing service is required. If bearing or journal appear defective, cause of failure should be determined before replacement.

* Remove crankshaft from block (see below). Measure the main bearing journals at each end twice (90° apart) using a micrometer, to determine diameter, journal taper and eccentricity. If journals are within tolerances, reinstall bearing caps at their specified torque. Using a telescope gauge and micrometer, measure bearing I.D. parallel to piston axis and at 30° on each side of piston axis. Subtract journal O.D. from bearing I.D. to determine oil clearance. If crankshaft journals appear defective, or do not meet tolerances, there is no need to measure bearings; for the crankshaft will require grinding and/or undersize bearings will be required. If bearing appears defective, cause for failure should be determined prior to replacement.

Checking the connecting rod bearing clearance:

Plastigage installed on connecting rod bearing journal
(© Chevrolet Div. G.M. Corp.)

Connecting rod bearing clearance is checked in the same manner as main bearing clearance, using Plastigage. Before removing the crankshaft, connecting rod side clearance also should be measured and recorded.

* Checking connecting rod bearing clearance, using a micrometer, is identical to checking main bearing clearance. If no other service

Procedure	*Method*

**Measuring Plastigage to determine
connecting rod bearing clearance**
(© Chevrolet Div. G.M. Corp.)

is required, the piston and rod assemblies need not be removed.

Removing the crankshaft:

Connecting rod matching marks
(© Ford Motor Co.)

Using a punch, mark the corresponding main bearing caps and saddles according to position (i.e., one punch on the front main cap and saddle, two on the second, three on the third, etc.). Using number stamps, identify the corresponding connecting rods and caps, according to cylinder (if no numbers are present). Remove the main and connecting rod caps, and place sleeves of plastic tubing over the connecting rod bolts, to protect the journals as the crankshaft is removed. Lift the crankshaft out of the block.

Remove the ridge from the top of the cylinder:

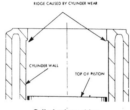

Cylinder bore ridge
(© Pontiac Div. G.M. Corp.)

In order to facilitate removal of the piston and connecting rod, the ridge at the top of the cylinder (unworn area; see illustration) must be removed. Place the piston at the bottom of the bore, and cover it with a rag. Cut the ridge away using a ridge reamer, exercising extreme care to avoid cutting too deeply. Remove the rag, and remove cuttings that remain on the piston. CAUTION: *If the ridge is not removed, and new rings are installed, damage to rings will result.*

Removing the piston and connecting rod:

Removing the piston
(© SAAB)

Invert the engine, and push the pistons and connecting rods out of the cylinders. If necessary, tap the connecting rod boss with a wooden hammer handle, to force the piston out. CAUTION: *Do not attempt to force the piston past the cylinder ridge* (see above).

Procedure	Method
Service the crankshaft:	Ensure that all oil holes and passages in the crankshaft are open and free of sludge. If necessary, have the crankshaft ground to the largest possible undersize.
	** Have the crankshaft Magnafluxed, to locate stress cracks. Consult a machinist concerning additional service procedures, such as surface hardening (e.g., nitriding, Tuftriding) to improve wear characteristics, cross drilling and chamfering the oil holes to improve lubrication, and balancing.
Removing freeze plugs:	Drill a hole in the center of the freeze plugs, and pry them out using a screwdriver or drift.
Remove the oil gallery plugs:	Threaded plugs should be removed using an appropriate (usually square) wrench. To remove soft, pressed in plugs, drill a hole in the plug, and thread in a sheet metal screw. Pull the plug out by the screw using pliers.
Hot-tank the block:	Have the block hot-tanked to remove grease, corrosion, and scale from the water jackets. NOTE: *Consult the operator to determine whether the camshaft bearings will be damaged during the hot-tank process.*
Check the block for cracks:	Visually inspect the block for cracks or chips. The most common locations are as follows: Adjacent to freeze plugs. Between the cylinders and water jackets. Adjacent to the main bearing saddles. At the extreme bottom of the cylinders. Check only suspected cracks using spot check dye (see introduction). If a crack is located, consult a machinist concerning possible repairs.
	** Magnaflux the block to locate hidden cracks. If cracks are located, consult a machinist about feasibility of repair.
Install the oil gallery plugs and freeze plugs:	Coat freeze plugs with sealer and tap into position using a piece of pipe, slightly smaller than the plug, as a driver. To ensure retention, stake the edges of the plugs. Coat threaded oil gallery plugs with sealer and install. Drive replacement soft plugs into block using a large drift as a driver.
	* Rather than reinstalling lead plugs, drill and tap the holes, and install threaded plugs.

Procedure	*Method*

Check the bore diameter and surface:

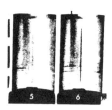

1, 2, 3 Piston skirt seizure resulted in this pattern. Engine must be rebored

4. Piston skirt and oil ring seizure caused this damage. Engine must be rebored

5, 6 Score marks caused by a split piston skirt. Damage is not serious enough to warrant reboring

7. Ring seized longitudinally, causing a score mark 1 3/16" wide, on the land side of the piston groove. The honing pattern is destroyed and the cylinder must be rebored

8. Result of oil ring seizure. Engine must be rebored

9. Oil ring seizure here was not serious enough to warrant reboring. The honing marks are still visible

Cylinder wall damage
(© Daimler-Benz A.G.)

Visually inspect the cylinder bores for roughness, scoring, or scuffing. If evident, the cylinder bore must be bored or honed oversize to eliminate imperfections, and the smallest possible oversize piston used. The new pistons should be given to the machinist with the block, so that the cylinders can be bored or honed exactly to the piston size (plus clearance). If no flaws are evident, measure the bore diameter using a telescope gauge and micrometer, or dial gauge, parallel and perpendicular to the engine centerline, at the top (below the ridge) and bottom of the bore. Subtract the bottom measurements from the top to determine taper, and the parallel to the centerline measurements from the perpendicular measurements to determine eccentricity. If the measurements are not within specifications, the cylinder must be bored or honed, and an oversize piston installed. If the measurements are within specifications the cylinder may be used as is, with only finish honing (see below). NOTE: *Prior to submitting the block for boring, perform the following operation(s).*

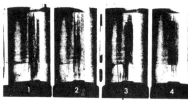

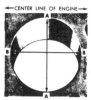

Cylinder bore measuring positions
(© Ford Motor Co.)

Measuring the cylinder bore with a telescope gauge
(© Buick Div. G.M. Corp.)

Determining the cylinder bore by measuring the telescope gauge with a micrometer
(© Buick Div. G.M. Corp.)

Measuring the cylinder bore with a dial gauge
(© Chevrolet Div. G.M. Corp.)

Procedure	Method
Check the block deck for warpage:	Using a straightedge and feeler gauges, check the block deck for warpage in the same manner that the cylinder head is checked (see Cylinder Head Reconditioning). If warpage exceeds specifications, have the deck resurfaced. NOTE: *In certain cases a specification for total material removal (Cylinder head and block deck) is provided. This specification must not be exceeded.*
* Check the deck height:	The deck height is the distance from the crankshaft centerline to the block deck. To measure, invert the engine, and install the crankshaft, retaining it with the center main cap. Measure the distance from the crankshaft journal to the block deck, parallel to the cylinder centerline. Measure the diameter of the end (front and rear) main journals, parallel to the centerline of the cylinders, divide the diameter in half, and subtract it from the previous measurement. The results of the front and rear measurements should be identical. If the difference exceeds .005″, the deck height should be corrected. NOTE: *Block deck height and warpage should be corrected concurrently.*
Check the cylinder block bearing alignment:  **Checking main bearing saddle alignment** (© Petersen Publishing Co.)	Remove the upper bearing inserts. Place a straightedge in the bearing saddles along the centerline of the crankshaft. If clearance exists between the straightedge and the center saddle, the block must be align-bored.
Clean and inspect the pistons and connecting rods: 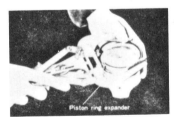 **Removing the piston rings** (© Subaru)	Using a ring expander, remove the rings from the piston. Remove the retaining rings (if so equipped) and remove piston pin. NOTE: *If the piston pin must be pressed out, determine the proper method and use the proper tools; otherwise the piston will distort.* Clean the ring grooves using an appropriate tool, exercising care to avoid cutting too deeply. Thoroughly clean all carbon and varnish from the piston with solvent. CAUTION: *Do not use a wire brush or caustic solvent on pistons.* Inspect the pistons for scuffing, scoring, cracks, pitting, or excessive ring groove wear. If wear is evident, the piston must be replaced. Check the connecting rod length by measuring the rod from the inside of the large end to the inside of the small end using calipers (see

Procedure	*Method*

Cleaning the piston ring grooves
(ⓒ Ford Motor Co.)

Connecting rod length checking dimension

illustration). All connecting rods should be equal length. Replace any rod that differs from the others in the engine.

* Have the connecting rod alignment checked in an alignment fixture by a machinist. Replace any twisted or bent rods.

* Magnaflux the connecting rods to locate stress cracks. If cracks are found, replace the connecting rod.

Fit the pistons to the cylinders:

Measuring the cylinder with a telescope gauge for piston fitting
(ⓒ Buick Div. G.M. Corp.)

Measuring the piston for fitting
(ⓒ Buick Div. G.M. Corp.)

Using a telescope gauge and micrometer, or a dial gauge, measure the cylinder bore diameter perpendicular to the piston pin, $2\frac{1}{2}''$ below the deck. Measure the piston perpendicular to its pin on the skirt. The difference between the two measurements is the piston clearance. If the clearance is within specifications or slightly below (after boring or honing), finish honing is all that is required. If the clearance is excessive, try to obtain a slightly larger piston to bring clearance within specifications. Where this is not possible, obtain the first oversize piston, and hone (or if necessary, bore) the cylinder to size.

Assemble the pistons and connecting rods:

Installing piston pin lock rings
(ⓒ Nissan Motor Co., Ltd.)

Inspect piston pin, connecting rod small end bushing, and piston bore for galling, scoring, or excessive wear. If evident, replace defective part(s). Measure the I.D. of the piston boss and connecting rod small end, and the O.D. of the piston pin. If within specifications, assemble piston pin and rod. CAUTION: *If piston pin must be pressed in, determine the proper method and use the proper tools; otherwise the piston will distort.* Install the lock rings; ensure that they seat properly. If the parts are not within specifications, determine the service method for the type of engine. In some cases, piston and pin are serviced as an assembly when either is defective. Others specify reaming the piston and connecting rods for an oversize pin. If the connecting rod bushing is worn, it may in many cases be replaced. Reaming the piston and replacing the rod bushing are machine shop operations.

Procedure	*Method*

Clean and inspect the camshaft:

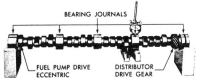

**Checking the camshaft
for straightness**
(© Chevrolet Motor
Div. G.M. Corp.)

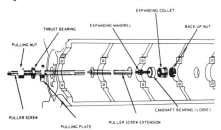

Camshaft lobe measurement
(© Ford Motor Co.)

Degrease the camshaft, using solvent, and clean out all oil holes. Visually inspect cam lobes and bearing journals for excessive wear. If a lobe is questionable, check all lobes as indicated below. If a journal or lobe is worn, the camshaft must be reground or replaced. NOTE: *If a journal is worn, there is a good chance that the bushings are worn.* If lobes and journals appear intact, place the front and rear journals in V-blocks, and rest a dial indicator on the center journal. Rotate the camshaft to check straightness. If deviation exceeds .001″, replace the camshaft.

* Check the camshaft lobes with a micrometer, by measuring the lobes from the nose to base and again at 90° (see illustration). The lift is determined by subtracting the second measurement from the first. If all exhaust lobes and all intake lobes are not identical, the camshaft must be reground or replaced.

Replace the camshaft bearings:

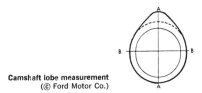

Camshaft removal and installation tool (typical)
(© Ford Motor Co.)

If excessive wear is indicated, or if the engine is being completely rebuilt, camshaft bearings should be replaced as follows: Drive the camshaft rear plug from the block. Assemble the removal puller with its shoulder on the bearing to be removed. Gradually tighten the puller nut until bearing is removed. Remove remaining bearings, leaving the front and rear for last. To remove front and rear bearings, reverse position of the tool, so as to pull the bearings in toward the center of the block. Leave the tool in this position, pilot the new front and rear bearings on the installer, and pull them into position. Return the tool to its original position and pull remaining bearings into position. NOTE: *Ensure that oil holes align when installing bearings.* Replace camshaft rear plug, and stake it into position to aid retention.

Finish hone the cylinders:

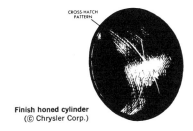

Finish honed cylinder
(© Chrysler Corp.)

Chuck a flexible drive hone into a power drill, and insert it into the cylinder. Start the hone, and move it up and down in the cylinder at a rate which will produce approximately a 60° cross-hatch pattern (see illustration). NOTE: *Do not extend the hone below the cylinder bore.* After developing the pattern, remove the hone and recheck piston fit. Wash the cylinders with a detergent and water solution to remove abrasive dust, dry, and wipe several times with a rag soaked in engine oil.

Procedure	*Method*
Check piston ring end-gap:  **Checking ring end-gap** (© Chevrolet Motor Div. G.M. Corp.)	Compress the piston rings to be used in a cylinder, one at a time, into that cylinder, and press them approximately 1″ below the deck with an inverted piston. Using feeler gauges, measure the ring end-gap, and compare to specifications. Pull the ring out of the cylinder and file the ends with a fine file to obtain proper clearance. CAUTION: *If inadequate ring end-gap is utilized, ring breakage will result.*
Install the piston rings: 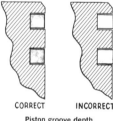 **Checking ring side clearance** (© Chrysler Corp.) 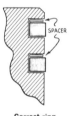 **CORRECT INCORRECT** Piston groove depth **Correct ring spacer installation**	Inspect the ring grooves in the piston for excessive wear or taper. If necessary, recut the groove(s) for use with an overwidth ring or a standard ring and spacer. If the groove is worn uniformly, overwidth rings, or standard rings and spacers may be installed without recutting. Roll the outside of the ring around the groove to check for burrs or deposits. If any are found, remove with a fine file. Hold the ring in the groove, and measure side clearance. If necessary, correct as indicated above. NOTE: *Always install any additional spacers above the piston ring.* The ring groove must be deep enough to allow the ring to seat below the lands (see illustration). In many cases, a "go-no-go" depth gauge will be provided with the piston rings. Shallow grooves may be corrected by recutting, while deep grooves require some type of filler or expander behind the piston. Consult the piston ring supplier concerning the suggested method. Install the rings on the piston, lowest ring first, using a ring expander. NOTE: *Position the ring markings as specified by the manufacturer (see car section).*
Install the camshaft:	Liberally lubricate the camshaft lobes and journals, and slide the camshaft into the block. CAUTION: *Exercise extreme care to avoid damaging the bearings when inserting the camshaft.* Install and tighten the camshaft thrust plate retaining bolts.
Check camshaft end-play:  **Checking camshaft end-play with a feeler gauge** (© Ford Motor Co.)	Using feeler gauges, determine whether the clearance between the camshaft boss (or gear) and backing plate is within specifications. Install shims behind the thrust plate, or reposition the camshaft gear and retest end-play.

Procedure	*Method*

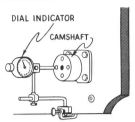

Checking camshaft end-play with a
dial indicator

* Mount a dial indicator stand so that the stem of the dial indicator rests on the nose of the camshaft, parallel to the camshaft axis. Push the camshaft as far in as possible and zero the gauge. Move the camshaft outward to determine the amount of camshaft end-play. If the end-play is not within tolerance, install shims behind the thrust plate, or reposition the camshaft gear and retest.

Install the rear main seal (where applicable):

Seating the rear
main seal
(© Buick Div. G.M. Corp.)

Position the block with the bearing saddles facing upward. Lay the rear main seal in its groove and press it lightly into its seat. Place a piece of pipe the same diameter as the crankshaft journal into the saddle, and firmly seat the seal. Hold the pipe in position, and trim the ends of the seal flush if required.

Install the crankshaft:

Home made bearing
roll-out pin
(© Pontiac Div.
G.M. Corp.)

Removal and installation of upper
bearing insert using a roll-out pin
(© Buick Div. G.M. Corp.)

Thoroughly clean the main bearing saddles and caps. Place the upper halves of the bearing inserts on the saddles and press into position. NOTE: *Ensure that the oil holes align.* Press the corresponding bearing inserts into the main bearing caps. Lubricate the upper main bearings, and lay the crankshaft in position. Place a strip of Plastigage on each of the crankshaft journals, install the main caps, and torque to specifications. Remove the main caps, and compare the Plastigage to the scale on the Plastigage envelope. If clearances are within tolerances, remove the Plastigage, turn the crankshaft 90°, wipe off all oil and retest. If all clearances are correct, remove all Plastigage, thoroughly

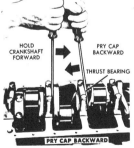

Aligning the thrust bearing
(© Ford Motor Co.)

Procedure	Method
	lubricate the main caps and bearing journals, and install the main caps. If clearances are not within tolerance, the upper bearing inserts may be removed, without removing the crankshaft, using a bearing roll out pin (see illustration). Roll in a bearing that will provide proper clearance, and retest. Torque all main caps, excluding the thrust bearing cap, to specifications. Tighten the thrust bearing cap finger tight. To properly align the thrust bearing, pry the crankshaft the extent of its axial travel several times, the last movement held toward the front of the engine, and torque the thrust bearing cap to specifications. Determine the crankshaft end-play (see below), and bring within tolerance with thrust washers.
Measure crankshaft end-play:  **Checking crankshaft end-play with a dial indicator** (© Ford Motor Co.) A 2908-A  **Checking crankshaft end-play with a feeler gauge** (© Chevrolet Div. (G.M. Corp.)	Mount a dial indicator stand on the front of the block, with the dial indicator stem resting on the nose of the crankshaft, parallel to the crankshaft axis. Pry the crankshaft the extent of its travel rearward, and zero the indicator. Pry the crankshaft forward and record crankshaft end-play. NOTE: *Crankshaft end-play also may be measured at the thrust bearing, using feeler gauges* (see illustration).
Install the pistons:	Press the upper connecting rod bearing halves into the connecting rods, and the lower halves into the connecting rod caps. Position the piston ring gaps according to specifications (see car section), and lubricate the pistons. Install a ring compresser on a piston, and press two long (8″) pieces of plastic tubing over the rod bolts. Using the plastic tubes as a guide, press the pistons into the bores and onto the crankshaft with a wooden hammer handle. After seating the rod on the crankshaft journal, remove the tubes and install the cap finger tight. Install the remaining pistons in the same man-

Procedure	*Method*

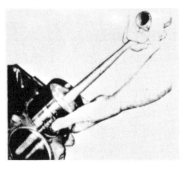

Tubing used as guide when installing
a piston
(© Oldsmobile Div. G.M. Corp.)

Installing a piston
(© Chevrolet Div. G.M. Corp.)

ner. Invert the engine and check the bearing clearance at two points (90° apart) on each journal with Plastigage. NOTE: *Do not turn the crankshaft with Plastigage installed.* If clearance is within tolerances, remove *all* Plastigage, thoroughly lubricate the journals, and torque the rod caps to specifications. If clearance is not within specifications, install different thickness bearing inserts and recheck. CAUTION: *Never shim or file the connecting rods or caps.* Always install plastic tube sleeves over the rod bolts when the caps are not installed, to protect the crankshaft journals.

Check connecting rod side clearance:

Checking connecting rod side clearance
(© Chevrolet Div. G.M. Corp.)

Determine the clearance between the sides of the connecting rods and the crankshaft, using feeler gauges. If clearance is below the minimum tolerance, the rod may be machined to provide adequate clearance. If clearance is excessive, substitute an unworn rod, and recheck. If clearance is still outside specifications, the crankshaft must be welded and reground, or replaced.

Inspect the timing chain:

Visually inspect the timing chain for broken or loose links, and replace the chain if any are found. If the chain will flex sideways, it must be replaced. Install the timing chain as specified. NOTE: *If the original timing chain is to be reused, install it in its original position.*

Procedure	*Method*
Check timing gear backlash and runout:  **Checking camshaft gear backlash** (© Chevrolet Div. G.M. Corp.)  **Checking camshaft gear runout** (© Chevrolet Div. G.M. Corp.)	Mount a dial indicator with its stem resting on a tooth of the camshaft gear (as illustrated). Rotate the gear until all slack is removed, and zero the indicator. Rotate the gear in the opposite direction until slack is removed, and record gear backlash. Mount the indicator with its stem resting on the edge of the camshaft gear, parallel to the axis of the camshaft. Zero the indicator, and turn the camshaft gear one full turn, recording the runout. If either backlash or runout exceed specifications, replace the worn gear(s).

Completing the Rebuilding Process

Following the above procedures, complete the rebuilding process as follows:

Fill the oil pump with oil, to prevent cavitating (sucking air) on initial engine start up. Install the oil pump and the pickup tube on the engine. Coat the oil pan gasket as necessary, and install the gasket and the oil pan. Mount the flywheel and the crankshaft vibrational damper or pulley on the crankshaft. NOTE: *Always use new bolts when installing the flywheel.* Inspect the clutch shaft pilot bushing in the crankshaft. If the bushing is excessively worn, remove it with an expanding puller and a slide hammer, and tap a new bushing into place.

Position the engine, cylinder head side up. Lubricate the lifters, and install them into their bores. Install the cylinder head, and torque it as specified in the car section. Insert the pushrods (where applicable), and install the rocker shaft(s) (if so equipped) or position the rocker arms on the pushrods. If solid lifters are utilized, adjust the valves to the "cold" specifications.

Mount the intake and exhaust manifolds, the carburetor(s), the distributor and spark plugs. Adjust the point gap and the static ignition timing. Mount all accessories and install the engine in the car. Fill the radiator with coolant, and the crankcase with high quality engine oil.

Break-in Procedure

Start the engine, and allow it to run at low speed for a few minutes, while checking for leaks. Stop the engine, check the oil level, and fill as necessary. Restart the engine, and fill the cooling system to capacity. Check the point dwell angle and adjust the ignition timing and the valves. Run the engine at low to medium speed (800-2500 rpm) for approximately ½ hour, and retorque the cylinder head bolts. Road test the car, and check again for leaks.

Follow the manufacturer's recommended engine break-in procedure and maintenance schedule for new engines.

4 · Emission Controls and Fuel System

Emission Controls

There are three types of automotive pollutants; crankcase fumes, exhaust gases and gasoline evaporation. The equipment that is used to limit these pollutants is commonly called emission control equipment.

Emission Control Usage Chart

Emission Control System	Engine
Air Injection	304 V8, 225 V6, F-Head
Thermostatically Controlled Air Cleaner (TAC)	1972 304 V8, 1973–76 232, 258 Sixes and 304 V8
Transmission Controlled Spark (TCS)	232, 258 Sixes, and 304 V8
Spark Coolant Temperature Override Switch (Spark CTO)	232, 258 Sixes and 304 V8
Fuel Tank Vapor Control	232, 258 Sixes, and 304 V8
Positive Crankcase Ventilation (PCV)	All engines

Emission Control System	Engine
Exhaust Gas Recirculation (EGR)	1973 304 V8, 1974 232, 258 Sixes, 1975 California 232, 258 Sixes and 304 V8, 1976 232, 258 Sixes and 304 V8
Backpressure Sensor (BPS)	1976 232, 258 Sixes and 304 V8
Exhaust Gas Recirculation Coolant Temperature Override Switch (EGR CTO)	1975–76 232, 258 Sixes and 304 V8
Catalytic Converter	1975–76 304 V8 and 1976 California 232 and 258 Sixes
Fuel Return System	1975–76 304 V8 and 1976 232, 258 Sixes
Choke Heat Bypass Valve (CHBPV)	1976 304 V8

PCV SYSTEM

The crankcase emission control equipment consists of a positive crankcase ventilation valve (PCV), a closed or open oil filler cap and hoses to connect this equipment.

When the engine is running, a small

portion of the gases which are formed in the combustion chamber during combustion leak by the piston rings and enter the crankcase. Since these gases are under pressure they tend to escape from the crankcase and enter into the atmosphere. If these gases were allowed to remain in the crankcase for any length of time, they would contaminate the engine oil and cause sludge to build up. If the gases are allowed to escape into the atmosphere, they would pollute the air, as they contain unburned hydrocarbons. The crankcase emission control equipment recycles these gases back into the engine combustion chamber where they are burned.

Crankcase gases are recycled in the following manner: while the engine is running, clean filtered air is drawn into the crankcase either directly through the oil filler cap, or through the carburetor air filter and then through a hose leading to the oil filler cap. As the air passes through the crankcase it picks up the combustion gases and carries them out of the crankcase, up through the PCV valve and into the intake manifold. After they enter the intake manifold they are drawn into the combustion chamber where they are burned.

The most critical component in the system is the PCV valve. This vacuum controlled valve regulates the amount of gases which are recycled into the combustion chamber. At low engine speeds the valve is partially closed, limiting the flow of gases into the intake manifold. As engine speed increases, the valve opens to admit greater quantities of the gases into the intake manifold. If the valve should become blocked or plugged, the gases will be prevented from escaping from the crankcases by the normal route. Since these gases are under pressure, they will find their own way out of the crankcase. This alternate route is usually a weak oil seal or gasket in the engine. As the gas escapes by the gasket, it also creates an oil leak. Besides causing oil leaks, a clogged PCV valve also allows these gases to remain in the crankcase for an extended period of time, promoting the formation of sludge in the engine.

The above explanation and the troubleshooting procedure which follows applies to all engines equipped with PCV systems.

Troubleshooting

With the engine running, pull the PCV valve and hose from the engine. Block off the end of the valve with your finger. The engine speed should drop at least 50 rpm when the end of the valve is blocked. If the engine speed does not drop at least 50 rpm, then the valve is defective and should be replaced.

Removal and Installation

1. Pull the PCV valve and hose from the engine.
2. Remove the PCV valve from the hose. Inspect the inside of the PCV valve hose. If it is dirty, disconnect it from the intake manifold and clean it.

To install, proceed as follows:
1. If the PCV valve hose was removed, connect it to the intake manifold.
2. Connect the PCV valve to its hose.
3. Install the PCV valve on the engine.

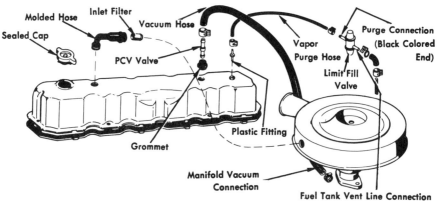

Positive crankcase ventilation and fuel tank vapor system components for the American Motors sixes

AIR INJECTION SYSTEM

All of the engines used in Jeeps at some point incorporated the air injection system for controlling the emission of exhaust gases into the atmosphere. Since this type of emission control system is common to all of the engines, it will be explained here.

The exhaust emission control air injection system consists of a belt driven air pump which directs compressed air through connecting hoses to a steel distribution manifold into stainless steel injection tubes in the exhaust port adjacent to each exhaust valve. The air, with its normal oxygen content, reacts with the hot, but incompletely burned exhaust gases and permits further combustion in the exhaust port or manifold.

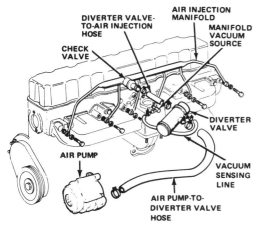

The air injection exhaust emission control system installed on the 232, 258 Sixes

Air Pump

The air injection pump is a positive displacement vane type which is permanently lubricated and requires little periodic maintenance. The only serviceable parts on the air pump are the filter, exhaust tube, and relief valve. The relief valve relieves the air flow when the pump pressure reaches a preset level. This occurs at high engine rpm. This serves to prevent damage to the pump and to limit maximum exhaust manifold temperatures.

NOTE: *On 1974–76 models the relief valve assembly is incorporated in the diverter valve. If the relief valve is believed to be defective, the diverter valve assembly must be replaced.*

Pump Air Filter

The air filter attached to the pump (all except American Motors engines), is a replaceable element type. The filter should be replaced every 12,000 miles under normal conditions and sooner under off-road use. Some models draw their air supply through the carburetor air filter.

The air pump on American Motors engines is equipped with a centrifugal fan-type air filter. This filter fan requires no servicing aside from replacement if damaged.

Air Delivery Manifold

The air delivery manifold distributes the air from the pump to each of the air delivery tubes in a uniform manner. A check valve is integral with the air delivery manifold. Its function is to prevent the reverse flow of exhaust gases to the pump should the pump fail. This reverse flow would damage the air pump and connecting hose.

Air Injection Tubes

The air injection tubes are inserted into the exhaust ports. The tubes project into the exhaust ports, directing air into the vicinity of the exhaust valve.

Anti-Backfire Valve

The anti-backfire diverter valve prevents engine backfire by briefly interrupting the air being injected into the exhaust manifold during periods of deceleration or rapid throttle closure. On the F-head and all of the American Motors engines the valve opens when a sudden increase in manifold vacuum overcomes the diaphragm spring tension. With the valve in the open position the air flow is directed to the atmosphere.

On the V6, the anti-backfire valve is what is commonly called a gulp valve. During rapid deceleration the valve is opened by the sudden high vacuum condition in the intake manifold and gulps air into the intake manifold.

Both of these valves prevent backfiring in the exhaust manifold. Both valves also prevent an over rich fuel mixture from being burned in the exhaust manifold, which would cause backfiring and possible damage to the engine.

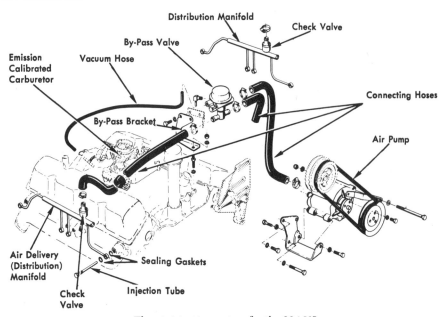

The air injection system for the 304 V8

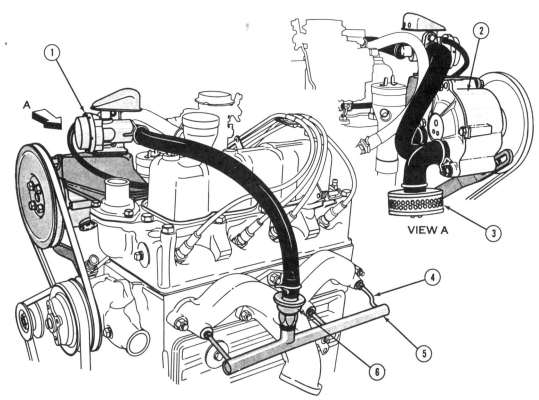

The air injection system for the F-head

1. Anti-backfire diverter valve	3. Pump air filter	5. Air delivery manifold
2. Air pump	4. Air injection tubes	6. Check valve

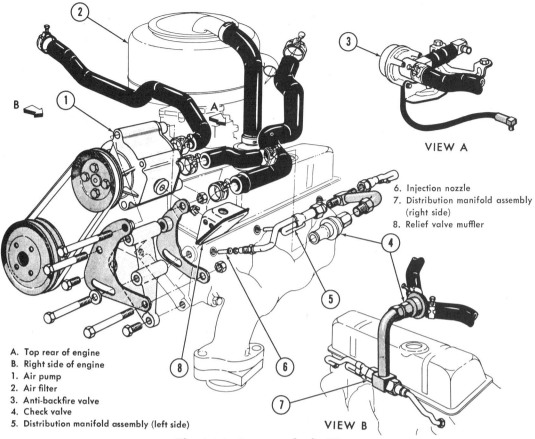

6. Injection nozzle
7. Distribution manifold assembly (right side)
8. Relief valve muffler

VIEW A

A. Top rear of engine
B. Right side of engine
1. Air pump
2. Air filter
3. Anti-backfire valve
4. Check valve
5. Distribution manifold assembly (left side)

VIEW B

The air injection system for the V6

Carburetor

The carburetors used on engines equipped with emission controls have specific flow characteristics that differ from the carburetors used on vehicles not equipped with emission control devices. The carburetors are identified by number. The correct carburetor should be used when replacement is necessary.

A carburetor dashpot is used on the F-head to control throttle closing speed.

NOTE: *All of the components discussed in the following paragraphs apply only to American Motors engines.*

THERMOSTATICALLY CONTROLLED AIR CLEANER SYSTEM (TAC)

232 and 258 Sixes

The TAC system applied to the AMC sixes consists of a two-piece heat shroud positioned on the exhaust manifold, a hot air hose, and an air duct and valve assembly located in the air cleaner snorkel.

The air duct and valve assembly incorporates an air valve, a thermostat mechanism, and a spring.

The temperature of the air entering the air cleaner is thermostatically regulated by the air duct and valve assembly. Cold air is supplied from the engine compartment and hot air from the shrouded exhaust manifold.

The thermostat unit in the air duct is exposed to incoming air on the air filter side of the air valve. The spring-loaded air valve is connected to the thermostat unit through linkage. The spring holds the valve in the closed (heat on), position until the thermostat overcomes the spring tension.

While the engine is warming up and the air temperature entering the air duct is less than 105° F, the thermostat is in the retracted position and the air valve is held in the closed (heat on) position.

As the temperature of the air passing over the thermostat unit rises, the thermostat starts to open and pulls the air valve

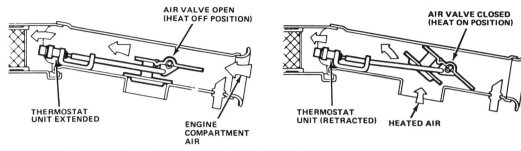

Operation of the thermostatically-controlled air cleaner (TAC) on the 232, 258 Sixes

down, closing off the heated air intake and opening the cool air intake, allowing cooler engine compartment air to enter the air cleaner.

When the temperature of the air reaches 130° F, the air valve is completely open to engine compartment air.

304 V8

This system consists of a heat shroud which is integral with the right side exhaust manifold, a hot air hose and a special air cleaner assembly equipped with a thermal sensor and a vacuum motor and air valve assembly.

The thermal sensor incorporates an air bleed valve which regulates the amount of vacuum applied to the vacuum motor, controlling the air valve position to supply either heated air from the exhaust manifold or air from the engine compartment.

During the warm-up period when underhood temperatures are low, the air bleed valve is closed and sufficient vacuum is applied to the vacuum motor to hold the air valve in the closed (heat on) position.

As the temperature of the air entering the air cleaner approaches approximately 115° F, the air bleed valve opens to decrease the amount of vacuum applied to the vacuum motor. The diaphragm spring in the vacuum motor then moves the air valve into the open (heat off) position, allowing only underhood air to enter the air cleaner.

The air valve in the air cleaner will also open, regardless of air temperature, during heavy acceleration to obtain maximum air flow through the air cleaner.

TRANSMISSION CONTROLLED SPARK SYSTEM

The purpose of this system is to reduce the emission of oxides of nitrogen by low-

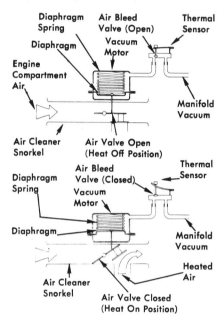

Opened and closed position of the thermostatically controlled air cleaner on the 304 V8

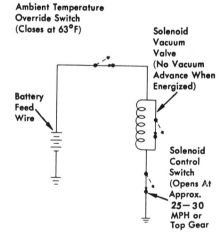

Diagram of the electrical circuit of the TCS system

ering the peak combustion pressure and temperature during the power stroke.

The system incorporates the following components:

Ambient Temperature Override Switch (1973 only)

This switch, located at the firewall, senses ambient temperatures and completes the electrical circuit from the battery to the solenoid vacuum valve when ambient temperatures are above 63° F.

Solenoid Vacuum Valve

This valve is attached to the ignition coil bracket at the right side of the engine (1973 V8 engines), right rear intake manifold (1974–76 V8), or to a bracket at the rear of the intake manifold (Sixes). When the valve is energized, carburetor vacuum is blocked off and the distributor vacuum line is vented to the atmosphere through a port in the valve, resulting in no vacuum advance. When the valve is de-energized, vacuum is applied to the distributor resulting in normal vacuum advance.

Solenoid Control Switch

This switch is located on the transmission on vehicles with manual transmissions. It opens or closes in relation to car speed and gear range. When the transmission is in high gear, the switch opens and breaks the ground circuit to the solenoid vacuum valve. In lower gear ranges the switch closes and completes the ground circuit to

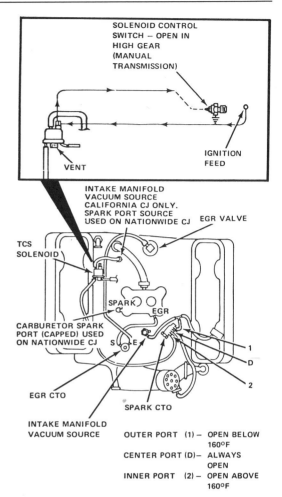

The TCS system installed on the 304 V8

the solenoid vacuum valve. The switch is operated by the transmission shifter shaft.

On vehicles equipped with an automatic transmission, the switch is located along the speedometer cable on the firewall. The switch is operated by speedometer cable rpm. At 32 to 36 mph (533–599 cable rpm), the switch will open the electorical ground circuit to the solenoid vacuum valve.

Coolant Temperature Override Switch

This switch is used only on the 304 V8. It is threaded into the thermostat housing. The switch reacts to coolant temperatures to route either intake manifold or carburetor vacuum to the distributor vacuum advance diaphragm.

When the coolant temperature is below 160° F, intake manifold vacuum is applied through a hose connection to the distribu-

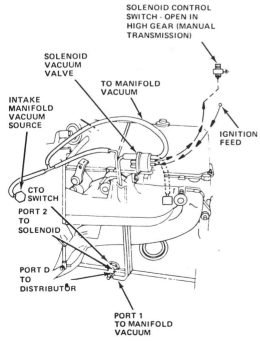

The TCS system installed on the 232, 258 Sixes

Emission Control Distributor Vacuum Application Chart For 1973 American Motors Engines

Manual Transmission Gear		Ambient (Air) Temperature	Coolant Temperature	Vacuum Applied to the Distributor
3 Speed	4 Speed			
1–2	1–2–3	Below 63° F	Below 160° F	Manifold
1–2	1–2–3	Below 63° F	Above 160° F	Carburetor
1–2	1–2–3	Above 63° F	Above 160° F	None
1–2	1–2–3	Above 63° F	Below 160° F	Manifold
3	4	Below 63° F	Below 160° F	Manifold
3	4	Below 63° F	Above 160° F	Carburetor
3	4	Above 63° F	Above 160° F	Carburetor
3	4	Above 63° F	Below 160° F	Manifold

Emission Control Distributor Vacuum Application Chart For 1794–76 American Motors Engines

Transmission			Coolant Temperature	Vacuum Source
3 Speed	4 Speed	Automatic		
1–2	1–2–3	Below 32–36 mph	Below 160° F	Manifold
1–2	1–2–3	Below 32–36 mph	Above 160° F	Through the Solenoid Vacuum Valve
3	4	Above 32–36 mph	Below 160° F	Manifold
3	4	Above 32–36 mph	Above 160° F	No Vacuum

tor advance diaphragm, resulting in full vacuum advance.

When the coolant temperature is above 160° F, intake manifold vacuum is blocked off and carburetor vacuum is then applied through the solenoid vacuum valve to the distributor advance diaphragm, resulting in decreased vacuum advance.

NOTE: *On 1974–76 vehicles made for California, intake manifold vacuum routed through the TCS solenoid is applied to the distributor when the coolant temperature is above 160° F.*

The relationship between distributor vacuum advance and the operation of the TCS system and coolant temperature override switch can be determined by referring to the Emission Control Distributor Vacuum Application Chart.

EXHAUST GAS RECIRCULATION (EGR) SYSTEM

The EGR system consists of a diaphragm actuated flow control valve (EGR valve), coolant temperature override switch

(EGR CTO), an exhaust backpressure sensor low temperature vacuum signal modulator (1973 only), high temperature vacuum signal modulator (1973 only), and connecting hoses.

The purpose of the EGR system is to limit the formation of nitrogen oxides by diluting the fresh air intake charge with a metered amount of exhaust gas, thereby reducing the peak temperatures of the burning gases in the combustion chambers.

EGR VALVE

The EGR valve is mounted on a machined surface at the rear of the intake manifold on V8 engines and on the side of the intake manifold on the Sixes. When a backpressure sensor is used, the EGR valve is mounted on a spacer which is an integral part of the backpressure sensor.

The valve is held in a normally closed position by a coil spring located above the diaphragm. A special fitting is provided at the carburetor to route ported (above the throttle plates) vacuum through the CTO and BPS (when used), and the high and

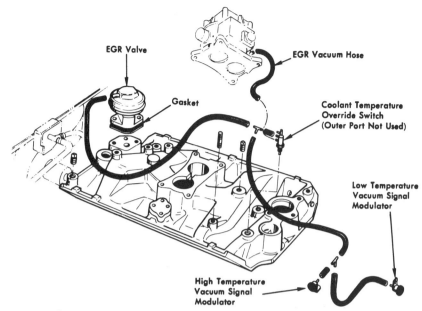

Exhaust Gas Recirculation Equipment for 1973 304 V8. The TVSMs are not used on 1974–76 Calif. models.

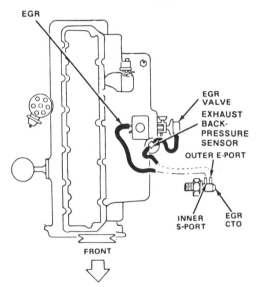

The EGR system on the 1974–76 232, 258 Sixes

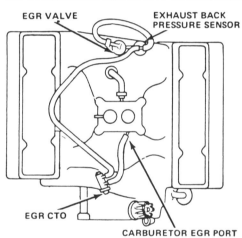

The EGR system on 1975 304 V8 California vehicles and all 1976 models

low temperature sensors (used in 1973 only), and hose connections to a fitting located above the diaphragm on the valve. A passage in the intake manifold directs exhaust gas from the exhaust crossover passage on V8s and from near the heat riser on the Sixes, to the EGR valve. When the diaphragm is actuated by vacuum, the valve opens and meters exhaust gas through special passages into the intake manifold below the carburetor.

COOLANT TEMPERATURE OVERRIDE SWITCH

This switch is located in the intake manifold at the coolant passage adjacent to the oil filler tube on V8s and on the left-side of the cylinder block on the Sixes. The outer port of the switch is open and not used on 1973–74 models, or is connected to either the EGR valve or BPS (when used). The inner port is connected by a hose to the EGR fitting at the carburetor. The center port (1973–74 only) is connected to the EGR valve. When coolant temperature is below 160° F, the center port of the switch is closed and no vacuum signal is applied to the EGR valve, therefore, no exhaust gas will flow through the valve. When the coolant temperature reaches 115° F (160° F in 1973 only), both the center port and the inner port of the switch are open and a vacuum signal is applied to the EGR valve. This vacuum signal is, however, subject to regulation by the low and high temperature signal modulators (1973 only) or BPS when used.

Low Temperature Vacuum Signal Modulator (1973 only)

This unit is located near the center of the radiator behind the grill opening. The low temperature vacuum signal modulator vacuum hose is connected by a plastic T-fitting to the EGR vacuum signal hose. The modulator is open when ambient temperatures are below 60° F. This causes a weakened vacuum signal to the EGR valve and a resultant decrease in the amount of exhaust gas being recirculated.

High Temperature Vacuum Signal Modulator (1973 only)

This unit is located at the firewall just to the right of the battery case. The high temperature vacuum signal modulator is connected to the EGR vacuum signal hose by a plastic T-fitting. The modulator opens when the underhood air temperatures reach 115° F and it causes a weakened vacuum signal to the EGR valve, thus reducing the amount of exhaust gases being recirculated.

EXHAUST BACKPRESSURE SENSOR (BPS)

This device is used on 1975 California vehicles and on all 1976 models in conjunction with the EGR system.

The BPS monitors exhaust backpressure and permits EGR operation only when engine operating conditions are favorable. The BPS units are variously calibrated, are not serviceable, and must be replaced with the identical part as a unit when necessary.

The BPS consists of a diaphragm valve and a spacer connected by a metal tube projecting into an exhaust port in the spacer body. The EGR valve mounts directly on the spacer.

In operation, the metal tube connecting the diaphragm valve to the spacer routes exhaust backpressure from the particular exhaust port to the sensor. When the backpressure reaches a certain level the diaphragm valve spring pressure is overcome, permitting a vacuum signal to the EGR valve, providing that the CTO switch is open.

Thus, EGR operation is only permitted when the engine is warmed up sufficiently and exhaust backpressure relatively high, such as during acceleration and at some cruising speeds. When temperature or backpressure conditions are not met, the vacuum signal is vented to the atmosphere from a vent at the diaphragm valve.

CATALYTIC CONVERTER

The catalytic converter is a muffler-like looking device inserted in the exhaust system. Exhaust gases flow through the converter where a chemical change takes place, reducing carbon monoxide and hydrocarbons to carbon dioxide and water; the latter two elements being harmless. The catalysts promoting this reaction are platinum and palladium-coated beads of alumina.

Because of the chemical reaction which does take place in the converter, the temperature of the converter during operation is higher than the exhaust gasses when they leave the engine. However, insulation keeps the outside skin of the converter about the same temperature as the muffler.

An improperly adjusted carburetor or ignition problem which would permit unburned fuel to enter the converter could produce excessive heat. Excessive heat in the converter could result in bulging or other distortion of the converter's shape. If the converter is heat-damaged and must be replaced, the ignition or carburetor problem must be corrected also.

FUEL TANK VAPOR EMISSION CONTROL SYSTEM

A closed fuel tank system is used to route raw fuel vapor from the fuel tank into the PCV system (1973 Sixes only) or air cleaner snorkle, where it is burned along with the fuel-air mixture. The system prevents raw fuel vapors from entering the atmosphere.

The fuel vapor system consists of internal fuel tank venting, a vacuum-pressure fuel tank filler cap, an expansion tank

(1972) or charcoal filled canister, limit fill valve (1972 only), liquid check valve, and internal carburetor venting.

On 1972 models only, fuel vapor pressure in the fuel tank forces the vapor through vent lines to the expansion tank or charcoal filled storage canister. The vapor then travels through a single vent line to the limit fill valve which regulates the vapor flow to the valve cover. The fuel tank vent line is routed through the limit fill valve to the valve cover on the left side on the 1972 V8. On the 1973 Sixes, it travels to the intake manifold and on the 304 V8 it is routed to the carburetor air cleaner.

On 1973–76 models, the fuel vapor is routed from the fuel tank through vapor vent hoses to the liquid check valve. From the liquid check valve, the fuel vapor is routed to the vapor storage canister which is filled with charcoal. When the engine is not operating the charcoal retains the vapors. When the engine is started vacuum from the air cleaner snorkle routed through a hose leading to the top of the vapor storage canister sucks the vapors from the storage canister. There are three nipples on the top of the canister; one for vapors coming from the fuel tank, one for vapors going to the air cleaner snorkle, and the other nipple is plugged (for use with 4 bbl carburetors on other AMC engines). Fresh air is drawn up through the canister from the bottom through a replaceable filter during operation.

Limit Fill Valve

This valve is essentially a combination vapor flow regulator and pressure relief valve. It regulates vapor flow from the fuel tank vent line into the valve cover. The valve consists of a housing, a spring loaded diaphragm and a diaphragm cover. As tank vent pressure increases, the diaphragm lifts permitting vapor to flow through. The pressure at which this occurs is 4–6 in. of water column. This action regulates the flow of vapors under severe conditions but generally prohibits the flow of vapor during normal temperature operation, thus minimizing driveability problems.

LIQUID CHECK VALVE

The liquid check valve prevents liquid fuel from entering the vapor lines leading to the storage canister. The check valve incorporates a float and needle valve assembly. If liquid fuel should enter the check valve, the float will rise and force the needle upward to close the vent passage. With no liquid fuel present in the check valve, fuel vapors pass freely from

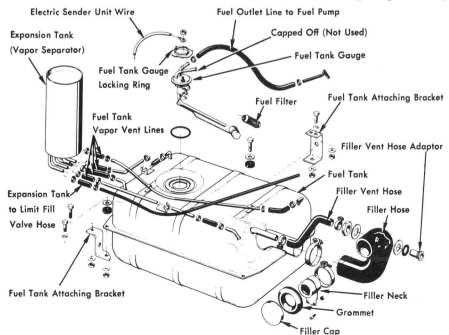

Fuel tank and vent lines for CJ-5 and CJ-6, 1972–73

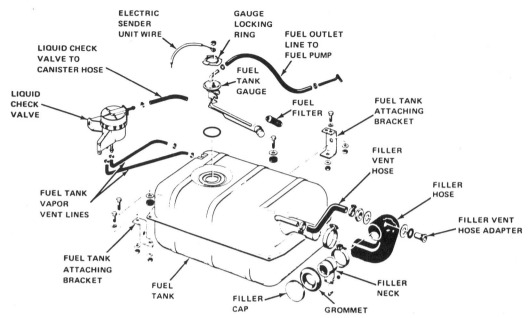

The fuel tank vapor emission control system on 1974–76 models

the tank, through the check valve, and on to the storage canister.

CHOKE HEAT BY-PASS VALVE (CHBPV)—1976 V8

When the engine is first started and begins to warm up, heated air from the exhaust crossover passage in the intake manifold is routed through a heat tube to the choke housing containing the thermostatic spring for regulating the choke flap. A thermostatic by-pass valve, which is integral with the choke heat tube, helps prevent premature choke valve opening during the early part of the warmup period. This is important when ambient temperatures are relatively low and adverse drivability could occur if the choke was opened too soon.

The thermostatic by-pass valve regulates the temperature of the hot airflow to the choke housing by allowing outside unheated air to enter the heat tube. A thermostatic disc in the valve is calibrated to close the valve at 75° F and open it at 55° F.

FUEL RETURN SYSTEM

The purpose of the fuel return system is to reduce high temperature fuel vapor problems. The system consists of a fuel return line to the fuel tank and a special fuel filter with an extra outlet nipple to which the return line is connected. During normal operation, a small amount of fuel is returned to the fuel tank. During periods of high underhood temperatures, vaporized fuel in the fuel line is returned to the fuel tank and not passed through the carburetor.

NOTE: *The extra nipple on the special fuel filter should be positioned upward to ensure proper operation of the system.*

EMISSION CONTROL CHECKS

ANTI-BACKFIRE DIVERTER VALVE

On the F-head, the anti-backfire valve remains open except when the throttle is closed rapidly from an open position.

To check the valve for proper operation, accelerate the engine in neutral, allowing the throttle to close rapidly. The valve is operating satisfactorily when no exhaust system backfire occurs. A further check can be made by removing the large hose that runs from the anti-backfire valve to the check valve and accelerating the engine and allowing the throttle to close rapidly. If there is an audible momentary interruption of the flow of air then it can be assumed that the valve is working correctly.

To check the valve on a V6, listen for backfire when the throttle is released quickly. If none exists, the valve is doing its job. To check further, remove the large hose that connects the valve with the air pump. Place a finger over the open end of the hose, not the valve, and accelerate the engine, allowing the throttle to close rapidly. The valve is operating satisfactorily if there is a momentary audible rush of air.

To check the diverter valve on American Motors engines, start the engine and let it idle. With the engine idling, there should be little or no air coming out the vents. When the engine is accelerated to 2,000–3,000 rpm, a strong flow of air should be felt at the vents. If the flow of air from the air pump is not diverted through the diverter valve vents when the engine is accelerated to the above mentioned rpm, check and make sure that the vacuum sensing line leading to the valve has vacuum and is not leaking or disconnected. The diverter valve should bleed air when 20 in. Hg or more vacuum is applied to the vacuum sensing line or when the output of the air pump exceeds 5 psi. When the engine is slowly accelerated, the diverter valve should begin to bleed off air between 2,500 and 3,500 rpm.

Check Valve

The check valve in the air distribution manifold prevents the reverse flow of exhaust gases to the pump in the event the pump should become inoperative or should exhaust pressure ever exceed the pump pressure.

To check this valve for proper operation, remove the air supply hose from the pump at the distribution manifold. With the engine running, listen for exhaust leakage where the check valve is connected to the distribution manifold. If leakage is audible, the valve is not operating correctly. A small amount of leakage is normal.

Air Pump

Check for the proper drive belt tension and adjust as necessary. Do not pry on the die cast pump housing. Check to see if the pump is discharging air. Remove the air outlet hose at the pump. With the engine running, air should be felt at the pump outlet opening.

EGR Valve

With the engine idling and at normal operating temperature, manually depress the EGR valve diaphragm. This should cause engine speed to drop about 200 rpm. This indicates that the EGR valve had been properly cutting off the flow of exhaust gas at idle and is operating properly.

If the engine speed did not change and the idle is smooth, exhaust gases are not reaching the combustion chambers. The probable cause of this is a plugged passage between the EGR valve and the intake manifold.

If the engine idle is rough and rpm is not affected by depressing the EGR valve diaphragm, the EGR valve is not closing off the flow of exhaust at idle like it's supposed to and there is most likely a fault in the hoses, hose routing, or the EGR valve itself.

NOTE: *The EGR valve can be removed and cleaned with a wire brush and a 9/16 in. drill coated with grease (to hold dirt particles) inserted in discharge passage. The drill should be held with a pair of pliers only.*

EGR CTO Switch

Before checking the operation of the EGR CTO switch, make sure that the engine coolant is below 100° F.

1. Check the vacuum lines for leaks and proper routing.

2. Disconnect the vacuum line at the backpressure sensor, if so equipped, or at the EGR valve, and connect the line to a vacuum gauge.

3. Operate the engine at 1,500 rpm. No vacuum should be indicated at the gauge. If vacuum is indicated, replace the EGR CTO switch.

4. Allow the engine to idle until the coolant temperature exceeds 115° F.

5. Accelerate the engine to 1,500 rpm. Vacuum should be present at the gauge. If not, replace the EGR CTO switch.

Exhaust BPS Unit

1. Make sure that all the EGR vacuum lines are routed correctly and are not leaking.

2. Install a "T" in the vacuum line between the EGR valve and BPS, and attach a vacuum gauge to the "T."

3. Start the engine and allow it to idle. No vacuum should be present.

If vacuum is indicated at idle speed, make sure of correct line connections. Also, be sure that manifold vacuum is not the source. If the carburetor is providing the vacuum, look for a partially open throttle plate which could cause premature ported vacuum to the BPS unit.

4. Accelerate the engine to 2,000 rpm and observe the vacuum gauge for the following:

a. If the coolant is below 115° F, no vacuum should be present;

b. With coolant temperature above 115° F, ported vacuum should be indicated;

c. If no vacuum is indicated at any time, make sure that vacuum is being applied to the inlet side of the BPS. If correct, remove the BPS and either clean it with a wire brush (if blocked) or replace it.

Spark CTO Switch

Before testing the spark CTO switch, make sure that the engine coolant temperature is below 160° F.

1. Remove all the hoses from the CTO switch and plug those which will create a vacuum leak.

2. Connect a vacuum line from a manifold vacuum source to the top port of the CTO switch.

3. Connect a vacuum gauge to the center port.

4. Start the engine. Manifold vacuum should be indicated on the gauge. If not, replace the switch.

5. With the engine still running and the coolant temperature still below 160° F, disconnect the vacuum line from the top port and connect it to the bottom port.

6. No vacuum should be indicated. Replace the switch if there is vacuum.

7. Allow the engine to run until the coolant temperature exceeds 160° F. Manifold vacuum should be indicated. If not, replace the CTO switch.

8. Disconnect the hose from the bottim port and connect it to the top port again. With the coolant temperature above 160° F, no vacuum should be indicated. If there is, replace the CTO switch.

Fuel System

FUEL PUMP

Removal and Installation, All Engines

1. Disconnect the inlet and outlet fuel lines.

2. Remove the two fuel pump body attaching nuts and lockwashers.

3. Pull the pump and gasket free of the engine. Make sure that the mating surfaces

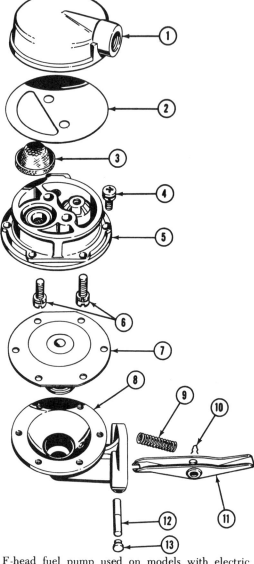

F-head fuel pump used on models with electric windshield wipers

1. Housing cover
2. Air dome diaphragm
3. Strainer
4. Screw and washer
5. Housing
6. Cover screw and lockwashers
7. Main diaphragm
8. Pump body
9. Cam lever return spring
10. Pin retainer
11. Cam lever
12. Cam lever pin
13. Lever seal shaft plug

of the fuel pump and the engine are clean.

4. Cement a new gasket to the mounting flange of the fuel pump.

5. Position the fuel pump on the engine block so that the lever of the fuel pump rests on the fuel pump cam of the camshaft.

6. Secure the fuel pump to the block with the two cap screws and lock washers.

7. Connect the intake and outlet fuel lines to the fuel pump.

Fuel Pump Testing

Volume Check

Disconnect the fuel line from the carburetor. Place the open end in a suitable container. Start the engine and operate it at normal idle speed. The pump should deliver at least one pint in 30 seconds.

Pressure Check

Disconnect the fuel line at the carburetor. Disconnect the fuel return line from the fuel filter if so equipped, and plug the nipple on the filter. Install a T-fitting on the open end of the fuel line and refit the line to the carburetor. Plug a pressure gauge into the remaining opening of the T-fitting. The hose leading to the pressure gauge should not be any longer than 6 inches. Start the engine and let it run at idle speed. Bleed any air out of the hose between the gauge and the T-fitting. Pressure readings @ rpm are given below.

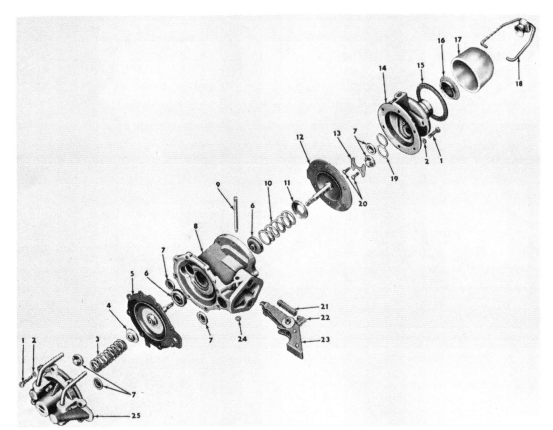

An exploded view of a fuel and vacuum pump for an F-head

1. Cover screw	10. Fuel diaphragm	19. Gasket
2. Lockwasher	11. Oil seal retainer	20. Screw
3. Diaphragm spring	12. Diaphragm and rod	21. Rocker arm spring
4. Spring seat	13. Valve retainer	22. Link spacer
5. Diaphragm and rod	14. Cover	23. Rocker arm
6. Oil seal	15. Gasket	24. Washer
7. Valve assembly	16. Screen	25. Body
8. Body	17. Bowl	
9. Rocker arm pin spring	18. Bail	

The fuel pump for the V6. This pump is not serviceable

1. Fuel outlet	2. Vapor return	3. Fuel inlet

F-Head—$2\frac{1}{2}$–$3\frac{3}{4}$ psi @ 1800 rpm.

NOTE: *The gauge should not be more than 16 in. above the outlet of the fuel pump.*

V6—$3\frac{3}{4}$ psi @ idle with the vapor return line squeezed off. $2\frac{1}{2}$ psi @ idle with the vapor return line open.

232, 258 Sixes—4–5 psi @ 500 rpm.

304 V8—5–$6\frac{1}{2}$ psi @ 500 rpm.

CARBURETORS

Removal and Installation
All Engines

To remove the carburetor from any engine, first remove the air cleaner from the top of the carburetor. Remove all lines and hoses, noting their positions to facilitate installation. Remove all throttle and choke linkage at the carburetor. Remove the carburetor attaching nuts which hold it to the intake manifold. Lift the carburetor from the engine along with the carburetor base gasket. Discard the gasket. Install the carburetor in the reverse order of removal, using a new base gasket.

Overhaul

ALL TYPES

Efficient carburetion depends greatly on careful cleaning and inspection during overhaul since dirt, gum, water, or varnish in or on the carburetor parts are often responsible for poor performance.

Overhaul your carburetor in a clean, dust-free area. Carefully disassemble the carburetor, referring often to the exploded views. Keep all similar and look-alike parts segregated during disassembly and cleaning to avoid accidental interchange during assembly. Make a note of all jet sizes.

When the carburetor is disassembled, wash all parts (except diaphragms, electric choke units, pump plunger, and any other plastic, leather, fiber, or rubber parts) in clean carburetor solvent. Do not leave parts in the solvent any longer than is necessary to sufficiently loosen the deposits. Excessive cleaning may remove the special finish from the float bowl and choke valve bodies, leaving these parts unfit for service. Rinse all parts in clean solvent and blow them dry with compressed air or allow them to air dry. Wipe clean all cork, plastic, leather, and fiber parts with a clean, lint-free cloth

Blow out all passages and jets with compressed air and be sure that there are no restrictions or blockages. Never use wire or similar tools to clean jets, fuel passages, or air bleeds. Clean all jets and valves separately to avoid accidental interchange.

Check all parts for wear or damage. If wear or damage is found, replace the defective parts. Especially check the following:

1. Check the float needle and seat for wear. If wear is found, replace the complete assembly.

2. Check the float hinge pin for wear and the float(s) for dents or distortion. Replace the float if fuel has leaked into it.

3. Check the throttle and choke shaft bores for wear or an out-of-round condition. Damage or wear to the throttle arm, shaft, or shaft bore will often require replacement of the throttle body. These parts require a close tolerance of fit; wear may allow air leakage, which could affect starting and idling.

NOTE: *Throttle shafts and bushings are not included in overhaul kits. They can be purchased separately.*

4. Inspect the idle mixture adjusting needles for burrs or grooves. Any such condition requires replacement of the needle, since you will not be able to obtain a satisfactory idle.

5. Test the accelerator pump check valves. They should pass air one way but not the other. Test for proper seating by

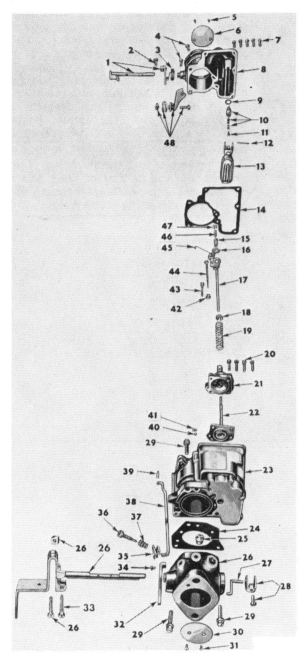

1. Choke shaft and lever
2. Screw
3. Choke lever spring
4. Screw and washer
5. Choke valve screw
6. Choke valve
7. Screw and washer
8. Air horn
9. Needle seat gasket
10. Needle spring and seat
11. Needle pin
12. Float pin
13. Float
14. Gasket
15. Pump spring
16. Metering rod arm
17. Pump link
18. Pump spring retainer
19. Vacuum diaphragm spring
20. Screw and washer
21. Diaphragm housing
22. Diaphragm
23. Body
24. Gasket
25. Idle port plug
26. Throttle body lever and shaft assembly
27. Pump link connector
28. Throttle shaft arm
29. Screw and washer
30. Throttle valve
31. Throttle valve screw
32. Fast idle arm
33. Adjusting screw
34. Body flange plug
35. Clevis clip
36. Idle adjusting screw
37. Idle screw spring
38. Fast idle connector rod
39. Pin spring
40. Ball check valve
41. Ball check valve retainer ring
42. Metering rod jet
43. Low speed jet
44. Metering rod
45. Metering rod spring
46. Inner pump spring
47. Pump spring retainer
48. Bracket and clamp assembly (choke and throttle)

An exploded view of a carburetor for the F-head

blowing and sucking on the valve. Replace the valve if necessary. If the valve is satisfactory, wash the valve again to remove breath moisture.

6. Check the bowl cover for warped surfaces with a straightedge.

7. Closely inspect the valves and seats for wear and damage, replacing as necessary.

8. After the carburetor is assembled,

check the choke valve for freedom of operation.

Carburetor overhaul kits are recommended for each overhaul. These kits contain all gaskets and new parts to replace those that deteriorate most rapidly. Failure to replace all parts supplied with the kit (especially gaskets) can result in poor performance later.

Some carburetor manufacturers supply

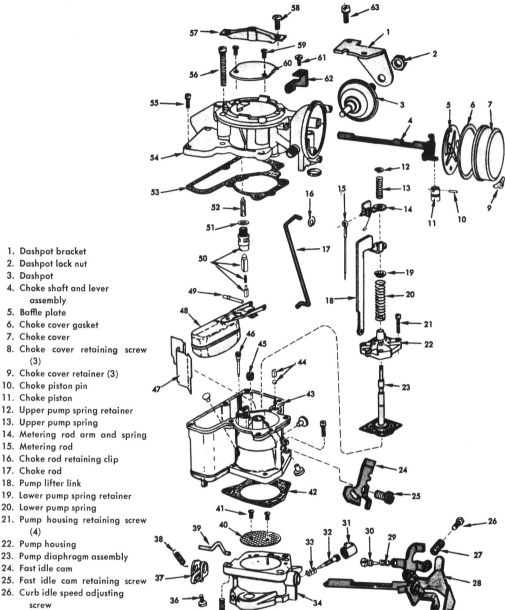

An exploded view of a model YF carburetor

1. Dashpot bracket
2. Dashpot lock nut
3. Dashpot
4. Choke shaft and lever assembly
5. Baffle plate
6. Choke cover gasket
7. Choke cover
8. Choke cover retaining screw (3)
9. Choke cover retainer (3)
10. Choke piston pin
11. Choke piston
12. Upper pump spring retainer
13. Upper pump spring
14. Metering rod arm and spring
15. Metering rod
16. Choke rod retaining clip
17. Choke rod
18. Pump lifter link
19. Lower pump spring retainer
20. Lower pump spring
21. Pump housing retaining screw (4)
22. Pump housing
23. Pump diaphragm assembly
24. Fast idle cam
25. Fast idle cam retaining screw
26. Curb idle speed adjusting screw
27. Curb idle screw spring
28. Throttle shaft and lever assembly
29. Fast idle screw spring
30. Fast idle speed adjusting screw
31. Idle limiter cap
32. Idle mixture screw
33. Idle mixture screw spring
34. Throttle body
35. Throttle body retaining screw (3)
36. Throttle shaft arm set screw
37. Throttle shaft arm
38. Throttle shaft return spring
39. Pump connector link
40. Throttle valve
41. Throttle valve retaining screw (2)

42. Throttle body gasket
43. Main body
44. Pump discharge check ball and weight
45. Metering rod jet
46. Low speed jet
47. Fuel bowl baffle
48. Float and lever assembly
49. Float pin
50. Needle and seat assembly
51. Needle seat gasket
52. Screen
53. Air horn gasket
54. Air horn

55. Short air horn retaining screw (3)
56. Long air horn retaining screw (3)
57. Air cleaner bracket
58. Air cleaner bracket retaining screw (2)
59. Choke valve retaining screw (2)
60. Choke valve
61. Choke lever retaining screw
62. Choke lever
63. Dashpot bracket retaining screw

1. Pivot pin
2. Modulator arm
3. Choke valve retaining screw (2)
4. Choke valve
5. Choke shaft
6. Air horn
7. Air horn retaining screw (4)
8. Air horn gasket
9. Float shaft retainer
10. Float and lever assembly
11. Needle retaining clip
12. Deflector
13. Needle and seat assembly
14. Needle seat gasket
15. Fuel bowl baffle
16. Float shaft
17. Curb idle adjusting screw
18. Curb idle adjusting screw spring
19. Throttle shaft and lever assembly
20. Dashpot
21. Dashpot locknut
22. Dashpot bracket
23. Dashpot bracket retaining screw
24. Throttle valve retaining screw (4)
25. Throttle valve (2)
26. Main jet (2)
27. Main body
28. Pump rod retainer
29. Pump rod
30. Elastomer valve
31. Pump return spring
32. Pump diaphragm
33. Pump lever pin
34. Pump cover
35. Pump lever
36. Pump cover retaining screw (4)
37. Fuel inlet fitting
38. Power valve gasket
39. Power valve
40. Power valve cover gasket

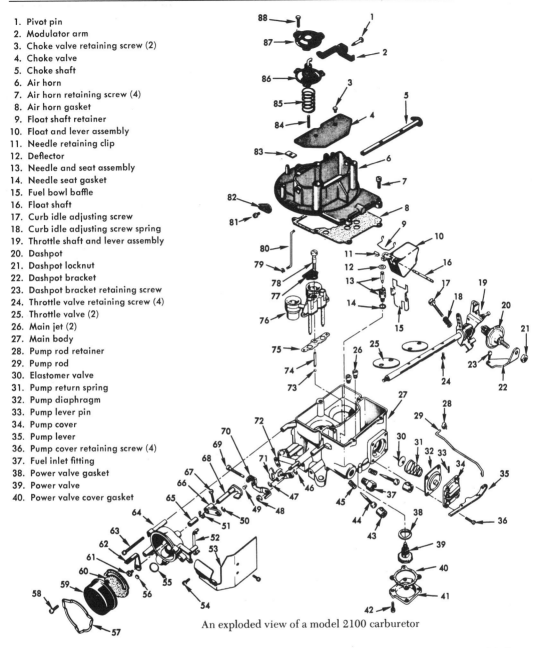

An exploded view of a model 2100 carburetor

41. Power valve cover
42. Power valve cover retaining screw (4)
43. Idle limiter cap (2)
44. Idle mixture screw (2)
45. Idle mixture screw spring (2)
46. Retainer
47. Retainer
48. Fast idle lever retaining nut
49. Fast idle lever pin
50. Retainer
51. Retainer
52. Fast idle cam rod
53. Choke shield
54. Choke shield retaining screw (2)
55. Piston passage plug
56. Heat passage plug

57. Choke cover retaining clamp
58. Choke cover retaining screw (3)
59. Choke cover
60. Choke cover gasket
61. Thermostat lever retaining screw
62. Thermostat lever
63. Choke housing retaining screw (3)
64. Choke housing
65. Choke shaft bushing
66. Fast idle cam lever
67. Fast idle cam lever adjusting screw
68. Thermostatic choke shaft
69. Fast idle speed adjusting screw
70. Fast idle lever
71. Fast idle cam
72. Choke housing gasket

73. Pump discharge check ball
74. Pump discharge weight
75. Booster venturi gasket
76. Booster venturi assembly
77. Air distribution plate
78. Pump discharge screw
79. Retainer
80. Choke rod
81. Choke lever retaining screw
82. Choke lever
83. Choke rod seal
84. Stop screw
85. Modulator return spring
86. Modulator diaphragm assembly
87. Modulator cover
88. Modulator retaining screw (3)

overhaul kits of three basic types: minor repair; major repair; and gasket kits. Basically, they contain the following:

Minor Repair Kits
    All gaskets
    Float needle valve
    Volume control screw
    All diaphragms
    Spring for the pump diaphragm

Major Repair Kits
    All jets and gaskets
    All diaphragms
    Float needle valve
    Volume control screw
    Pump ball valve
    Main jet carrier
    Float
    Complete intermediate rod
    Intermediate pump lever
    Complete injector tube
    Some cover hold-down screws and washers

Gasket Kits
    All gaskets

After cleaning and checking all components, reassemble the carburetor, using new parts and referring to the exploded view. When reassembling, make sure that all screws and jets are tight in their seats, but do not overtighten, as the tips will be distorted. Tighten all screws gradually, in rotation. Do not tighten needle valves into their seats; uneven jetting will result. Always use new gaskets. Be sure to adjust the float level when reassembling.

Float and Fuel Level Adjustment

F-Head

1. Remove and invert the bowl cover.
2. Remove the bowl cover gasket.

3. Allow the weight of the float to rest on the needle and spring. Be sure that there is no compression of the spring other than by the weight of the float.

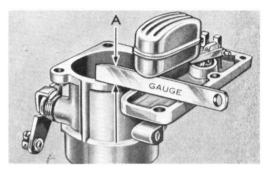

Adjusting the float level on an F-head carburetor

4. Adjust the level by bending the float arm lip that contacts the needle (not the arm) to provide $17/64$ in. of clearance on models made during and after 1968. On models prior to 1968 the clearance is to be set at $5/16$ in.

V6

The procedure for adjusting the float level of the two barrel carburetor installed

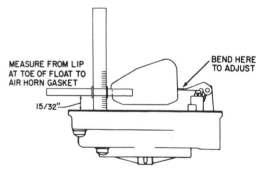

Adjusting the float level on a V6 carburetor

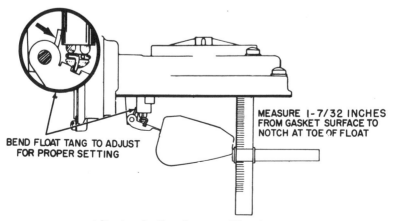

Adjusting the float drop on a V6 carburetor

on the V6 is the same as the procedure for the F-head up to step 4.

The actual measurement is taken from the air horn gasket to the lip at the toe of the float. This distance should be $^{15}/_{32}$ in. To adjust the float level, bend the float arm as required.

The float drop adjustment is accomplished in the following manner: With the bowl cover turned in the upright position, measure the distance from the gasket to the notch at the toe of the float. Bend the tang as required to obtain a measurement of $1^{7}/_{32}$ in.

232, 258 Sixes

Remove and invert the air horn assembly and remove the gasket. Measure the distance between the top of the float at the free end, and the air horn casting. The measurement should be $^{29}/_{64}$–$^{31}/_{64}$ in. Adjust by bending the float lever.

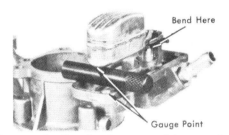

Adjusting the float level on a model YF carburetor

NOTE: *The fuel inlet needle must be held off its seat while bending the float lever in order to prevent damage to the needle and seat.*

To adjust the float drop, hold the air horn in the upright position and measure the distance between the top of the float, at the extreme outer end, and the air horn

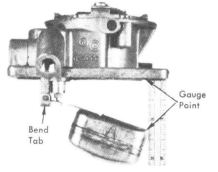

Adjusting the float drop on a model YF carburetor

casting. The measurement should be $1\frac{1}{4}$ in. to 1973, $1\frac{3}{8}$ in. 1974–76. Adjust by bending the tab at the rear of the float lever.

304 V8

With the air horn assembly and the gasket removed, raise the float by pressing down on the float tab until the fuel inlet needle is lightly seated. Using a T-scale, measure the distance from the fuel bowl machined surface to either corner of the float at the free end. The measurement should be $\frac{3}{4}$ in. through 1975, $^{59}/_{64}$ in. 1976. To adjust bend the float tab and hold the fuel inlet needle off its seat in order to prevent damage to the seat and the tip of the needle.

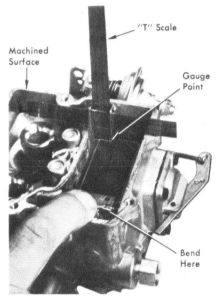

Adjusting the float level on a model 2100 carburetor

Fast Idle Linkage Adjustment

NOTE: *With air cleaner removed.*

F-Head

With the choke held in the wide open position, the lip on the fast-idle rod should contact the boss on the body casting. Adjust it by bending the fast idle link at the offset in the link.

V6

No fast idle speed adjustment is required. Fast idle is controlled by the curb idle speed adjustment screw. If the curb

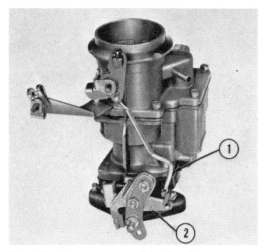

Fast idle adjustment on an F-head carburetor

1. Fast idle connector rod   2. Fast idle link

idle speed is set correctly and the choke rod is properly adjusted, fast idle speed will be correct.

232, 258 SIXES THROUGH 1973

Partially open the throttle and close the choke valve to rotate the fast idle cam into the cold start position. While holding the choke valve closed, release the throttle. With the fast idle cam in this position, the fast idle adjusting screw must be aligned with the index mark at the back side of the cam. Adjust by bending the choke rod at its upper angle.

232, 258 SIXES 1974–76

Position the fast idle screw on the second step of the fast idle cam, against the shoulder of the high step on the cam. Ad-

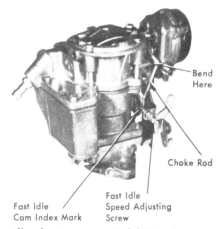

Fast idle adjustment on a Model YF carburetor

just by bending the choke plate connecting rod to obtain $1\frac{3}{64}$ in. clearance between the lower edge of the choke plate and the air horn wall.

304 V8

Push down on the fast idle cam lever until the fast idle speed adjusting screw is contacting the second step (index), and against the shoulder of the high step. Measure the clearance between the lower edge of the choke valve and air horn wall. Adjust by turning the fast idle cam lever screw to obtain $1\frac{9}{64}$ in. through 1975 and $\frac{1}{8}$ in. 1976. Adjust the automatic choke.

Fast idle adjustment for model 2100 carburetor

Choke Linkage Adjustment

F-HEAD AND V6

The choke is manually operated by a cable that runs from the dash mounted control pull knob to the set screw on the choke actuating arm. To adjust the choke, loosen the set screw at the choke actuating lever and push in the dash knob as far as it will go. Open the choke plate as far as it will go and hold it with your finger while the set screw is tightened.

232, 258 SIXES AND 304 V8

The automatic choke setting is made by loosening the choke cover retaining screws and rotating the cover in the desired direction as indicated by an arrow on the face of the cover. In all cases the automatic choke spring housing cover is set to 1 or 2 notches to the rich side. This setting will be satisfactory for most driving conditions. However, if the engine stumbles or stalls on acceleration during warmup, the choke may be set richer or leaner no more than two graduations from the original setting.

Unloader Adjustment

232, 258 SIXES

With the throttle held fully open, apply pressure on the choke valve toward the closed position and measure the clearance between the lower edge of the choke valve and the air horn wall. The measurement should be $\frac{1}{4}$ in. 1971–73, $\frac{9}{32}$ in. 1974–76. Adjust by bending the tang on the throttle lever which contacts the fast idle cam. Bend toward the cam to increase the clearance.

NOTE: *Do not bend the unloader downward from a horizontal plane. After making the adjustment, make sure the unloader tang does not contact the main body flange when the throttle is fully open. Final unloader adjustment must always be done on the vehicle. The throttle should be fully opened by depressing the accelerator pedal to the floor. This is to assure that full throttle is obtained.*

Unloader adjustment on the model YF carburetor

304 V8

With the throttle held fully open, apply pressure on the choke valve toward the closed position and measure the clearance between the lower edge of the choke valve and the air horn wall. The setting should be $\frac{1}{4}$ in. Adjust by bending the tang on the fast idle lever, which is located on the

throttle linkage. Refer to the "Note" under the procedure for adjusting the unloader on the Sixes.

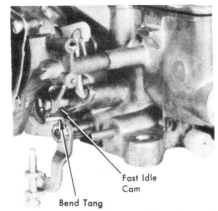

Unloader adjustment on the model 2100 carburetor

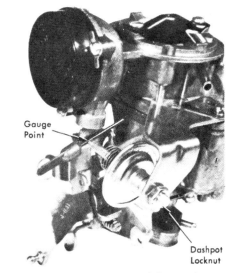

Dashpot adjustment on the model YF carburetor

Dashpot adjustment on the model 2100 carburetor

Dashpot Adjustment

ALL ENGINES

With the throttle set at curb idle position fully depress the dashpot stem and measure the clearance between the stem and the throttle lever. Adjust by loosening the lock nut and turning the dashpot.

Dashpot Stem-to-Throttle Lever Clearance (in.)

	'72	'73	'74	'75	'76
232	$3/32$	$3/32$	$3/32$	$5/64$	$5/64$
258	$3/32$	$3/32$	$3/32$	$5/64$	$5/64$
304	$7/64$	$9/64$	$9/64$	$3/32$	$5/64$

Carburetor Specifications

All measurements in in.

Engine	Model	Low Speed Jet	Metering Rod Jet Size	Float Level	Float Drop	Fast Idle Cam Linkage	Automatic Choke Valve Setting	Fast Idle Speed ▲ (rpm)	Choke Unloader	Initial Choke Valve Clearance
F-Head	Carter YF 938S 938SA 938SC 938SD 4002–S 4366–S③	0.028	0.0935	$5/16$①	——	②	——	——	——	Manual Choke
V6	Rochester 2G 7026082 7027082	——	0.051	$13/32$④	$17/8$	⑤	——	——	——	Manual Choke
232, 258 Sixes	Carter YF 6288S	0.036	0.101	$29/64$	$11/4$	Index Mark⑥	Index	1600	$19/64$	$15/64$
	64013	0.033	0.101	$29/64$	$11/4$	Index Mark	1 Rich	1600	$9/32$	$7/32$
	6431, 6511, 7029, 7040, 7041	0.033	0.101	$31/64$	$13/8$	$3/16$	1 Rich	1600	$9/32$	$7/32$
	7084	0.035	0.101	$31/64$	$13/8$	$13/64$	2 Rich	1600	$9/32$	$7/32$
	7109	0.033	0.101	$31/64$	$13/8$	$13/64$	2 Rich	1600	$9/32$	$7/32$
	7083	0.036	0.101	$31/64$	$13/8$	$13/64$	1 Rich	1600	$9/32$	$7/32$
	7085	0.035	0.101	$31/64$	$13/8$	$13/64$	1 Rich	1600	$9/32$	$7/32$
304 V8	Autolite 2100 2DM2	0.028	——	$3/8$⑦	——	$1/8$	1 Rich	1600	$13/64$	$9/64$
	3DM2	0.035	——	$3/4$⑧	——	$1/8$	1 Rich	1600	$1/4$	$1/8$
	4DMJ2	0.035	——	$25/32$⑧	——	$1/8$	2 Rich	1600	$1/4$	$9/64$

Engine	Model	Low Speed Jet	Metering Rod Jet Size	Float Level	Float Drop	Fast Idle Cam Linkage	Automatic Choke Valve Setting	Fast Idle Speed ▲ (rpm)	Choke Unloader	Initial Choke Valve Clearance
	4DM2	0.035	——	$^{25}\!/_{32}$⑧	——	$\frac{1}{8}$	2 Rich	1600	$\frac{1}{4}$	$\frac{1}{8}$
	5DM2J, 5DM2	0.035	——	$^{25}\!/_{32}$⑧	——	$\frac{1}{8}$	2 Rich	1600	$\frac{1}{4}$	$^{9}\!/_{64}$
	6DM2J	0.028	——	$^{15}\!/_{16}$⑧	——	$\frac{1}{8}$	1 Rich	1600	$\frac{1}{4}$	$^{9}\!/_{64}$
	6DM2	0.031	——	$^{15}\!/_{16}$⑧	——	$\frac{1}{8}$	2 Rich	1600	$\frac{1}{4}$	$\frac{1}{8}$
	6DA2J	0.032	——	$^{15}\!/_{16}$⑧	——	$\frac{1}{8}$	1 Rich	1600	$\frac{1}{4}$	$^{9}\!/_{64}$

▲ On second step of fast idle cam
① $^{17}\!/_{64}$ on Models YF–4002–S and YF–4366–S
② With the choke held wide open, the lip of the fast idle rod should contact the boss on the body casting
③ With exhaust emission control
④ $1^{5}\!/_{32}$ on 2G–7027082 only
⑤ Fast idle is controlled by the curb idle adjustment
⑥ Choke closed
⑦ Dry measurement
⑧ Wet measurement on vehicle

5 · Chassis Electrical

Understanding and Troubleshooting Electrical Systems

For any electrical system to operate, it must make a complete circuit. This simply means that the power flow from the battery must make a complete circle. When an electrical component is operating, power flows from the battery to the component, passes through the component causing it to perform its function (lighting a light bulb), and then returns to the battery through the ground of the circuit. This ground is usually (but not always) the metal part of the car on which the electrical component is mounted.

Perhaps the easiest way to visualize this is to think of connecting a light bulb with two wires attached to it to your car battery. The battery in your car has two posts; negative and positive. If one of the two wires attached to the light bulb was attached to the negative post of the battery and the other wire was attached to the positive post of the battery, you would have a complete circuit. Current from the battery would flow out one post, through the wire attached to it and then to the light bulb, where it would pass through causing it to light. It would then leave the

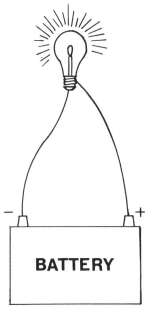

A complete circuit

light bulb, travel through the other wire, and return to the other post of the battery.

The normal automotive circuit differs from this simple example in two ways. First, instead of having a return wire from the bulb to the battery, the light bulb returns the current to the battery through the chassis of the vehicle. Since the negative battery cable is attached to the chassis and the chassis is made of electrically conductive metal, the chassis of the vehicle

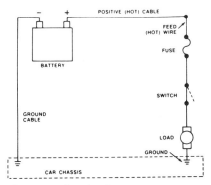

A simple automotive circuit

can serve as a ground wire to complete the circuit. Secondly, most automotive circuits contain switches to turn components on and off as required.

There are many types of switches, but the most common simply serves to prevent the passage of current when it is turned off. Since the switch is a part of the circle necessary for a complete circuit, it operates to leave an opening in the circuit, and thus an incomplete or open circuit, when it is turned off.

Some electrical components which require a large amount of current to operate also have a relay in their circuit. Since these circuits carry a large amount of current, the thickness of the wire in the circuit (gauge size) is also greater. If this large wire were connected from the component to the control switch on the instrument panel, and then back to the component, a voltage drop would occur in the circuit. To prevent this potential drop in voltage, an electromagnetic switch (relay) is used. The large wires in the circuit are connected from the car battery to one side of the relay, and from the opposite side of the relay to the component. The relay is normally open, preventing current from passing through the circuit. An additional, smaller, wire is connected from the relay to the control switch for the circuit. When the control switch is turned on, it grounds the smaller wire from the relay and completes the circuit. This closes the relay and allows current to flow from the battery to the component. The horn, headlight, and starter circuits are three which commonly use relays.

Did you ever notice how your instrument panel lights get brighter the faster your car goes? This happens because your alternator (which supplies the battery)

puts out more current at speeds above idle. This is normal. However, it is possible for larger surges of current to pass through the electrical system of your car. If this surge of current were to reach an electrical component, it could burn it out. To prevent this from happening, fuses are connected into the current supply wires of most of the major electrical systems of your car. The fuse serves to head off the surge at the pass. When an electrical current of excessive power passes through the component's fuse, the fuse blows out and breaks the circuit, saving it from destruction.

The fuse also protects the component from damage if the power supply wire to the component is grounded before the current reaches the component.

Let us here interject another rule to the complete circle circuit. *Every complete circuit from a power source must include a component which is using the power from the power source.* If you were to disconnect the light bulb (from the previous example of a lightbulb being connected to the battery by two wires) from the wires and touch the two wires together (please take my word for this; don't try it), the result would be shocking. You probably haven't seen so many sparks since the Fourth of July. A similar thing happens (on a smaller scale) when the power supply wire to a component or the electrical component itself becomes grounded before the normal ground connection for the circuit. To prevent damage to the system, the fuse for the circuit blows to interrupt the circuit—protecting the components from damage. Because grounding a wire from a power source makes a complete circuit—less the required component to use the power—this phenomenon is called a short circuit. The most common causes of short circuits are: the rubber insulation on a wire breaking or rubbing through to expose the current carrying core of the wire to a metal part of the car, or a shorted switch.

Some electrical systems on the car are protected by a circuit breaker which is, basically, a self-repairing fuse. When either of the above-described events takes place in a system which is protected by a circuit breaker, the circuit breaker opens the circuit the same way a fuse does. However, when either the short is removed from the circuit or the surge subsides, the circuit breaker resets itself and does not have to be replaced as a fuse does.

The final protective device in the chassis electrical system is a fuse link. A fuse link is a wire that acts as a fuse. It is connected between the battery and the fuse box. Since the fuse link protects all the chassis electrical components, it is the probable cause of trouble when none of the electrical components function, unless the battery is disconnected or dead.

Electrical problems generally fall into one of three areas:

1. The component itself is not functioning.

2. The component that is not functioning is not receiving current.

3. The component is not properly grounded.

Problems that fall into the second category are by far the most complicated. It is the current supply system to the component which contains all the switches, relays, fuses, etc.

The electrical system can be checked with a test light and a jumper wire. A test light is a device that looks like a pointed screwdriver with a wire attached to it. It has a light bulb in its handle. A jumper wire is a piece of insulated wire with an alligator clip attached to each end. To check the system you must follow the wiring diagram of the vehicle being worked on. A wiring diagram is a road map of the car's electrical system.

If a light bulb is not working you must follow a systematic plan to determine which of the three causes is at fault.

1. The first thing to do, of course, is examine the bulb and/or test it to make sure that it is not burned out. Replace the bulb, if necessary, and try the new one to see if it works. If it does, you've solved the problem; if the new bulb fails to light, continue on to Step 2.

2. Turn on the switch that controls the inoperable bulb.

3. Disconnect the power supply wire from the bulb.

4. Attach the ground wire on the test light to a good metal ground.

5. Touch the probe end of the test light to the end of the power supply wire that was disconnected from the bulb. If the bulb is receiving current, the test light will go on.

NOTE: *If the bulb is one which works only when the ignition key is turned on (turn signal), make sure the key is turned on.*

If the test light does not go on, then the problem is in the circuit between the battery and the bulb. As mentioned before, this includes all the switches, fuses, and relays in the system. Turn to the wiring diagram and find the bulb on the diagram. Follow the wire that runs back to the battery. The problem is an open circuit between the battery and the bulb. If the fuse is blown and, when replaced, immediately blows again, there is a short circuit in the system which must be located and repaired. If there is a switch in the system, bypass it with a jumper wire. This is done by connecting one end of the jumper wire to the power supply wire into the switch and the other end of the jumper wire to the wire coming out of the switch. Again, consult the wiring diagram. If the test light lights with the jumper wire installed, the switch or whatever was bypassed is defective.

NOTE: *Never substitute the jumper wire for the bulb, as the bulb is the component required to use the power from the power source.*

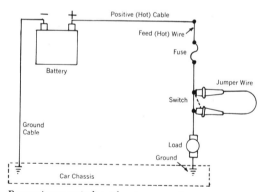

Bypassing a switch with a jumper wire

6. If the bulb in the test light goes on, then the current is getting to the bulb that is not working in the car. This eliminates the first of the three possible causes. Connect the power supply wire and connect a jumper wire from the bulb to a good metal ground. Do this with the switch which controls the bulb turned on, and also the ignition switch turned on if it is required for the light to work. If the bulb works with the jumper wire installed, then it has

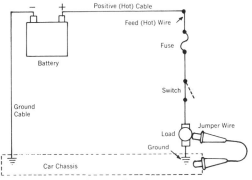

Checking for a bad ground with a jumper wire

a bad ground. This is usually caused by the metal area on which the bulb mounts to the car being coated with some type of foreign matter.

The above test procedure can be applied to any of the components of the

chassis electrical system by substituting the component that is not working for the light bulb. Remember that for any electrical system to work, all connections must be clean and tight.

Heater

BLOWER

Removal and Installation

1. Disconnect the battery ground cable.
2. Disconnect the electrical connections:
   a. Heater switch
   b. Ground wire
   c. Battery connector
3. Remove the screws that hold the

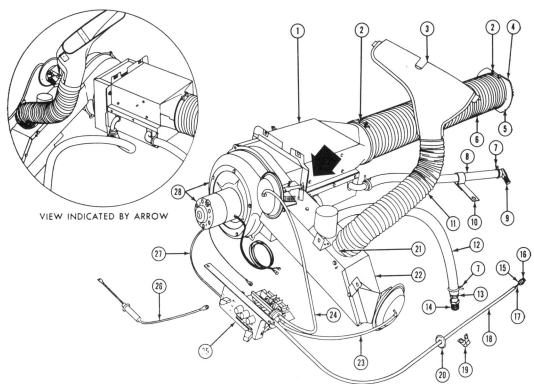

VIEW INDICATED BY ARROW

Heater assembly for a Jeep made prior to 1972. Heaters from early model Jeeps are less complicated

1. Heater assembly	11. Defroster hose	21. Defroster bushing
2. Hose clamp	12. Hot water hose	22. Heat distributor assembly
3. Defroster nozzle	13. Heater nipple	23. Heater control tube
4. Air duct screen	14. Reducing bushing	24. Heater control tube
5. Air duct and heater collar	15. Inverted flared tube nut	25. Heater control assembly
6. Air duct intake tube	16. Inverted flared tube connector	26. Fuse holder assembly
7. Hose clamp	17. Heater vacuum to engine tube	27. Bowden wire (control panel to
8. Straight hot water hose	18. Heater control tube	heater)
9. Heater tube elbow	19. Clip	28. Blower and air inlet assembly
10. Heater hose support bracket	20. Grommet	

motor to the heater assembly and remove the blower motor housing and motor.

4. Remove fan and blower motor from blower motor housing.

5. Reverse the procedure to install.

CORE

Removal and Installation

THROUGH 1974

1. Drain the cooling system.
2. Mark the duct halves to be sure they are reassembled properly.
3. Remove the screws that fasten the two halves of the duct together.
4. Remove the screws that secure the heater core to the duct.
5. Remove the heater core from the vehicle.
6. Install in reverse order of the above procedure.

1975–76

1. Drain about two quarts of coolant from the radiator.
2. Disconnect the battery cables, remove the battery and battery box.
3. Disconnect the heater hoses.

4. Disconnect the damper door control cables.

5. Disconnect the blower motor wiring harness at the switch and ground wire at the instrument panel.

6. Remove the glove box.

7. Disconnect the water drain hose and defroster hose.

8. Disconnect the heater-to-air deflector duct at the heater housing.

9. Remove the nuts from the heater housing studs in the engine compartment and remove the heater housing assembly.

10. Remove the heater core from the heater housing.

11. Install the heater core in the reverse order of removal, refill the radiator, run the engine and check for leaks.

Windshield Wipers

MOTOR

Removal and Installation

PRIOR TO 1972

On Jeeps made prior to 1972, remove the windshield wiper assembly from the

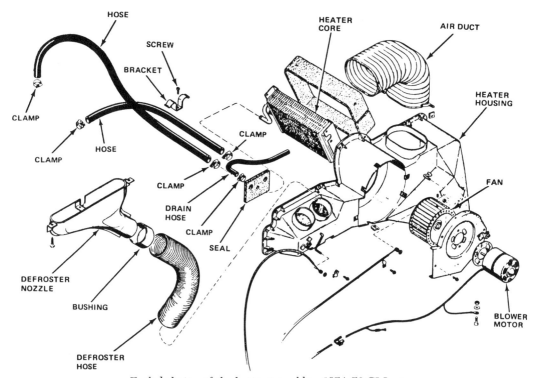

Exploded view of the heater assembly—1974–76 CJ Jeeps

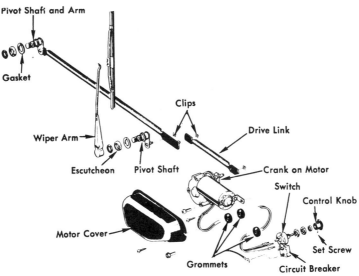

Wiper assembly for American Motors Jeeps—1972–75. The motor and cover are on the inside on 1976 models.

pivot shaft. Remove the vacuum hose or wire from the motor. Remove all attaching screws that hold the motor to the windshield assembly and remove the motor from the vehicle. Install in the reverse order.

To remove the wiper motor from 1972 and later Jeeps, follow the procedure given below:

1. Remove the extreme left plastic hole plug from the bottom of the windshield frame air duct and disconnect the drive link from the motor crank.

2. Loosen the wiper control knob set screw.

3. Remove the control switch and mark the location of the wires on the switch prior to removing them from the switch.

4. Remove the motor cover and the motor.

5. Install in the reverse order of the above procedure.

NOTE: *The motor cover must be sealed when installing.*

LINKAGE

Removal and Installation

NOTE: *Jeeps made prior to 1972 have no windshield wiper linkage.*

PRIOR TO 1976

1. Remove the wiper arms and pivot shaft nuts, washers, escutcheons and gaskets.

2. Disconnect the drive arm from the motor crank.

3. Remove the individual links where necessary, to remove the pivot shaft bodies without excessive interference.

4. Reverse the procedure for installation.

1976

1. Remove the wiper arms.

2. Remove the nuts attaching the pivots to the windshield frame.

3. Remove the necessary components from the top of the windshield frame.

4. Remove the windshield hold-down knobs and fold the windshield forward.

5. Remove the access hole covers on both sides of the windshield.

6. Disconnect the wiper motor drive link from the left wiper pivot.

7. Remove the wiper pivot shafts and linkage from the access hole.

8. Install the linkage in the reverse order.

Instrument Cluster

Removal and Installation

THROUGH 1975

1. Disconnect one battery cable.

2. Separate the speedometer cable from the speedometer head.

3. Remove the screws that hold up the

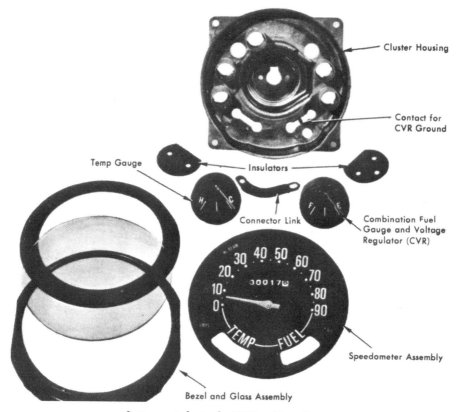

Instrument cluster for 1972 and later Jeeps

heater control bracket. (1972 and later Jeeps only)

4. Remove the attaching nuts that hold the cluster to the dash.

5. Remove the gauge wires and cluster lamps and remove the cluster assembly.

6. Install in the reverse order. After installing the cluster, connect the battery and check all of the lights and gauges for proper operation.

1976

1. Disconnect the negative battery cable.

2. Disconnect the speedometer cable from the back of the speedometer.

3. Remove the radio, if so equipped, and the voltmeter.

4. Remove the instrument cluster attaching nuts and remove the cluster.

5. Disconnect the instrument cluster electrical connectors and remove the cluster from the vehicle.

6. Install in the reverse order.

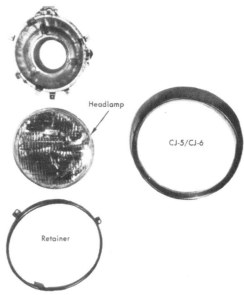

Head light assembly for 1972 and later Jeeps

Lighting (Headlights)

Removal and Installation

1. Remove the one lower attaching screw from the headlight door. Pull the door out slightly at the bottom and push up to disengage the upper retaining tab.

2. Remove the door.

3. Remove the three retaining screws from the retaining ring.

4. Pull the headlamp out and disconnect the wire harness.

When installing the headlamp, the number "2" is placed at the top of the lamp.

5. Install in reverse order of the above procedure. Check for proper seating of the lamp in its mounting ring and check for proper alignment.

Head light adjustment points for the 1972 and later Jeeps

Fuse Application Chart

Fuse Application	Fuse (Amp)
Early F-Head (6 volt)	
Directional Signal	SFE-14
Heater	SFE-14
Early F-Head (12 volt)	
Directional Signal	SFE-9
Heater	SFE-9
Late F-Head and V6	
Heater	15 amp
Backup Lights	9 amp
Windshield Wiper	14 amp
Directional Signal	14 amp
4-way Flasher	14 amp
1972–75	
Backup Lights	9 amp
Brake Failure	9 amp
Cigar Lighter	14 amp
Directional Signal	9 amp
4-way Flasher	14 amp
Head Lights	25 amp circuit breaker
Heater	15 amp
Windshield Wiper/Washer	6 amp circuit breaker
1976	
Heater	25 amp
Backup Lights and Cigar Lighter	15 amp
Tail and Stop Lights	20 amp
Cluster Feed, Brake Failure and Parking Brake Warning	3 amp
Directional Signal	10 amp
Headlights	25 amp circuit breaker
Panel Lights	3 amp
Radio	10 amp (5 amp inline)

NOTE: *There is one fusible link on Jeep Universals. It is in the wire running from the positive side of the battery to the fuse box on the firewall.*

Light Bulb Specifications

Bulb Application	Early F-Head (6 Volt)	Early F-Head (12 Volt)	Late F-Head and V6	1972 and Later (All Engines)
Headlights	5040-S or 6006	5400-S or 6012	6012	6012③
Parking Lights or Marker Reflector	63	67	1157	194
Park and Directional Signal	1158	1176 or 1034	1157	1157A①
Stop, Tail, and Directional Signal	1158	1034	1157	1157

Light Bulb Specifications (cont.)

Bulb Application	Early F-Head (6 Volt)	Early F-Head (12 Volt)	Late F-Head and V6	1972 and Later (All Engines)
Indicator Lamps:				
Headlight Beam	51	53–57	53–57	57②
Directional Signal	51	53	53	57②
Charge Lamp	51	53–57	53–57	57②
Oil Pressure	51	57	57	57②
Instrument Lamp	55	57	57	57
License	——	——	1155	1155
Back-up	——	——	1156	1156
Clock	——	——	——	1816
Steering Column Automatic Transmission Indicator	——	——	——	1816
Courtesy	——	——	——	89
Hazard Warning Flasher	——	——	——	552
Oil Pressure Gauge	——	——	——	1895
Radio	——	——	——	1893
Tachometer	——	——	——	1895
Voltmeter	——	——	——	1895

① 1157NA on 1973–75 models
② 53 on 1973–76 models
③ 6014—1974 and later

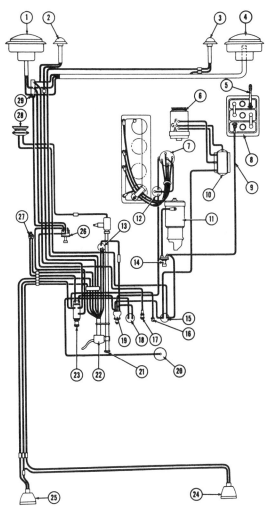

Wiring diagram for model CJ-3B up to serial number 35522

1. Left headlamp
2. Left parking lamp
3. Right parking lamp
4. Right headlamp
5. Negative ground cable
6. Generator
7. Distributor
8. Battery
9. Positive cable
10. Voltage regulator
11. Starting motor
12. Ignition coil
13. Signal flasher
14. Starting switch
15. Ammeter
16. Dash light
17. Tell-tale light
18. Fuel guage
19. Ignition switch
20. Fuel guage sending unit
21. Horn button
22. Directional signal switch
23. Light switch
24. Right tail and stop lamp
25. Left tail and stop lamp
26. Dimmer switch
27. Stop light switch
28. Horn
29. Junction block

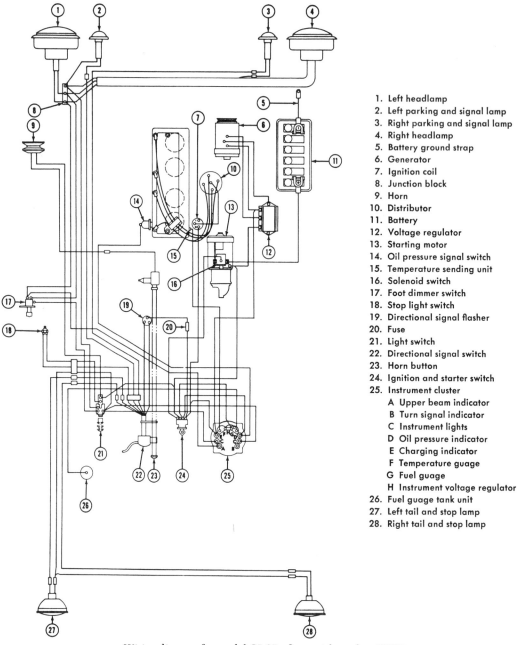

1. Left headlamp
2. Left parking and signal lamp
3. Right parking and signal lamp
4. Right headlamp
5. Battery ground strap
6. Generator
7. Ignition coil
8. Junction block
9. Horn
10. Distributor
11. Battery
12. Voltage regulator
13. Starting motor
14. Oil pressure signal switch
15. Temperature sending unit
16. Solenoid switch
17. Foot dimmer switch
18. Stop light switch
19. Directional signal flasher
20. Fuse
21. Light switch
22. Directional signal switch
23. Horn button
24. Ignition and starter switch
25. Instrument cluster
    A Upper beam indicator
    B Turn signal indicator
    C Instrument lights
    D Oil pressure indicator
    E Charging indicator
    F Temperature guage
    G Fuel guage
    H Instrument voltage regulator
26. Fuel guage tank unit
27. Left tail and stop lamp
28. Right tail and stop lamp

Wiring diagram for model CJ-3B after serial number 35522

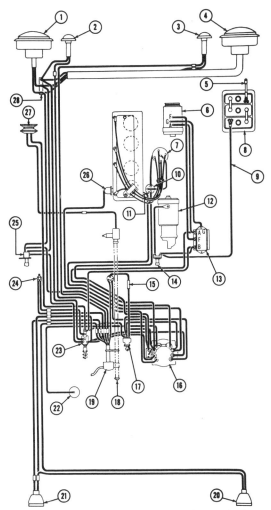

Wiring diagram for models CJ-5 and CJ-6 before
serial number 49248 CJ-5 and 12577 CJ-6

1. Left headlamp
2. Left parking lamp
3. Right parking lamp
4. Right headlamp
5. Negative ground cable
6. Generator
7. Distributor
8. Battery
9. Positive cable
10. Ignition coil
11. Temperature sending
    unit
12. Starting motor
13. Volatge regulator
14. Starting switch

15. Fuse
16. Instrument switch
17. Ignition switch
18. Horn button
19. Directional signal switch
20. Right tail and stop lamp
21. Left tail and stop lamp
22. Fuel guage sending unit
23. Light switch
24. Stop light switch
25. Dimmer switch
26. Oil pressure sending
    unit
27. Horn
28. Junction block

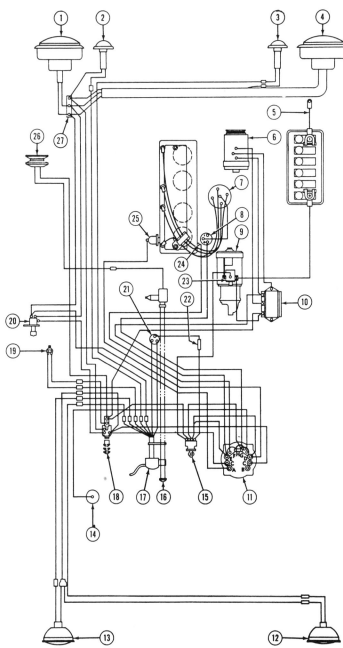

1. Left headlamp
2. Left parking and directional lamp
3. Right parking and directional lamp
4. Right headlamp
5. Battery ground cable
6. Generator
7. Distributor
8. Ignition coil
9. Starting motor
10. Voltage regulator
11. Instrument cluster
     A Upper beam indicator
     B Turn signal indicator
     C Instrument lights
     D Oil pressure indicator
     E Charging indicator
     F Temperature guage
     G Fuel guage
     H Instrument voltage regulator
12. Right tail and stop lamp
13. Left tail and stop lamp
14. Fuel guage tank unit
15. Ignition and starter switch
16. Horn button
17. Directional signal switch
18. Light switch
19. Stop light switch
20. Foot dimmer switch
21. Directional signal flasher
22. Fuse
23. Solenoid switch
24. Temperature sending unit
25. Oil pressure signal switch
26. Horn
27. Junction block

Wiring diagram for models CJ-5 and CJ-6 after serial number
49248 CJ-5 and 12577 CJ-6

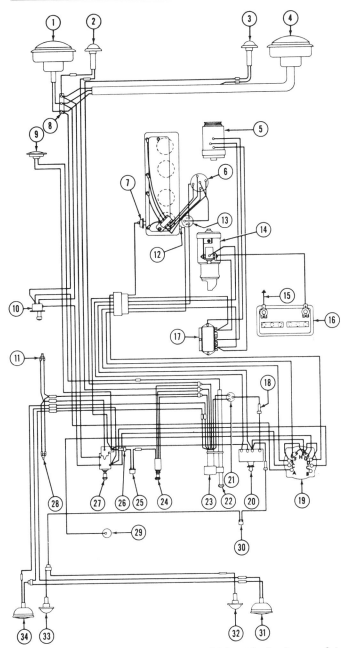

1. Left headlamp
2. Left parking and signal lamp
3. Right parking and signal lamp
4. Right headlamp
5. Generator
6. Ignition distributor
7. Oil pressure sending unit
8. Junction block
9. Horn
10. Foot dimmer switch
11. Stop light switch—front
12. Temperature sending unit
13. Ignition coil
14. Starting motor
15. Battery ground cable
16. Battery
17. Voltage regulator
18. Fuse
19. Instrument cluster
    A Hi-beam indicator
    B Auxiliary
    C Instrument lights
    D Oil pressure indicator
    E Charging indicator
    F Temperature indicator
    G Fuel guage
    H Instrument voltage reglator
20. Ignition and starter switch
21. Flasher (directional signal)
22. Horn button
23. Directional signal switch
24. 4-Way flasher switch
25. Flasher (4-way)
26. Fuse
27. Main light switch
28. Stop light switch—rear
29. Fuel guage tank unit
30. Back-up light switch
31. Right tail and stop lamp
32. Right back-up lamp
33. Left back-up lamp
34. Left tail and stop lamp

Wiring diagram for models CJ-5 and CJ-6 with the late model F-head engine

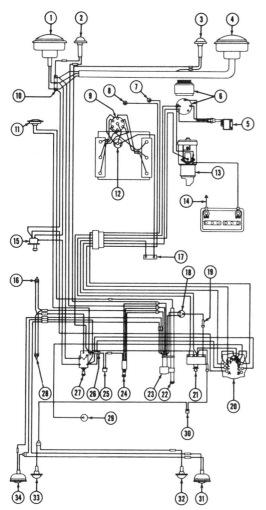

Wiring diagram for models CJ-5 and CJ-6 with the V6 engine

1. Left headlamp
2. Left parking and signal lamp
3. Right parking and signal lamp
4. Right headlamp
5. Voltage regulator
6. Alternator
7. Oil pressure sender
8. Temperature sender
9. Ignition distributor
10. Junction block
11. Horn
12. Ignition coil
13. Starting motor
14. Battery ground cable
15. Foot dimmer switch
16. Stop light switch—front
17. Ballast
18. Flasher (directional signal)
19. Fuse
20. Instrument cluster
   A Hi-beam indicator
   B Auxiliary
   C Instrument lights
   D Oil pressure indicator
   E Charging indicator
   F Temperature indicator
   G Fuel guage
   H Instrument voltage regulator
21. Ignition and starter switch
22. Horn button
23. Directional signal switch
24. 4-Way flasher switch
25. Flasher (4-way)
26. Fuse
27. Main light switch
28. Stop light switch—rear
29. Fuel guage tank unit
30. Back-up light switch
31. Right tail and stop lamp
32. Right back-up lamp
33. Left back-up lamp
34. Left tail and stop lamp

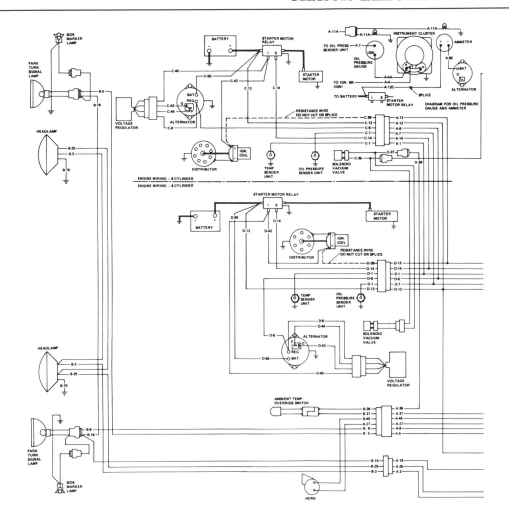

Wiring diagram for 1972–73 models

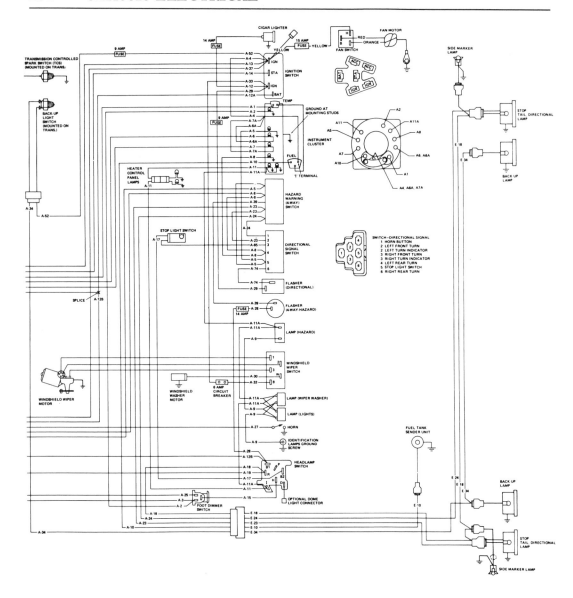

No.	GA.	Color	Instrument and Control Harness
A–1	18	Blue-yellow tr.	Cluster "A" temp. to connector (temp. sender)
A–2	18	White-red tr.	Cluster "L" Hi-beam indicator to dimmer switch (hi-beam)
	14	Red-white tr.	Dimmer switch (hi-beam) to headlamp junction block (hi-beam)
A–3	18	Green-white tr.	Cluster "K" ignition to ignition switch (ignition term.)
	18	Black-white tr.	Cluster "J" right turn indicator to directional signal switch (right turn)
A–4	16	Black	Directional signal switch (right turn) to directional signal lamp (right turn)
A–5	18	Gray	Cluster "H" (charge indicator) to connector (alternator auxiliary term.)
A–6	18	Purple	Cluster "G" (oil indicator) to connector (oil pressure sender)
	18	Yellow-black tr.	Cluster "E" left turn indicator to directional signal switch (left turn)
A–7	16	Yellow	Directional signal switch (left turn) to directional signal light (left turn)
A–8	18	Black-yellow tr.	Cluster "D" ground to instrument panel ground (mounting)
A–9	18	White	Cluster "C" gas guage to connector (frame harness)
A–10	18	Red-blue tr.	Cluster "B" panel lights to dimmer switch to connector (gear selector)
A–11	14	Green	Ignition switch (ignition term.) to resistance wire
A–14	16	Light blue	Connector (ignition switch starter term.) to connector (neutral safety switch)
A–14A	16	Light blue	Connector (neutral safety switch) to connector (starter motor starter term.)
A–15	10	Red	Auxiliary circuit breaker to connector (solenoid "B" term.)
A–16	14	Red-white tr.	Light switch circuit breaker to auxiliary circuit breaker
A–17	14	Red-white tr.	Ignition switch "B" term. to auxiliary circuit breaker
A–18	14	Red-white tr.	Auxiliary circuit breaker to horn relay
A–19	14	Red-white tr.	Cigar lighter to auxiliary circuit
A–20	16	Brown	Auxiliary circuit breaker to stop light switch
A–21	14	Green	Light switch "H" term. to foot dimmer switch "B" term.
A–22	16	Light blue	Light switch (parking term.) to headlamp junction block (parking term.)
A–23	16	Yellow	Light switch (tail light term.) to instrument dimmer switch
A–23	16	Yellow	Instrument dimmer switch to connector (frame harness tail lamps)
A–24	18	Green-white tr.	Connector (ignition switch accessory term.) to connector (backup light switch)
A–25	18	Green-white tr.	Connector (backup light switch—standard) to connector (backup light switch—auto) to connector (frame harness—backup lights)
A–26	16	Black	Foot dimmer switch (low-beam) to headlamp junction block (low-beam)
A–27	16	Brown	Connector (turn signal switch) to connector (stop light switch)
A–28	18	Black-yellow tr.	Connector (steering column horn button) to horn relay
A–29	16	Light blue	Connector (turn signal switch) to connector (signal lamp rear left)
A–30	16	Orange	Connector (turn signal switch) to connector (signal lamp rear right)
A–33	14	Red-white tr.	Auxiliary circuit breaker to flasher (hazard warning)
A–34	18	Red	Ignition switch (accessory term.) (fused) to flasher (directional signal)
A–35	16	Orange	Connector (vacuum solenoid switch) to connector (temp. override switch)
A–36	16	Orange	Connector (ignition switch—ignition term.) to connector (temp. override switch)

No.	GA.	Color	Harness Assembly—Headlights, Parking and Signal Lamps
B–1	14	Red-white tr.	Connector (circuit breaker—auxiliary feed) to horn relay (battery)
B–2	18	Black-yellow tr.	Connector (steering column—horn button) to horn relay (horn button)
B–3	16	Yellow	Connector (turn signal switch—left turn) to connector (directional signal lamp—left turn)
B–4	16	Black	Connector (turn signal switch—right turn) to connector (directional signal lamp—right turn)
B–5	16	Light blue	Junction block (parking term.) to connector (parking lamp—left) to connector (parking lamp—right)
B–6	14	Red-white tr.	Junction block (hi-beam) to connector (headlamp hi-beam—left) to connector (headlamp hi-beam—right)
B–7	16	Black	Junction block (low-beam) to connector (headlamp low-beam—left) to connector (headlamp low-beam—right)
B–8	18	Black-white tr.	Headlamp ground to ground mounting (2 cables)
B–9	16	Orange	Connector (vacuum solenoid switch) to connector (temp. override switch)
B–10	16	Orange	Connector ignition switch ignition term. to connector temp. override switch

No.	GA.	Color	Engine Harness (V-8)
C–1	14	Green	Resistance wire (ignition) to coil (+) term.
C–2	14	Green	Coil (+) term. to starting solenoid (ignition)
C–3	16	Yellow	Starter solenoid (ignition) to alternator regulator (ignition)
C–4	16	Light blue	Connector (ignition switch—starter term.) to starter solenoid (starter term.)
C–5	18	Purple	Connector (oil pressure indicator) to oil pressure sender
C–6	18	Blue-yellow tr.	Connector (temp. indicator) to temp. sender
C–7	18	Gray	Connector (cluster "H" term.) to alternator (auxiliary term.) to alternator regulator (auxiliary term.)
C–8	18	Green-white tr.	Alternator regulator (field term.) to alternator (field term.)
C–9	16	Black	Alternator regulator (ground term.) to alternator (ground)
C–10	10	Red	Starter solenoid ("B" term.) to connector (circuit breaker—feed)
C–11	10	Yellow	Starter solenoid ("B" term.) to alternator (output term.)
C–12	16	Brown	Connector (transistor solenoid) (T.C.S.) vacuum switch
C–13	16	Black	Connector (sensor switch) (T.C.S.) to vacuum switch

No.	GA.	Color	Engine Harness (6 Cyl.)
D–1	14	Green	Resistance wire (ignition) to coil (+) term.
D–2	14	Green	Coil (+) term. to starting solenoid (ignition)
D–3	16	Yellow	Starter solenoid (ignition) to alternator regulator (ignition)
D–4	16	Light blue	Connector (ignition switch—starter term.) to starter solenoid (starter term.)
D–5	18	Purple	Connector (oil pressure indicator) to oil pressure sender
D–6	18	Blue-yellow tr.	Connector (temperature indicator) to temperature sender
D–7	18	Gray	Connector (cluster "H" term.) to alternator (auxiliary term.) to alternator regulator (auxiliary term.)
D–8	18	Green-white tr.	Alternator regulator (field term.) to alternator (field term.)
D–9	16	Black	Alternator regulator (ground term.) to alternator (ground term.)
D–10	10	Red	Starter solenoid ("B" term.) to connector (circuit breaker feed)
D–11	10	Yellow	Starter solenoid ("B" term.) to alternator (output term.)

NO.	GA.	COLOR	INSTRUMENT AND CONTROL HARNESS
A-1	18	BLUE W/TR	CONNECTOR (TEMPERATURE SENDER) TO TEMPERATURE GAUGE INDICATOR
A-2	18	WHITE	FOOT DIMMER SWITCH (HI-BEAM) TO INSTRUMENT CLUSTER (HI-BEAM INDICATOR)
A-3	14	RED W/TR	FOOT DIMMER SWITCH (HI-BEAM) TO HEADLAMP CONNECTOR (HI-BEAM)
A-4	14	GREEN	IGNITION SWITCH (IGNITION TERMINAL) TO INSTRUMENT CLUSTER VOLTAGE REGULATOR
A-4-A	14	GREEN	IGNITION SWITCH (IGNITION TERMINAL) TO INSTRUMENT CLUSTER VOLTAGE REGULATOR TO OIL PRESSURE GAUGE INDICATOR (IGNITION TERMINAL)
A-5	18	BLACK W/TR	CONNECTOR SIGNAL LAMP FRONT RIGHT TO HAZARD WARNING SWITCH TO DIRECTIONAL SIGNAL SWITCH TO CLUSTER LAMP RIGHT TURN
A-6-A	18	GRAY	CONNECTOR (ALTERNATOR REGULATOR) TO INSTRUMENT CLUSTER TO INSTRUMENT VOLTAGE REGULATOR
A-7	18	PURPLE	CONNECTOR (OIL PRESSURE SENDER) TO OIL PRESSURE INDICATOR TO INSTRUMENT VOLTAGE REGULATOR
A-7-A	18	PURPLE	CONNECTOR (OIL PRESSURE SENDER) TO OIL PRESSURE GAUGE
A-8	18	YELLOW W/TR	CONNECTOR SIGNAL LAMP FRONT LEFT TO HAZARD WARNING SWITCH TO DIRECTIONAL SIGNAL SWITCH TO CLUSTER LAMP LEFT TURN
A-9	16	BLACK	(GROUND) FLASH MOUNTING TO LIGHT SWITCH, WIPER & HAZARD LIGHTS
A-10	18	WHITE	CONNECTOR (FRAME HARNESS-GAS GAUGE TANK UNIT) TO INSTRUMENT CLUSTER GAS GAUGE INDICATOR
A-11	18	RED W/TR	HEADLAMP SWITCH "I" TERMINAL TO INSTRUMENT CLUSTER LIGHTS TO HEATER LAMP
A-11-A	18	RED W/TR	HEADLAMP SWITCH "I" TERMINAL TO LAMPS, (LIGHTS, WIPER, HAZARD) TO INSTRUMENT CLUSTER LAMPS
A-12	10	RED	SPLICE TO CONNECTOR (STARTING MOTOR SOLENOID-BATTERY TERMINAL)
A-12-A	12	RED	SPLICE TO CONNECTOR (IGNITION SWITCH-BATTERY)
A-12-B	14	RED	SPLICE TO CONNECTOR (LIGHT SWITCH) "B-1"
A-12-C	12	RED	SPLICE TO AMMETER (+) TERMINAL
A-13	14	GREEN	IGNITION SWITCH (IGNITION TERMINAL) TO CONNECTOR COIL (+) TERMINAL
A-14	16	LT. BLUE	IGNITION SWITCH (START TERMINAL) TO CONNECTOR (STARTING MOTOR SOLENOID-START TERMINAL)
A-15	14	GREEN	FOOT DIMMER SWITCH "B" TERMINAL TO LIGHT SWITCH "H" TERMINAL
A-17	16	BROWN	LIGHT SWITCH-BATTERY "B-2" TO CONNECTOR (STOP LIGHT SWITCH)
A-18	16	YELLOW	LIGHT SWITCH "R" TERMINAL TO CONNECTOR (FRAME HARNESS-TAIL LIGHTS)
A-19	16	LT. BLUE	LIGHT SWITCH "R" TERMINAL TO CONNECTOR (PARKING TERMINAL)
A-23	16	LT. BLUE	CONNECTOR-FRAME HARNESS REAR LEFT TO HAZARD WARNING SWITCH TO DIRECTIONAL SIGNAL SWITCH (LEFT TURN)
A-24	16	ORANGE	CONNECTOR-FRAME HARNESS REAR RIGHT TO HAZARD WARNING SWITCH TO DIRECTIONAL SIGNAL SWITCH (RIGHT TURN)
A-25	16	BLACK	FOOT DIMMER SWITCH (LO-BEAM) TO HEADLAMP CONNECTOR (LO-BEAM)
A-27	18	BLACK W/TR	HORN TERMINAL TO CONNECTOR (HORN BUTTON)
A-30	18	YELLOW	WINDSHIELD WIPER SWITCH TO WINDSHIELD WASHER MOTOR
A-33	14	RED W/TR	WINDSHIELD WIPER SWITCH "B" TO IGNITION (ACCESSORY TERMINAL)
A-34	18	GREEN W/TR	CONNECTOR (BACK-UP LIGHT SWITCH) TO CONNECTOR (FRAME HARNESS-BACK-UP LIGHTS)
A-37	16	ORANGE	TRANSMISSION CONTROL SWITCH TO IGNITION TERMINAL OF IGNITION SWITCH
A-38	16	PINK	HAZARD FLASHER TO HAZARD SWITCH
A-45	14	RED W/TR	CONNECTOR (HORN TERMINAL) TO SPLICE
A-52	18	GREEN W/TR	IGNITION SWITCH (IGNITION TERMINAL) FUSED TO CONNECTOR (BACK-UP LIGHT SWITCH)
A-55	10	YELLOW	CONNECTOR (STARTING MOTOR-BATTERY SIDE) TO AMMETER (-) TERMINAL
A-65	16	BROWN	CONNECTOR (TURN SIGNAL SWITCH) TO CONNECTOR (STOP LIGHT SWITCH)
A-74	18	WHITE	CONNECTOR (TURN SIGNAL SWITCH-FLASHER TERMINAL) TO CONNECTOR (FLASHER)

NO.	GA.	COLOR	HARNESS ASSEMBLY-HEADLAMP, PARKING & SIGNAL LAMPS
B-3	14	RED W/TR	CONNECTOR (HI-BEAM) TO CONNECTOR
B-5	18	BLACK W/TR	CONNECTOR (TURN SIGNAL SWITCH-RIGHT TURN) TO CONNECTOR (DIRECTIONAL SIGNAL LAMP RIGHT TURN)
B-6	18	YELLOW W/TR	CONNECTOR (TURN SIGNAL SWITCH-LEFT TURN) TO CONNECTOR (DIRECTIONAL SIGNAL LAMP LEFT TURN)
B-19	16	LT. BLUE	CONNECTOR (PARKING TERMINAL) TO CONNECTOR
B-25	16	TAN	CONNECTOR (LO-BEAM) TO CONNECTOR
B-27	18	BLACK W/TR	CONNECTOR (STEERING COLUMN-HORN BUTTON) TO HORN TERMINAL
B-45	14	RED W/TR	CONNECTOR (TO HORN TERMINAL)
B-70	16	BLACK	HEADLAMP GROUND TO GROUND MOUNTING (2 CABLES)

NO.	GA.	COLOR	HARNESS ASSEMBLY ENGINE
C-1	18	BLUE W/TR	CONNECTOR (TEMPERATURE INDICATOR TO TEMPERATURE SENDER)
C-6	18	GRAY	CONNECTOR ALTERNATOR (REGULATOR TERMINAL) TO CONNECTOR
C-7	18	PURPLE	CONNECTOR (OIL PRESSURE INDICATOR) TO OIL PRESSURE SENDER
C-12	10	RED	STARTING MOTOR SOLENOID ("B" TERMINAL) TO CONNECTOR
C-14	16	LT. BLUE	CONNECTOR (IGNITION SWITCH START TERMINAL) TO STARTING MOTOR SOLENOID (STARTING TERMINAL)
C-35	16	BLACK	CONNECTOR TRANSMISSION SOLENOID (T.C.S.) TO VACUUM SOLENOID SWITCH
C-37	16	ORANGE	CONNECTOR (VACUUM SOLENOID SWITCH) TO CONNECTOR
C-38	20	PINK	CONNECTOR (IGNITION SWITCH-IGNITION TERMINAL) TO COIL (+) TERMINAL-RESISTANCE WIRE (6 CYLINDER, 1.80 Ω – 8 CYLINDER, 1.35 Ω MAXIMUM AT 76°F.)
C-40	16	YELLOW	STARTING MOTOR SOLENOID (IGNITION) TO ALTERNATOR REGULATOR (IGNITION)
C-42	14	GREEN	COIL (+) TERMINAL TO STARTING MOTOR SOLENOID (IGNITION)
C-43	14	BLACK	ALTERNATOR REGULATOR (GROUND TERMINAL) TO ALTERNATOR (GROUND)
C-44	18	GREEN W/TR	ALTERNATOR REGULATOR (FIELD TERMINAL) TO ALTERNATOR (FIELD TERMINAL)
C-55	10	YELLOW	STARTING MOTOR SOLENOID ("B" TERMINAL) TO ALTERNATOR (OUTPUT TERMINAL)

NO.	GA.	COLOR	CHASSIS WIRING HARNESS
E-10	18	WHITE	CONNECTOR (GAS GAUGE-INSTRUMENT UNIT) TO CONNECTOR (GAS GAUGE-TANK UNIT)
E-18	16	YELLOW	CONNECTOR (LIGHT SWITCH-"R" TERMINAL) TO CONNECTOR (TAIL LAMPS & REAR MARKER LAMPS) TO CONNECTOR
E-23	16	LT. BLUE	CONNECTOR (TURN SIGNAL SWITCH) TO CONNECTOR (LEFT STOP & SIGNAL LAMPS)
E-24	16	ORANGE	CONNECTOR (TURN SIGNAL SWITCH) TO CONNECTOR (RIGHT STOP & SIGNAL LAMPS)
E-34	18	GREEN W/TR	CONNECTOR (BACK-UP LIGHT SWITCH) TO CONNECTOR (BACK-UP LAMPS)

W/TR = WITH TRACER

Wiring diagram legend—1974 model CJ Jeeps

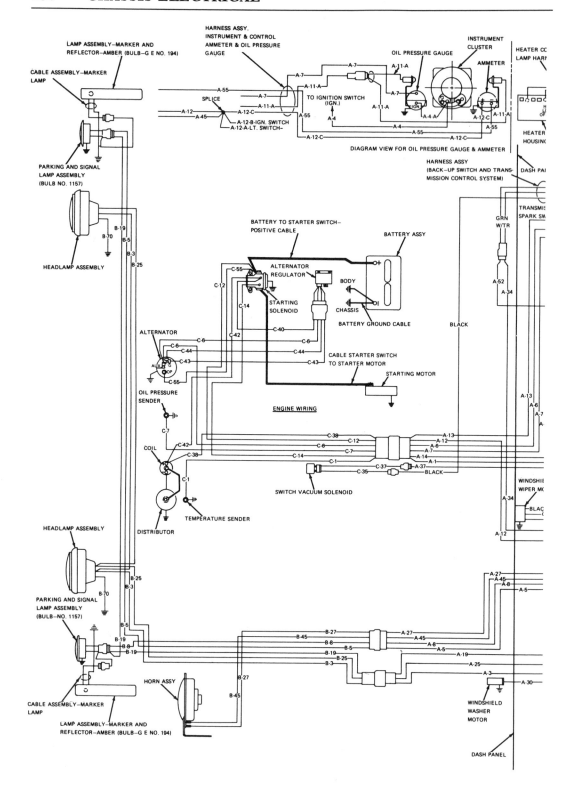

Wiring diagram—1974 model CJ Jeeps

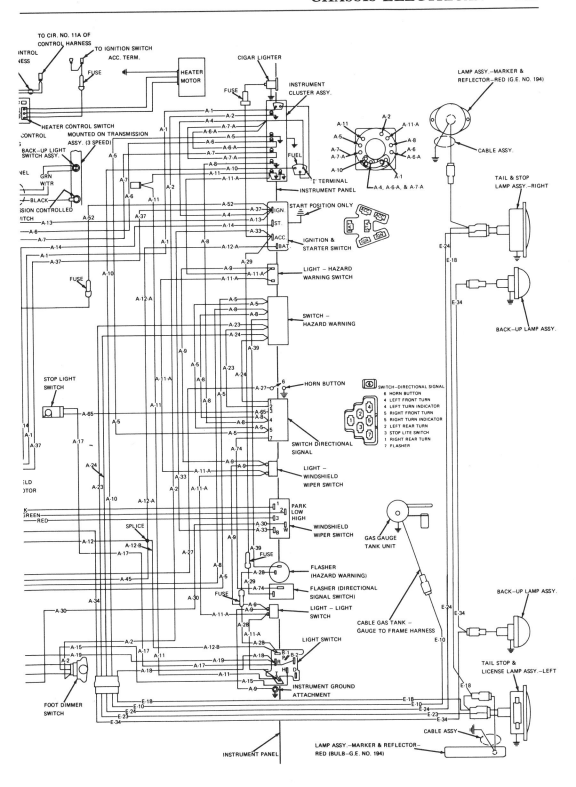

Wiring diagram—1974 model CJ Jeeps

NO.	GA.	COLOR	INSTRUMENT AND CONTROL HARNESS
1	18	PURPLE W/TR	BULKHEAD CONNECTOR (TEMPERATURE SENDER) TO TEMPERATURE GAUGE
2	18	GRAY W/TR	FOOT DIMMER SWITCH (HI-BEAM) TO INSTRUMENT CLUSTER (HI-BEAM INDICATOR)
3	14	GRAY W/TR	FOOT DIMMER SWITCH (HI-BEAM) TO BULKHEAD CONNECTOR (HI-BEAM)
4	18	RED	FUSE PANEL (CLUSTER FEED) TO INSTRUMENT CONSTANT VOLTAGE REGULATOR
4A	18	RED	INSTRUMENT CONSTANT VOLTAGE REGULATOR (IGNITION TERMINAL) TO OIL PRESSURE GAUGE (IGNITION TERMINAL)
5A	18	GREEN	BULKHEAD CONNECTOR (RIGHT TURN & HAZARD FRONT) TO HAZARD SWITCH
5B	18	GREEN	HAZARD SWITCH TO STEERING COLUMN CONNECTOR (RIGHT TURN & HAZARD FRONT)
5C	18	GREEN	STEERING COLUMN CONNECTOR TO INSTRUMENT CLUSTER LAMP (RIGHT TURN)
7	18	PURPLE	BULKHEAD CONNECTOR (OIL PRESSURE SENDER) TO OIL PRESSURE GAUGE
8A	18	GREEN W/TR	BULKHEAD CONNECTOR (LEFT TURN & HAZARD FRONT) TO HAZARD SWITCH
8B	18	GREEN W/TR	HAZARD SWITCH TO STEERING COLUMN CONNECTOR (LEFT TURN & HAZARD FRONT)
8C	18	GREEN W/TR	STEERING COLUMN CONNECTOR TO INSTRUMENT CLUSTER LAMP (LEFT TURN)
9A	18	BLACK	WINDSHIELD WIPER & WASHER SWITCH LIGHT TO INSTRUMENT PANEL LIGHTS GROUND
9B	18	BLACK	WINDSHIELD WIPER & WASHER SWITCH LIGHT TO LIGHT SWITCH LIGHT
9C	18	BLACK	INSTRUMENT PANEL LIGHTS GROUND TO HAZARD LIGHT
9D	18	BLACK	HAZARD LIGHT TO VOLTMETER (−) TERMINAL
10	18	PINK	BULKHEAD CONNECTOR (FRAME HARNESS-FUEL SENDER UNIT) TO INSTRUMENT CLUSTER FUEL GAUGE (S-TERMINAL)
11A	18	ORANGE	FUSE PANEL (LIGHTS - ACCESSORIES) TO SPLICE "D"
11B	18	ORANGE	LIGHT SWITCH LIGHT TO WINDSHIELD WIPER & WASHER SWITCH LIGHT
11C	18	ORANGE	SPLICE "D" TO WINDSHIELD WIPER & WASHER SWITCH LIGHT
11D	18	ORANGE	SPLICE "D" TO HAZARD LIGHT
11E	18	ORANGE	SPLICE "D" TO SPLICE "C"
11F	18	ORANGE	SPLICE "C" TO RIGHT INSTRUMENT PANEL LIGHT
11G	18	ORANGE	SPLICE "C" TO LEFT INSTRUMENT PANEL LIGHT CONNECTOR
11H	18	ORANGE	LEFT INSTRUMENT PANEL LIGHT CONNECTOR TO LEFT INSTRUMENT PANEL LIGHT
11J	18	ORANGE	SPLICE "C" TO INSTRUMENT CLUSTER OIL PRESSURE GAUGE LIGHT
11K	18	ORANGE	SPLICE "C" TO INSTRUMENT CLUSTER VOLTMETER LIGHT
12A	10	RED	BULKHEAD CONNECTOR (ALTERNATOR & VOLTAGE REGULATOR) TO SPLICE "A"
12B	12	RED	BULKHEAD CONNECTOR (HORN) TO SPLICE "A"
12C	12	RED	FUSE PANEL (TRAFFIC HAZARD) TO SPLICE "A"
12D	12	RED	SPLICE "A" TO LIGHT SWITCH (BATTERY FEED)
12E	12	RED	SPLICE "A" TO IGNITION SWITCH
12F	12	RED	FUSE PANEL (CIGAR LIGHTER) TO SPLICE "A"
13A	14	RED W/TR	BULKHEAD CONNECTOR (COIL) TO TACHOMETER CONNECTOR
13B	14	RED W/TR	TACHOMETER CONNECTOR TO IGNITION SWITCH
14	16	LT BLUE	BULKHEAD CONNECTOR (STARTING MOTOR SOLENOID) TO IGNITION SWITCH
15	14	RED W/TR	LIGHT SWITCH (FOOT DIMMER SWITCH FEED) TO FOOT DIMMER SWITCH
17	14	RED W/TR	FUSE PANEL (TAIL - STOP) TO STOP LIGHT SWITCH
18	16	WHITE	BULKHEAD CONNECTOR (CHASSIS HARNESS - TAIL LAMPS) TO BULKHEAD CONNECTOR - HEADLAMP HARNESS MARKER LIGHTS
19	16	WHITE	BULKHEAD CONNECTOR (MARKER LAMPS) TO LIGHT SWITCH (PARKING LAMPS)
23	16	LT GREEN W/TR	BULKHEAD CONNECTOR (CHASSIS HARNESS LEFT TURN & HAZARD) TO HAZARD SWITCH (LEFT TURN & HAZARD - REAR)
23A	16	LT GREEN W/TR	HAZARD SWITCH TO STEERING COLUMN CONNECTOR (LEFT TURN & HAZARD - REAR)
24	16	LT GREEN	BULKHEAD CONNECTOR (CHASSIS HARNESS RIGHT TURN & HAZARD) TO HAZARD SWITCH (RIGHT TURN & HAZARD - REAR)
24A	16	LT GREEN	HAZARD SWITCH TO STEERING COLUMN CONNECTOR (RIGHT TURN & HAZARD - REAR)
25	16	GRAY	BULKHEAD CONNECTOR (HEADLAMPS) TO FOOT DIMMER SWITCH (LO-BEAM)
26	14	RED W/TR	FUSE PANEL (HEATER - BATTERY) TO HEATER BLOWER SWITCH
27	14	BLACK W/TR	BULKHEAD CONNECTOR TO HORN BUTTON
30	16	YELLOW	BULKHEAD CONNECTOR (WINDSHIELD WIPER & WASHER) TO WINDSHIELD WIPER & WASHER SWITCH
33	14	RED W/TR	FUSE PANEL (RADIO) TO WINDSHIELD WIPER & WASHER SWITCH
34	16	WHITE W/TR	BULKHEAD CONNECTOR (BACK-UP LIGHT SWITCH) TO BULKHEAD CONNECTOR (CHASSIS HARNESS - BACK-UP LIGHTS)
39	16	PINK	FUSE PANEL (TRAFFIC HAZARD FLASH) TO HAZARD FLASHER
52	16	RED	FUSE PANEL (BACK-UP LAMPS) TO BULKHEAD CONNECTOR (BACK-UP LIGHT SWITCH)
57	18	BLACK	BULKHEAD CONNECTOR (BRAKE FAILURE SWITCH) TO BRAKE WARNING LIGHT (GROUND)
60	14	RED	CIGAR LIGHTER CONNECTOR TO CIGAR LIGHTER
65	16	RED W/TR	STOP LIGHT SWITCH TO STEERING COLUMN CONNECTOR (BRAKE SWITCH & HAZARD FEED)
66	18	RED W/TR	FUSE PANEL (PANEL LAMPS) TO LIGHT SWITCH (PANEL LIGHTS FEED)
67A	12	YELLOW	FUSE PANEL LAMPS TO IGNITION SWITCH
67B	18	YELLOW	IGNITION SWITCH TO INSTRUMENT CLUSTER VOLTMETER (+) TERMINAL
74	18	RED W/TR	FUSE PANEL (FLASH - DIRECTIONAL SIGNAL) TO STEERING COLUMN CONNECTOR (FLASHER & DIRECTIONAL SIGNAL FEED)
75	12	RED W/TR	IGNITION SWITCH TO SPLICE "B"
75A	12	RED W/TR	FUSE PANEL (HEATER - BATTERY) TO SPLICE "B"
75B	12	RED W/TR	FUSE PANEL LAMPS TO SPLICE "B"
77	16	BLACK	BULKHEAD CONNECTOR (BRAKE FAILURE SWITCH) TO BRAKE WARNING LIGHT CONNECTION
78	16	RED W/TR	BULKHEAD CONNECTOR (ALTERNATOR - VOLTAGE REGULATOR) TO SPLICE "B" IN CIRCUIT 75
77A	16	BLACK	FUSE PANEL (WARNING LIGHT) TO BRAKE WARNING LIGHT
			HARNESS ASSEMBLY – HEADLAMP, PARKING AND SIGNAL LAMP
3A	14	GRAY W/TR	BULKHEAD CONNECTOR (HI-BEAM) TO LEFT HEADLAMP CONNECTOR (HI-BEAM)
3B	14	GRAY W/TR	LEFT HEADLAMP CONNECTOR (HI-BEAM) TO RIGHT HEADLAMP CONNECTOR (HI-BEAM)
5A	16	GREEN	BULKHEAD CONNECTOR (RIGHT TURN SIGNAL) TO RIGHT TURN SIGNAL SPLICE "K"
5B	16	GREEN	RIGHT TURN SPLICE "K" TO RIGHT SIDE MARKER LAMP ASSEMBLY
5C	16	GREEN	RIGHT TURN SPLICE "K" TO RIGHT FRONT PARK & TURN SIGNAL LAMP ASSEMBLY
8A	16	GREEN W/TR	BULKHEAD CONNECTOR (LEFT TURN SIGNAL) TO LEFT TURN SIGNAL SPLICE "H"
8B	16	GREEN W/TR	LEFT TURN SPLICE "H" TO LEFT SIDE MARKER LAMP ASSEMBLY
8C	16	GREEN W/TR	LEFT TURN SPLICE "H" TO LEFT FRONT PARK & TURN SIGNAL LAMP ASSEMBLY
19A	16	WHITE	BULKHEAD CONNECTOR (PARKING LIGHTS) TO SPLICE "J"
19B	16	WHITE	PARKING LIGHTS SPLICE "J" TO LEFT SIDE MARKER LAMP ASSEMBLY
19C	16	WHITE	PARKING LIGHTS SPLICE "L" TO RIGHT FRONT PARK & TURN SIGNAL LAMP ASSEMBLY
19D	16	WHITE	PARKING LIGHTS SPLICE "M" TO LEFT FRONT PARK & TURN SIGNAL LAMP ASSEMBLY
19E	16	WHITE	PARKING LIGHTS SPLICE "L" TO RIGHT SIDE MARKER LAMP ASSEMBLY
19F	16	WHITE	LEFT PARKING LAMPS SPLICE "M" TO RIGHT PARKING LAMPS SPLICE "L"
19G	16	WHITE	SPLICE "J" TO SPLICE "M"
25A	16	GRAY	BULKHEAD CONNECTOR (LO-BEAM) TO LEFT HEADLAMP CONNECTOR (LO-BEAM)
25B	16	GRAY	LEFT HEADLAMP CONNECTOR (LO-BEAM) TO RIGHT HEADLAMP CONNECTOR (LO-BEAM)
27	14	BLACK W/TR	BULKHEAD CONNECTOR (HORN) TO HORN ASSEMBLY
30	16	YELLOW	BULKHEAD CONNECTOR (WINDSHIELD WIPER & WASHER SWITCH) TO WINDSHIELD WASHER MOTOR
45	14	RED W/TR	BULKHEAD CONNECTOR (HORN) TO HORN ASSEMBLY
57	16	BLACK	BULKHEAD CONNECTOR (BRAKE FAILURE SWITCH) CONNECTOR TO BRAKE FAILURE SWITCH
70	16	BLACK	LEFT AND RIGHT HEADLAMP GROUND TERMINALS TO GROUND MOUNTING
77	16	BLACK W/TR	BULKHEAD CONNECTOR (BRAKE FAILURE SWITCH) TO BRAKE FAILURE SWITCH CONNECTOR TO BRAKE FAILURE SWITCH

W/TR = WITH TRACER

Wiring diagram legend—1975 model CJ Jeeps

NO.	GA.	COLOR	HARNESS ASSEMBLY – ENGINE (SIX CYLINDER)
1	18	PURPLE W/TR	BULKHEAD CONNECTOR (TEMPERATURE GAUGE) TO TEMPERATURE SENDER
7	18	PURPLE	BULKHEAD CONNECTOR (OIL PRESSURE GAUGE) TO OIL PRESSURE SENDER
12A	14	RED	5/16 STUD TO SPLICE "E" (FUSIBLE LINK IN ALTERNATOR/REGULATOR CIRCUIT)
12B	10	RED	SPLICE "E" TO 1/4 STUD (ALTERNATOR/REGULATOR CIRCUIT)
12C	10	RED	BULKHEAD CONNECTOR (ALTERNATOR/REGULATOR) TO SPLICE "F" AT FUSIBLE LINK
12D	14	RED	SPLICE "F" TO 5/16 STUD (FUSIBLE LINK IN ALTERNATOR/REGULATOR CIRCUIT)
12E	14	RED	1/4 STUD TO ALTERNATOR/REGULATOR ASSEMBLY
13	14	RED W/TR	BULKHEAD CONNECTOR (IGNITION SWITCH) TO COIL (+) TERMINAL
14	16	LT BLUE	BULKHEAD CONNECTOR (IGNITION SWITCH) TO STARTING MOTOR SOLENOID (STARTING TERMINAL)
34	18	WHITE W/TR	BULKHEAD CONNECTOR (BACK-UP LAMPS) TO BACK-UP LIGHT SWITCH CONNECTOR
34A	18	WHITE W/TR	BACK-UP LIGHT SWITCH CONNECTOR TO BACK-UP LIGHT SWITCH
35	16	RED W/TR	BACK-UP LIGHT SWITCH CONNECTOR TO VACUUM SOLENOID SWITCH
37	16	ORANGE	BACK-UP LIGHT SWITCH CONNECTOR TO VACUUM SOLENOID SWITCH
37A	16	ORANGE	BACK-UP LIGHT SWITCH CONNECTOR TO TRANSMISSION CONTROLLED SPARK SWITCH (T.C.S.)
52	18	WHITE W/TR	BULKHEAD CONNECTOR (BACK-UP LAMPS) TO BACK-UP LIGHT SWITCH CONNECTOR
52A	18	WHITE W/TR	BACK-UP LIGHT SWITCH CONNECTOR TO BACK-UP LIGHT SWITCH
78	24	BLACK W/TR	BULKHEAD CONNECTOR (ALTERNATOR/REGULATOR) TO ALTERNATOR & VOLTAGE REGULATOR
79	16	GREEN	COIL (–) TERMINAL TO ELECTRONIC IGNITION PACK
80	16	BLUE	DISTRIBUTOR TO ELECTRONIC IGNITION PACK
81	16	YELLOW	DISTRIBUTOR TO ELECTRONIC IGNITION PACK
82	16	RED W/TR	COIL (+) TERMINAL TO ELECTRONIC IGNITION PACK
			HARNESS ASSEMBLY – ENGINE (V-8)
1*	18	PURPLE W/TR	BULKHEAD CONNECTOR (TEMPERATURE GAUGE) TO TEMPERATURE SENDER
7*	18	PURPLE	BULKHEAD CONNECTOR (OIL PRESSURE GAUGE) TO OIL PRESSURE SENDER
12A*	14	RED	5/16 STUD TO SPLICE "E" (FUSIBLE LINK IN ALTERNATOR CIRCUIT)
12B	10	RED	SPLICE "E" TO 1/4 STUD (ALTERNATOR CIRCUIT)
12C*	10	RED	BULKHEAD CONNECTOR (ALTERNATOR) TO SPLICE "F" AT FUSIBLE LINK
12D*	14	RED	SPLICE "F" TO 5/16 STUD (FUSIBLE LINK IN ALTERNATOR CIRCUIT)
13	14	RED W/TR	BULKHEAD CONNECTOR (IGNITION SWITCH) TO SPLICE "G"
13A	14	RED W/TR	SPLICE "G" TO COIL (+) TERMINAL
14*	16	LT BLUE	BULKHEAD CONNECTOR (IGNITION SWITCH) TO STARTING MOTOR SOLENOID (STARTING TERMINAL)
34*	18	WHITE W/TR	BULKHEAD CONNECTOR (BACK-UP LIGHTS) TO BACK-UP LIGHT SWITCH CONNECTOR
34A*	18	WHITE W/TR	BACK-UP LIGHT SWITCH CONNECTOR TO BACK-UP LIGHT SWITCH
40	16	YELLOW	SPLICE "G" (CIRCUIT NO. 13) TO VOLTAGE REGULATOR
41	18	GRAY	VOLTAGE REGULATOR TO ALTERNATOR
43	18	BLACK	VOLTAGE REGULATOR TO ALTERNATOR
44	18	GREEN	VOLTAGE REGULATOR TO ALTERNATOR
52	18	WHITE.W/TR	BULKHEAD CONNECTOR (BACK-UP LIGHTS) TO BACK-UP LIGHT SWITCH CONNECTOR
52A	18	WHITE W/TR	BACK-UP LIGHT SWITCH CONNECTOR TO BACK-UP LIGHT SWITCH
79	16	GREEN	COIL (–) TERMINAL TO ELECTRONIC IGNITION PACK
80	16	BLUE	DISTRIBUTOR TO ELECTRONIC IGNITION PACK
81	16	YELLOW	DISTRIBUTOR TO ELECTRONIC IGNITION PACK
82	16	RED W/TR	SPLICE "G" (CIRCUIT NO. 13) TO ELECTRONIC IGNITION PACK
			HARNESS ASSEMBLY – CHASSIS
10	16	PINK	BULKHEAD CONNECTOR (FUEL GAUGE – INSTRUMENT UNIT) TO CONNECTOR (FUEL TANK SENDING UNIT)
18	16	WHITE	BULKHEAD CONNECTOR (TAIL LAMPS) TO CONNECTOR (LEFT TAIL, STOP & LICENSE LAMP)
18A	16	WHITE	CONNECTOR (LEFT TAIL, STOP & LICENSE LAMP) TO CONNECTOR (LEFT REAR MARKER LAMP)
18B	16	WHITE	CONNECTOR (LEFT REAR MARKER LAMP) TO CONNECTOR (RIGHT TAIL & STOP LAMP)
18C	16	WHITE	CONNECTOR (RIGHT TAIL & STOP LAMP) TO CONNECTOR (RIGHT REAR MARKER LAMP)
23	16	LT GREEN W/TR	BULKHEAD CONNECTOR (LEFT TURN & HAZARD) TO CONNECTOR (LEFT TAIL, STOP & LICENSE LAMP)
24	16	LT GREEN	BULKHEAD CONNECTOR (RIGHT TURN & HAZARD) TO CONNECTOR (RIGHT TAIL & STOP LAMP)
34	18	WHITE W/TR	BULKHEAD CONNECTOR (BACK-UP LIGHTS) TO CONNECTOR (LEFT BACK-UP LAMP)
34A	18	WHITE W/TR	CONNECTOR (LEFT BACK-UP LAMP) TO CONNECTOR (RIGHT BACK-UP LAMP)
			HARNESS ASSEMBLY – DIRECTIONAL SIGNAL SWITCH
5B	18	GREEN	CONNECTOR (STEERING COLUMN) TO RIGHT FRONT POSITION CONTACT
8B	18	GREEN W/TR	CONNECTOR (STEERING COLUMN) TO LEFT FRONT POSITION CONTACT
23A	16	LT GREEN W/TR	CONNECTOR (STEERING COLUMN) TO LEFT REAR POSITION CONTACT
24A	16	LT GREEN	CONNECTOR (STEERING COLUMN) TO RIGHT REAR POSITION CONTACT
65	16	RED W/TR	CONNECTOR (STEERING COLUMN) TO BRAKE SWITCH POSITION CONTACTS
74	18	RED W/TR	CONNECTOR (STEERING COLUMN) TO FLASHER POSITION CONTACT

(*) COMBINED WITH 6 CYLINDER WIRING

W/TR = WITH TRACER

Wiring diagram legend—1975 model CJ Jeeps

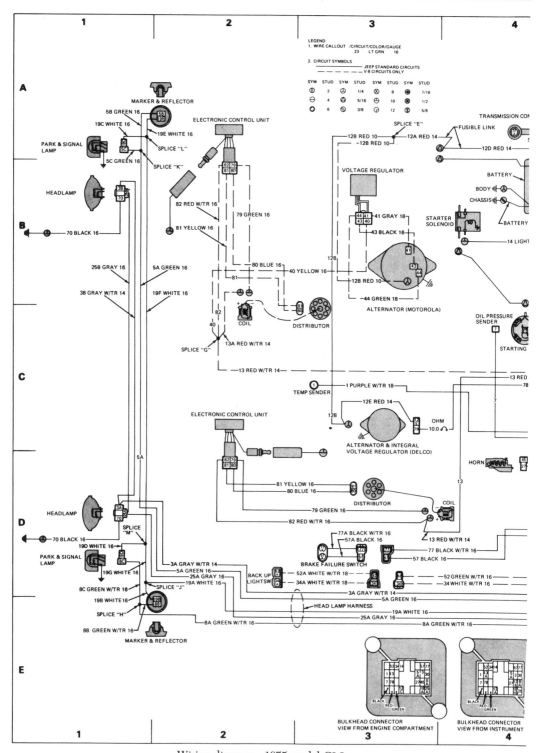

Wiring diagram—1975 model CJ Jeeps

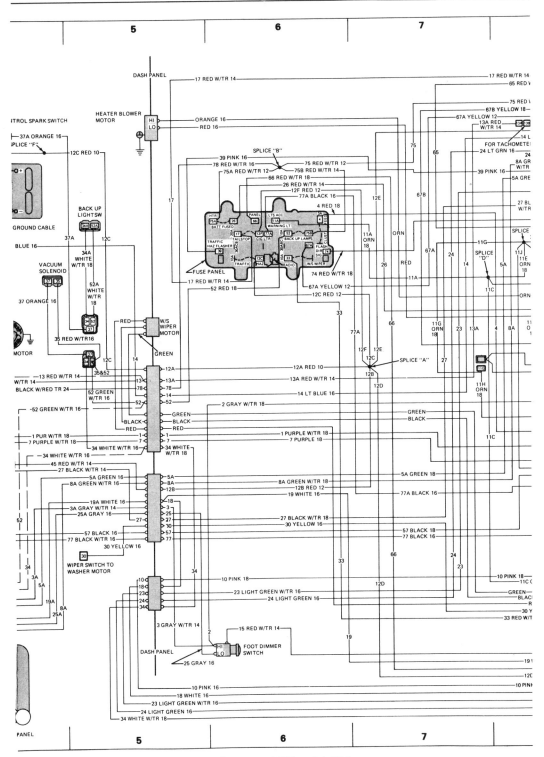

Wiring diagram—1975 model CJ Jeeps

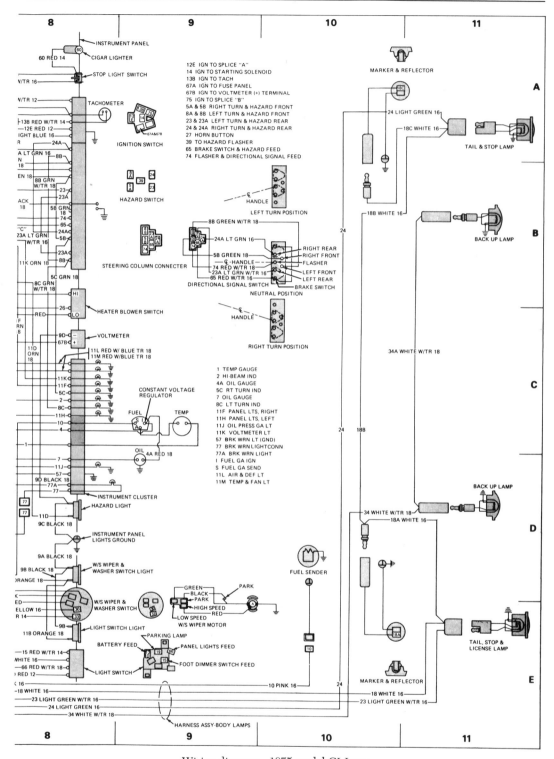

Wiring diagram—1975 model CJ Jeeps

NO.	GA.	COLOR	INSTRUMENT AND CONTROL HARNESS
1	18	PURPLE W/TR	BULKHEAD CONNECTOR (TEMPERATURE SENDER) TO TEMPERATURE GAUGE
2	18	GRAY W/TR	FOOT DIMMER SWITCH (HI-BEAM) TO INSTRUMENT CLUSTER (HI-BEAM INDICATOR)
3	14	GRAY W/TR	FOOT DIMMER SWITCH (HI-BEAM) TO BULKHEAD CONNECTOR (HI-BEAM)
4	18	RED	FUSE PANEL (CLUSTER FEED) TO INSTRUMENT CONSTANT VOLTAGE REGULATOR
4A	18	RED	INSTRUMENT CONSTANT VOLTAGE REGULATOR (IGNITION TERMINAL) TO OIL PRESSURE GAUGE (IGNITION TERMINAL)
5A	18	GREEN	BULKHEAD CONNECTOR (RIGHT TURN & HAZARD FRONT) TO HAZARD SWITCH
5B	18	GREEN	HAZARD SWITCH TO STEERING COLUMN CONNECTOR (RIGHT TURN & HAZARD FRONT)
5C	18	GREEN	STEERING COLUMN CONNECTOR TO INSTRUMENT CLUSTER LAMP (RIGHT TURN)
7	18	PURPLE	BULKHEAD CONNECTOR (OIL PRESSURE SENDER) TO OIL PRESSURE GAUGE
8A	18	GREEN W/TR	BULKHEAD CONNECTOR (LEFT TURN & HAZARD FRONT) TO HAZARD SWITCH
8B	18	GREEN W/TR	HAZARD SWITCH TO STEERING COLUMN CONNECTOR (LEFT TURN & HAZARD FRONT)
8C	18	GREEN W/TR	STEERING COLUMN CONNECTOR TO INSTRUMENT CLUSTER LAMP (LEFT TURN)
9A	18	BLACK	SPLICE "F" TO INSTRUMENT PANEL LIGHT GROUND
9B	18	BLACK	SPLICE "F" TO LIGHT SWITCH LIGHT
9C	18	BLACK	SPLICE "F" TO WIPER & WASHER SWITCH LIGHT
9D	18	BLACK	SPLICE "F" TO CIGAR LIGHTER
9E	18	BLACK	SPLICE "F" TO VOLTMETER
9F	18	BLACK	SPLICE "F" TO AIR LIGHT
9G	18	BLACK	AIR LIGHT TO HEAT LIGHT
9H	18	BLACK	HEAT LIGHT TO DEF. LIGHT
9J	18	BLACK	DEF. LIGHT TO FAN LIGHT
10	18	PINK	FRAME HARNESS (FUEL SENDER UNIT) TO INSTRUMENT CLUSTER FUEL GAUGE (S-TERMINAL)
11A	18	ORANGE	FUSE PANEL (LIGHTS-ACCESSORIES) TO SPLICE "A"
11B	18	ORANGE	SPLICE "A" TO STEERING COLUMN CONNECTOR
11C	18	ORANGE	SPLICE "A" TO LIGHT SWITCH LIGHT
11D	18	ORANGE	SPLICE "A" TO WIPER AND WASHER SWITCH LIGHT
11E	18	ORANGE	SPLICE "A" TO SPLICE "C"
11F	18	ORANGE	SPLICE "C" TO CLUSTER LIGHT
11G	18	ORANGE	SPLICE "C" TO CLUSTER LIGHT
11H	18	ORANGE	SPLICE "C" TO OIL PRESSURE GAUGE LIGHT
11J	18	ORANGE	SPLICE "C" TO VOLTMETER LIGHT
11K	18	ORANGE	SPLICE "C" TO AIR LIGHT CONNECTOR
11L	18	ORANGE	AIR LIGHT CONNECTOR TO HEAT LIGHT CONNECTOR
11M	18	ORANGE	HEAT LIGHT CONNECTOR TO DEF. LIGHT CONNECTOR
11N	18	ORANGE	DEF. LIGHT CONNECTOR TO FAN LIGHT CONNECTOR
12A	10	RED	BULKHEAD CONNECTOR (ALTERNATOR & VOLTAGE REGULATOR) TO SPLICE "P"
12B	12	RED	SPLICE "P" TO HORN RELAY
12C	12	RED	FUSE PANEL (TRAFFIC HAZARD) TO SPLICE "P"
12D	12	RED	SPLICE "P" TO LIGHT SWITCH (BATTERY FEED)
12E	12	RED	SPLICE "P" TO IGNITION SWITCH
12F	12	RED	FUSE PANEL (CIGAR LIGHTER) TO SPLICE "P"
13A	14	RED W/TR	BULKHEAD CONNECTOR (COIL) TO TACHOMETER CONNECTOR
13B	14	RED W/TR	TACHOMETER CONNECTOR TO IGNITION SWITCH
14	16	LT BLUE	BULKHEAD CONNECTOR (STARTING MOTOR SOLENOID) TO NEUTRAL SAFETY SWITCH CONNECTOR
14A	16	LT BLUE	IGNITION SWITCH TO NEUTRAL SAFETY SWITCH CONNECTOR
15	14	RED W/TR	LIGHT SWITCH (FOOT DIMMER SWITCH FEED) TO FOOT DIMMER SWITCH
16	18	BLACK	LIGHT SWITCH TO COURTESY LAMP GROUND CONNECTOR
17	14	RED W/TR	FUSE PANEL (TAIL-STOP) TO STOP LIGHT SWITCH
18	16	WHITE	BULKHEAD CONNECTOR TO CHASSIS HARNESS (TAIL LAMPS)
19	16	WHITE	BULKHEAD CONNECTOR (MARKER LAMPS) TO LIGHT SWITCH (PARKING LAMPS)
23	16	LT GREEN W/TR	STEERING COLUMN CONNECTOR (LEFT TURN & HAZARD-REAR) TO FRAME HARNESS CONNECTOR
24	16	LT GREEN W/TR	STEERING COLUMN CONNECTOR TO FRAME HARNESS CONNECTOR
25	16	GRAY	BULKHEAD CONNECTOR (HEADLAMPS) TO FOOT DIMMER SWITCH (LO-BEAM)
26	14	RED W/TR	FUSE PANEL (HEATER-BATTERY) TO HEATER BLOWER SWITCH
27	18	BLACK W/TR	STEERING COLUMN CONNECTOR TO HORN RELAY
30	16	YELLOW	BULKHEAD CONNECTOR (WINDSHIELD WIPER & WASHER) TO WINDSHIELD WIPER & WASHER SWITCH
33	16	RED W/TR	FUSE PANEL (RADIO) TO WINDSHIELD WIPER & WASHER SWITCH
34B	18	WHITE W/TR	BULKHEAD CONNECTOR (BACK-UP LIGHT SWITCH) TO BULKHEAD CONNECTOR (CHASSIS HARNESS - BACK-UP LIGHTS)
39	16	PINK	FUSE PANEL (TRAFFIC HAZARD) TO STEERING COLUMN CONNECTOR
45	16	RED W/TR	BULKHEAD CONNECTOR TO HORN RELAY
51	16	ORANGE	LIGHT SWITCH TO COURTESY LAMP FEED CONNECTOR
52	18	RED	FUSE PANEL (BACK-UP LAMPS) TO BULKHEAD CONNECTOR (BACK-UP LIGHT SWITCH - MAN. TRANS.)
52B	18	RED	FUSE PANEL (BACK-UP LAMPS) TO BULKHEAD CONNECTOR (BACK-UP LIGHT SWITCH - AUTO. TRANS.)
54	16	YELLOW	BULKHEAD CONNECTOR TO AUTOMATIC TRANSMISSION KICKDOWN SWITCH
56	16	ORANGE	BULKHEAD CONNECTOR TO EMERGENCY DRIVE LIGHT
57A	18	BLACK	BULKHEAD CONNECTOR (BRAKE FAILURE SWITCH) TO IGNITION SWITCH
57B	18	BLACK	BULKHEAD CONNECTOR TO SPLICE "E"
57C	18	BLACK	SPLICE "E" TO PARKING BRAKE SWITCH CONNECTOR
57D	18	BLACK	SPLICE "E" TO BRAKE WARNING LIGHT CONNECTOR
60	14	RED	BACK-UP SWITCH TO CIGAR LIGHTER CONNECTOR
65	16	RED W/TR	STOP LIGHT SWITCH TO STEERING COLUMN CONNECTOR (BRAKE SWITCH & HAZARD FEED)
66	18	RED W/TR	FUSE PANEL (PANEL LAMPS) TO LIGHT SWITCH (PANEL LIGHTS FEED)
67A	12	YELLOW	FUSE PANEL LAMPS TO IGNITION SWITCH
67B	18	YELLOW	IGNITION SWITCH TO INSTRUMENT CLUSTER VOLTMETER (+) TERMINAL
68	16	YELLOW	AUTOMATIC TRANSMISSION KICKDOWN SWITCH TO FUSE PANEL (CLUSTER FEED)
74	18	RED W/TR	FUSE PANEL (FLASH - DIRECTIONAL SIGNAL) TO STEERING COLUMN CONNECTOR (FLASHER & DIRECTIONAL SIGNAL FEED)
75A	12	RED W/TR	IGNITION SWITCH TO SPLICE "B"
75B	12	RED W/TR	FUSE PANEL LAMPS TO SPLICE "B"
75C	12	RED W/TR	FUSE PANEL (HEATER - BATTERY) TO SPLICE "B"
77	16	BLACK W/TR	IGNITION SWITCH TO BRAKE WARNING LIGHT CONNECTION

W/TR = WITH TRACER

Wiring diagram legend—1976 model CJ Jeeps

NO.	GA.	COLOR	HARNESS ASSEMBLY – HEADLAMP, PARKING AND SIGNAL LAMP
3A	14	GRAY W/TR	BULKHEAD CONNECTOR (HI-BEAM) TO LEFT HEADLAMP CONNECTOR (HI-BEAM)
3B	14	GRAY W/TR	LEFT HEADLAMP CONNECTOR (HI-BEAM) TO RIGHT HEADLAMP CONNECTOR (HI-BEAM)
5A	16	GREEN	BULKHEAD CONNECTOR (RIGHT TURN SIGNAL) TO RIGHT TURN SIGNAL SPLICE "N"
5B	16	GREEN	RIGHT TURN SPLICE "N" TO RIGHT SIDE MARKER LAMP ASSEMBLY
5C	16	GREEN	RIGHT TURN SPLICE "N" TO RIGHT FRONT PARK & TURN SIGNAL LAMP ASSEMBLY
8A	16	GREEN W/TR	BULKHEAD CONNECTOR (LEFT TURN SIGNAL) TO LEFT TURN SIGNAL SPLICE "L"
8B	16	GREEN W/TR	LEFT TURN SPLICE "L" TO LEFT SIDE MARKER LAMP ASSEMBLY
8C	16	GREEN W/TR	LEFT TURN SPLICE "L" TO LEFT FRONT PARK & TURN SIGNAL LAMP ASSEMBLY
19A	16	WHITE	BULKHEAD CONNECTOR (PARKING LIGHTS) TO SPLICE "M"
19B	16	WHITE	PARKING LIGHTS SPLICE "M" TO LEFT SIDE MARKER LAMP ASSEMBLY
19C	16	WHITE	PARKING LIGHTS SPLICE "O" TO RIGHT FRONT PARK & TURN SIGNAL LAMP ASSEMBLY
19D	16	WHITE	PARKING LIGHTS SPLICE "M" TO LEFT FRONT PARK & TURN SIGNAL LAMP ASSEMBLY
19E	16	WHITE	PARKING LIGHTS SPLICE "O" TO RIGHT SIDE MARKER LAMP ASSEMBLY
19F	16	WHITE	LEFT PARKING LAMPS SPLICE "M" TO RIGHT PARKING LAMPS SPLICE "O"
25A	16	GRAY	BULKHEAD CONNECTOR (LO-BEAM) TO LEFT HEADLAMP CONNECTOR (LO-BEAM)
25B	16	GRAY	LEFT HEADLAMP CONNECTOR (LO-BEAM) TO RIGHT HEADLAMP CONNECTOR (LO-BEAM)
45	14	RED W/TR	BULKHEAD CONNECTOR (HORN) TO HORN ASSEMBLY
57A	16	BLACK	BULKHEAD CONNECTOR (BRAKE FAILURE SWITCH) TO BRAKE FAILURE SWITCH CONNECTOR TO BRAKE FAILURE SWITCH
70	16	BLACK	LEFT AND RIGHT HEADLAMP GROUND TERMINALS TO GROUND MOUNTING
77	16	BLACK W/TR	BULKHEAD CONNECTOR (BRAKE FAILURE SWITCH) TO BRAKE FAILURE SWITCH CONNECTOR TO BRAKE FAILURE SWITCH
			HARNESS ASSEMBLY – ENGINE (SIX CYLINDER)
1	18	PURPLE W/TR	BULKHEAD CONNECTOR (TEMPERATURE GAUGE) TO TEMPERATURE SENDER
7	18	PURPLE	BULKHEAD CONNECTOR (OIL PRESSURE GAUGE) TO OIL PRESSURE SENDER
12A	14	RED	5/16 STUD TO SPLICE "E" (FUSIBLE LINK IN ALTERNATOR/REGULATOR CIRCUIT)
12B	10	RED	SPLICE "E" TO 1/4 STUD (ALTERNATOR/REGULATOR CIRCUIT)
12C	10	RED	BULKHEAD CONNECTOR (ALTERNATOR/REGULATOR) TO SPLICE "F" AT FUSIBLE LINK
12D	14	RED	SPLICE "F" TO 5/16 STUD (FUSIBLE LINK IN ALTERNATOR/REGULATOR CIRCUIT)
12E	14	RED W/TR	1/4 STUD TO ALTERNATOR/REGULATOR ASSEMBLY
13	14	RED W/TR	BULKHEAD CONNECTOR (IGNITION SWITCH) TO COIL (+) TERMINAL
14	16	LT BLUE	BULKHEAD CONNECTOR (IGNITION SWITCH) TO STARTING MOTOR SOLENOID (STARTING TERMINAL)
30	16	YELLOW	BULKHEAD CONNECTOR TO WINDSHIELD WASHER MOTOR
34	16	WHITE W/TR	BULKHEAD CONNECTOR (BACK-UP LAMPS) TO BACK-UP LIGHT SWITCH CONNECTOR
34A	18	WHITE W/TR	BACK-UP LIGHT SWITCH CONNECTOR TO BACK-UP LIGHT SWITCH
35	16	GREEN W/TR	BULKHEAD CONNECTOR TO TCS SYSTEM CONNECTOR
52	16	WHITE W/TR	BULKHEAD CONNECTOR (BACK-UP LAMPS) TO BACK-UP LIGHT SWITCH CONNECTOR
52A	18	WHITE W/TR	BACK-UP LIGHT SWITCH CONNECTOR TO BACK-UP LIGHT SWITCH
54	16	YELLOW	BULKHEAD CONNECTOR TO KICKDOWN CONNECTOR
56	16	ORANGE	BULKHEAD CONNECTOR TO QUADRA-TRAC EMERGENCY DRIVE CONNECTOR
73	16	RED W/TR	TCS SYSTEM CONNECTOR TO ANTI-DIESEL SOLENOID CONNECTOR
78	24	BLACK W/TR	BULKHEAD CONNECTOR (ALTERNATOR/REGULATOR) TO ALTERNATOR & VOLTAGE REGULATOR
79	16	GREEN	COIL (–) TERMINAL TO ELECTRONIC IGNITION PACK
80	16	BLUE	DISTRIBUTOR TO ELECTRONIC IGNITION PACK
81	16	YELLOW	DISTRIBUTOR TO ELECTRONIC IGNITION PACK
82	16	RED W/TR	COIL (+) TERMINAL TO ELECTRONIC IGNITION PACK
			HARNESS ASSEMBLY – ENGINE (V-8)
1*	18	PURPLE W/TR	BULKHEAD CONNECTOR (TEMPERATURE GAUGE) TO TEMPERATURE SENDER
7*	18	PURPLE	BULKHEAD CONNECTOR (OIL PRESSURE GAUGE) TO OIL PRESSURE SENDER
12A*	14	RED	5/16 STUD TO SPLICE "G" (FUSIBLE LINK IN ALTERNATOR CIRCUIT)
12B	10	RED	SPLICE "G" TO 1/4 STUD (ALTERNATOR CIRCUIT)
12C*	10	RED	BULKHEAD CONNECTOR (ALTERNATOR) TO SPLICE "K" AT FUSIBLE LINK
12D*	14	RED	SPLICE "H" TO 5/16 STUD (FUSIBLE LINK IN ALTERNATOR CIRCUIT)
13	14	RED W/TR	BULKHEAD CONNECTOR (IGNITION SWITCH) TO SPLICE "K"
13A	14	RED W/TR	SPLICE "K" TO COIL (+) TERMINAL
14*	16	LT BLUE	BULKHEAD CONNECTOR (IGNITION SWITCH) TO STARTING MOTOR SOLENOID (STARTING TERMINAL)
30	16	YELLOW	BULKHEAD CONNECTOR TO WINDSHIELD WASHER MOTOR
34*	16	WHITE W/TR	BULKHEAD CONNECTOR (BACK-UP LAMPS) TO BACK-UP LIGHT SWITCH CONNECTOR
34A*	18	WHITE W/TR	BACK-UP LIGHT SWITCH CONNECTOR TO BACK-UP LIGHT SWITCH
40	16	YELLOW	SPLICE "G" (CIRCUIT NO. 12) TO VOLTAGE REGULATOR
43	16	BLACK	VOLTAGE REGULATOR TO ALTERNATOR
44	18	GREEN	VOLTAGE REGULATOR TO ALTERNATOR
52	16	GREEN W/TR	BULKHEAD CONNECTOR (BACK-UP LIGHTS) TO BACK-UP LIGHT SWITCH CONNECTOR
52A	18	WHITE W/TR	BACK-UP LIGHT SWITCH CONNECTOR TO BACK-UP LIGHT SWITCH
54	16	YELLOW	BULKHEAD CONNECTOR TO KICKDOWN CONNECTOR
56	16	ORANGE	BULKHEAD CONNECTOR TO QUADRA-TRAC EMERGENCY DRIVE CONNECTOR
79	16	GREEN	COIL (–) TERMINAL TO ELECTRONIC IGNITION PACK
80	16	BLUE	DISTRIBUTOR TO ELECTRONIC IGNITION PACK
81	16	YELLOW	DISTRIBUTOR TO ELECTRONIC IGNITION PACK
82	16	RED W/TR	SPLICE "K" (CIRCUIT NO. 13) TO ELECTRONIC IGNITION PACK
			HARNESS ASSEMBLY – CHASSIS
10	16	PINK	BULKHEAD CONNECTOR (FUEL GAUGE – INSTRUMENT UNIT) TO CONNECTOR (FUEL TANK SENDING UNIT)
18	16	WHITE	BULKHEAD CONNECTOR (TAIL LAMPS) TO CONNECTOR (LEFT TAIL, STOP & LICENSE LAMP)
18A	16	WHITE	CONNECTOR (LEFT TAIL, STOP & LICENSE LAMP) TO CONNECTOR (LEFT REAR MARKER LAMP)
18B	16	WHITE	CONNECTOR (LEFT REAR MARKER LAMP) TO CONNECTOR (RIGHT TAIL & STOP LAMP)
18C	16	WHITE	CONNECTOR (RIGHT TAIL & STOP LAMP) TO CONNECTOR (RIGHT REAR MARKER LAMP)
23	16	LT GREEN W/TR	CONNECTOR (LEFT TURN & HAZARD) TO CONNECTOR (LEFT TAIL, STOP & LICENSE LAMP)
24	16	LT GREEN	CONNECTOR (RIGHT TURN & HAZARD) TO CONNECTOR (RIGHT TAIL & STOP LAMP)
34C	18	WHITE W/TR	CONNECTOR (BACK-UP LAMPS) TO LEFT TAIL, STOP & BACK-UP LAMP CONNECTOR
34D	18	WHITE W/TR	LEFT TAIL, STOP & BACK-UP LAMP CONNECTOR TO RIGHT TAIL, STOP & BACK-UP LAMP CONNECTOR

(*) COMBINED WITH 6 CYLINDER WIRING
W/TR = WITH TRACER

Wiring diagram legend—1976 model CJ Jeeps

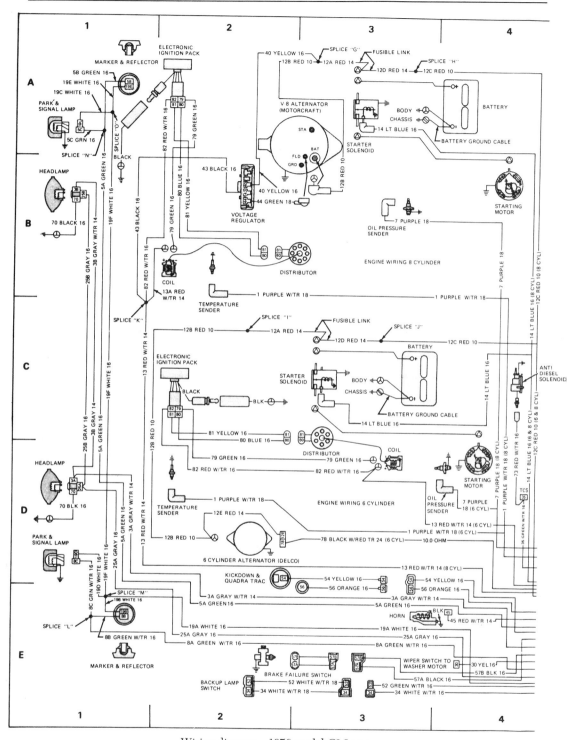

Wiring diagram—1976 model CJ Jeeps

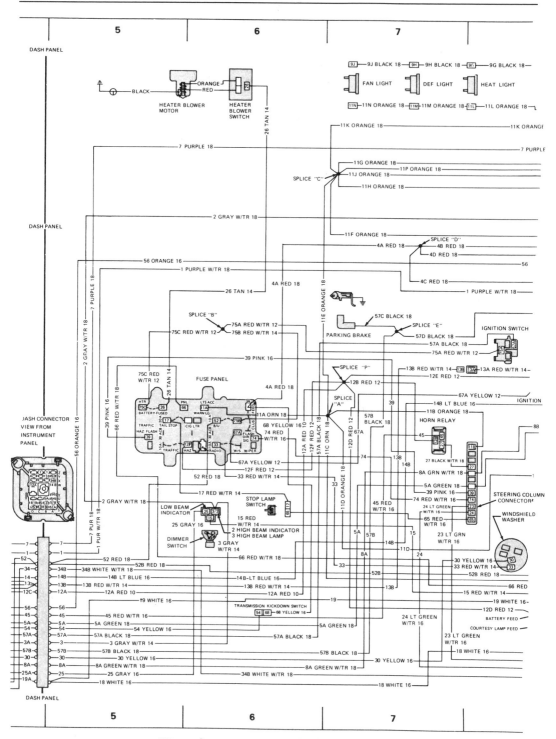

Wiring diagram—1976 model CJ Jeeps

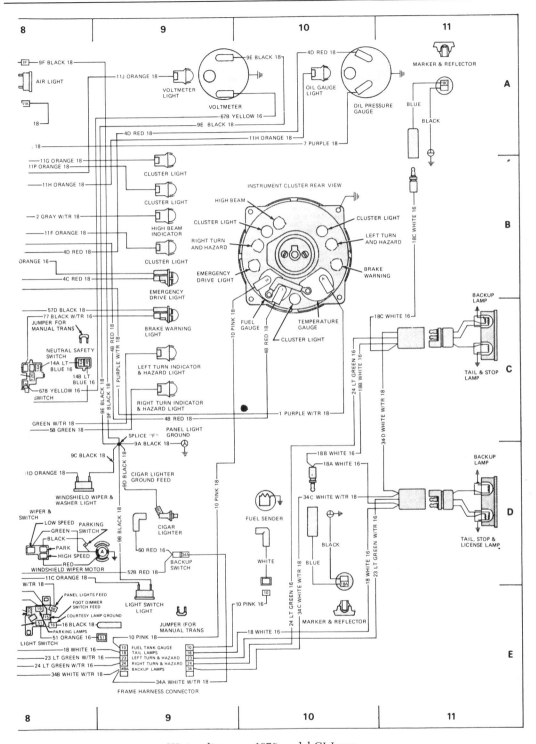

Wiring diagram—1976 model CJ Jeeps

6 · Clutch and Transmission

Manual Transmission

Removal and Installation

PRIOR TO 1972

The following removal and installation procedures apply to Jeeps made prior to 1972. These procedures apply generally to the 3 speed and 4 speed transmissions in all models. For model applications, refer to the chart at the end of this chapter. Minor differences between models that affect the removal and installation procedures are noted. The transmission and transfer case are removed from the vehicle as a unit and separated as necessary. Removal and installation procedures for Jeeps made in 1972–76 are given separately later in this section.

Remove the transmission and transfer case from Jeeps made prior to 1972 as follows:

1. Drain the transmission and transfer case. Replace the drain plugs.

2. Remove the floor pan inspection plate.

3. Remove the shift lever and shift housing assembly and its gasket from the transmission. On the CJ-5A and CJ-6A, remove the remote control shift rods.

4. Remove the set screw from the transfer case shift lever pivot pin. Remove

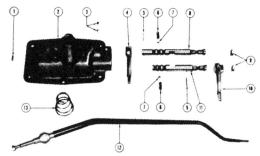

The Warner T-14A 3 speed transmission shifter control mechanism

1. Control lever housing pin
2. Control housing
3. Interlock plunger and plug
4. Second-third shift fork
5. Shift fork pin
6. Poppet spring
7. Poppet ball
8. Second-third shift rail
9. Shift rail caps
10. Low-reverse shift fork
11. Low-reverse shift rail
12. Shift lever
13. Shift lever support spring

the pivot pin, shift levers and shift lever springs. On the CJ-5A and CJ-6A, remove the pivot pin cotter key and the adjusting rod attaching nut to remove the shift lever.

5. If the vehicle is equipped with power take-off, remove the shift lever plate screws and lift out the lever.

6. Disconnect the front and rear propeller shafts from the transfer case. If the vehicle is equipped with power take-off,

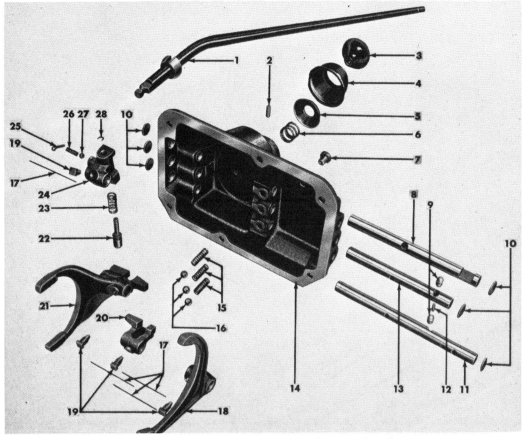

The Warner T-98A 4 speed transmission shifter control mechanism

1. Shift lever	11. Low and second shift rail	21. Direct and third shift fork
2. Control housing pin	12. Shift rail interlock pin	22. Reverse plunger
3. Shift handle	13. Direct and third shift rail	23. Reverse plunger spring
4. Control housing cap	14. Control housing	24. Reverse rail end
5. Washer	15. Shift rail poppet spring	25. Cotter pin
6. Control lever spring	16. Shift rail poppet ball	26. Reverse plunger poppet spring
7. Breather assembly	17. Lockwire	27. Reverse plunger poppet ball
8. Reverse shift rail	18. Low and second shift fork	28. C-washer
9. Shift rail interlock plunger	19. Lock screw	
10. Expansion plug	20. Shift rail end	

disconnect the transfer case end of the power take-off drive shaft.

7. Disconnect the speedometer cable at the transfer case.

8. Disconnect the hand brake cable.

9. Disconnect the clutch release cable at the bellcrank yoke end.

10. Place jacks under the transmission and engine. Place a block of wood between the oil pan and jack to protect the oil pan from possible damage.

11. Remove the nuts which hold the rear mounting to the frame cross member.

12. Remove the transfer case snubbing rubber bolt nut at the cross member.

13. Remove the bolts which hold the cross member to the frame side rails and remove the cross member.

14. Remove the bolts which hold the transmission to the flywheel bellhousing.

15. Force the transmission to the right to disengage the clutch control lever tube ball joint.

16. Lower the jacks under the engine and transmission. Slide the transmission and transfer case assembly toward the rear of the vehicle until the clutch shaft clears the flywheel housing.

17. Lower the jack under the transmission. Remove the transmission and transfer case assembly from under the vehicle.

18. Install in reverse order of removal

taking note of the following points concerning the 4 speed transmission:

When installing the front adapter plate, insert the bearing retainer into the adapter plate and position the adapter plate against the flywheel housing. With the adapter plate cap screws tight, make sure the bearing can be removed freely. If it can not be removed, relocate the adapter plate and tighten again to test the proper location of the adapter plate.

When installing the rear adapter plate, be sure that the cap screw heads do not protrude beyond the adapter plate face and that they do not interfere with the transfer case fitting tightly against the rear adapter plate.

1972–1976

1. Remove all floor lever knobs, trim rings and boots.

2. On the three speed models, remove the floor pan section from above the transmission shift control and remove the lever assembly from the transmission. On the four speed models, remove the shift control housing cap, washer, spring, shift lever and pin.

3. Remove the transfer case shift lever and bracket assembly.

4. Raise the vehicle.

5. Index mark the driveshafts for proper alignment at installation.

6. Remove the front propeller shaft.

7. Disconnect the front end of the rear propeller shaft from the transfer case.

8. Disconnect the clutch cable and remove the cable mounting bracket from the transfer case on 1972 models only.

9. Disconnect the speedometer cable, back-up light switch wires, transmission controlled spark advance, and parking brake cable if connected to the cross member.

10. If equipped with a V8 engine, disconnect the exhaust pipe at the manifolds and lower them.

Support the transmission with a transmission jack. Disconnect the support cross-member from the frame side rail.

11. Remove the bolts that attach the transmission to the clutch housing.

12. Lower the transmission slightly.

13. Move the transmission and transfer case assembly and crossmember backward far enough for the transmission clutch shaft to clear the clutch housing.

14. Remove the assembly from under the vehicle.

15. Install in the reverse order of removal taking note of the following points prior to installing the transmission:

Position the wave washer and the throw-out bearing and sleeve assembly in the throwout fork. Center the bearing over the pressure plate release levers.

Protect the splines and throw-out bearing alignment and slowly slide the transmission into position. Some maneuvering may be necessary in order to match the transmission input shaft splines and the clutch driven plate splines.

Linkage Adjustment—CJ-5A and CJ-6A

First disconnect the shift rods from the remote control levers. Check for binding of the remote control shaft on the steering column and make the necessary adjustments to eliminate any binding condition.

If the shift is not smooth and positive, first make sure that the transmission is in Neutral and then remove the shift rods at the transmission by removing the clevis pins. Slip a short piece of snug fitting $\frac{1}{4}$ in. aligning rod through the gearshift levers and housing.

This places the shift lever and clutch assemblies in the Neutral position. Adjust the shift rod yokes at the transmission end so that the clevis pins can be installed freely without moving the shift levers on the transmission. Remove the alignment pin.

If shifting from First to Second is difficult or the transmission hangs up in First gear, shorten the Low and Reverse rod one turn at a time until the condition is corrected. Usually three turns are required.

Should the fault continue after completing the above adjustment, check further as follows. First, remove the lubricating fitting from the shifter housing.

Use a narrow feeler gauge which will enter the opening for the lubricator and check the clearance between the faces of the shifting clutches. The clearance should be 0.015 in. to 0.031 in. If the clearance is greater, the assembly must be removed for adjustment. The shift dog, which engages the clutch slots should not have more than 0.009 in. clearance in the slots. If the clearance between the clutch grooves and cross

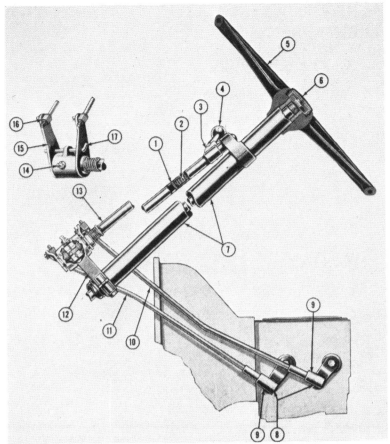

1. Stop screw
2. Bias spring
3. Gearshift lever
4. Lever ball
5. Steering wheel
6. Horn button
7. Column and bearing
8. End nuts
9. Shift rod ends
10. Shift rod
11. Shift rod
12. Cross-shift bracket
13. Control shaft
14. Lubrication fitting
15. Lever and clutch
16. Adjusting yoke
17. Aligning rod

Remote control transmission shift linkage for the CJ-5A and CJ-6A

pins is too great, these parts must be replaced.

To remove the remote control housing from the steering column for repairs, the following procedure is suggested:

1. Remove the shifting rods from the transmission and also from the steering column remote control clutch levers.

2. Remove the gearshift lever fulcrum pin and the gearshift lever.

3. Remove the plates on the toe board at the steering post.

4. Remove the two screws that hold the remote control housing to the steering post and lift the housing from the positioning pin.

5. Remove the assembly down through the floor pan.

6. Remove the lower clutch and shift lever from the housing by turning counterclockwise.

7. Remove the upper clutch and shift lever in the same manner.

8. Wash all of the parts in a suitable cleaning solution and replace all worn parts before reassembling.

9. Assemble the upper clutch assembly in the housing making sure that the alignment hole in the housing faces the engine. Turn the upper lever assembly in as far as it will go and then back off one full turn until the hole in the clutch lever aligns with the hole in the housing.

10. Assemble the lower clutch lever assembly in the housing until the faces of the clutches contact, then back off not more than one-half of a turn which should bring the aligning hole in the lever in line with the hole in the housing. If the one-half turn does not bring the alignment hole into the proper position, it will be necessary to grind off the face of the lower clutch so that it can be backed off one-half turn from contact with the upper clutch. The proper clearance of 0.015 in. is obtained when the lower clutch is backed off one-half turn.

11. Assemble the unit to the steering

post in the reverse order of removal and adjust the remote control rods.

12. If, after assembly, the shifter dog catches on the edge of the slot in the clutch when moving the lever up and down, disconnect the shift rod at the transmission end and either lengthen or shorten it slightly to correct this condition.

Clutch

Vehicles with the F-head engine have a 8½ or 9¼ in. clutch plate. The clutch is either a three pressure spring, three fingered Auburn clutch or a six pressure spring, three fingered Rockford clutch.

Auburn clutch assembly for the F-head

1. Driven plate and hub	7. Release lever
2. Pressure plate	8. Return spring
3. Pivot pin	9. Adjusting screw
4. Bracket	10. Jam nut
5. Spring cup	11. Washer
6. Pressure spring	

Rockford clutch assembly for the F-head

1. Driven plate and hub
2. Pressure plate
3. Backing plate and pressure spring

Jeeps with the V6 engine have a General Motors diaphragm type clutch.

Vehicles made during 1972 to 1976 have a 10½ in. direct spring pressure type clutch.

When the clutch pedal is depressed, linkage moves the clutch fork, which pivots on a ball stud and activates the throwout bearing. The throwout bearing then depresses the fingers, or in the case of the V6, the prongs of the diaphragm spring.

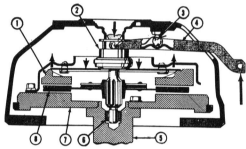

A cutaway view of a V6 clutch also showing the clutch release action

1. Pressure plate	5. Engine crankshaft
2. Throwout bearing	6. Pilot bearing
3. Pivot point	7. Flywheel
4. Clutch fork	8. Driven plate

The fingers or prongs are mounted on pivot pins, which reverse the direction of force. Force is then applied directly to the retracting springs or fingers, thus lifting the pressure plate from the drive plate and disengaging the clutch.

The removal and installation procedures for the F-head, V6, and 1972–76 clutches will be given separately in the following paragraphs due to differences in the recommended procedures.

Removal and Installation

F-Head

1. Remove the transmission and transfer case from the vehicle.

2. Remove the flywheel housing.

3. Mark the clutch pressure plate and engine flywheel with a center punch so the clutch assembly may be installed in the same position after adjustments or replacement are complete.

4. Loosen the clutch pressure plate bracket bolts equally, a little at a time, to prevent distortion and relieve the clutch springs evenly. Remove the bolts.

5. Remove the pressure plate assembly

(bracket and pressure plate) and driven plate from the flywheel. The driven plate will just be resting on the pressure plate housing since it usually is mounted on the input shaft of the transmission, which has been removed. Be careful that it does not fall down and cause injury.

6. Replace the clutch assembly in the reverse order of removal taking note of the following items:

The clutch release bearing (throwout bearing) is lubricated at time of assembly and no attempt should be made to lubricate it. Put a small amount of grease in the pilot bushing. Install the driven plate with the short end of the hub toward the flywheel. Use a spare transmission main shaft or an aligning arbor to align the pressure plate assembly and the driven plate. Leave the arbor in place while tightening the pressure plate screws evenly a turn or two at a time.

7. Install in reverse order of removal.

V6

1. Remove the transmission and transfer case.

2. Remove the clutch throwout bearing and pedal return spring from the clutch fork.

3. Remove the flywheel housing from the engine.

4. Disconnect the clutch fork from the ball stud by forcing it toward the center of the vehicle.

5. Mark the clutch cover and flywheel with a center punch so that the cover can later be installed in the same position on the flywheel. This is necessary to maintain engine balance.

6. Loosen the clutch attaching bolts alternately, one turn at a time to avoid distorting the clutch cover flange, until the diaphragm spring is released.

7. Support the pressure plate and cover assembly while removing the last of the bolts; remove the pressure plate and driven plate from the flywheel.

8. If it is necessary to disassemble the pressure plate assembly, note the position of the grooves on the edge of the pressure plate and cover. These marks must be aligned during assembly to maintain balance. The clutch diaphragm spring and two pivot rings are riveted to the clutch cover. Inspect the spring, rings and cover for excessive wear or damage. If there is a

defect, replace the complete cover assembly.

9. Replace the clutch assembly in reverse order of the removal procedure, taking note of the following:

Use extreme care at all times not to get the clutch driven plate dirty in any way. Lightly lubricate the inside of the clutch driven plate's spline with a coat of wheel bearing grease. Do the same to the input shaft of the transmission. Wipe off all excess grease so that none will fly off and get onto the driven plate. Lubricate the throwout bearing collar, the ball stud and the clutch fork with wheel bearing grease. Use a pilot shaft or a spare transmission main shaft to align the driven shaft and the clutch pressure plate when attaching the assembly to the flywheel. Tighten down on the clutch-to-flywheel attaching bolts alternately so that the clutch is drawn squarely into position on the flywheel. Each bolt must be tightened one turn at a time to avoid bending the clutch cover flange. Torque the bolts to 30–40 ft lbs.

1972–1976

1. Remove the transmission.

2. Remove the starter.

3. Remove the throwout bearing and sleeve assembly.

4. Remove the bell housing.

5. Mark the clutch cover, pressure plate and the flywheel with a center punch so that these parts can be later installed in the same position on the flywheel.

6. Remove the clutch cover-to-flywheel attaching bolts. When removing these bolts, loosen them in rotation, one or two turns at a time, until the spring tension is released. The clutch cover is a steel stamping which could be warped by improper removal procedures, resulting in clutch chatter when reused.

7. Remove the clutch assembly from the flywheel. Install in reverse order of removal referring to the paragraph at the end of the removal and installation procedure for the V6 clutch.

Clutch Pedal Adjustment— Prior to 1972

As the clutch facings wear out the free travel of the clutch pedal diminishes. When sufficient wear occurs, the pedal clearance must be adjusted to 1–1½ in.

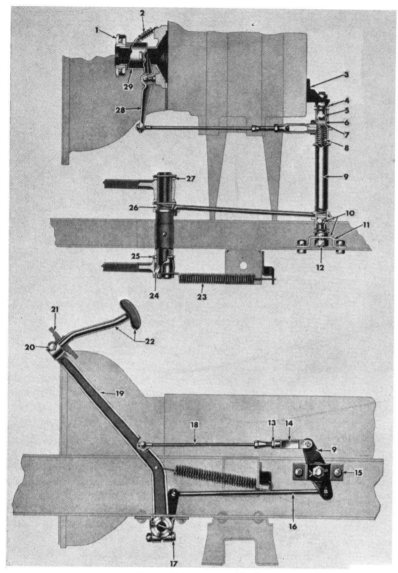

1. Clutch release bearing
2. Carrier spring
3. Bracket
4. Dust seal
5. Ball stud
6. Pad
7. Retainer
8. Control tube spring
9. Control lever and tube
10. Ball stud and bracket
11. Frame bracket
12. Ball stud nut
13. Yoke lock nut
14. Adjusting yoke
15. Bolt
16. Pedal release rod
17. Pedal clamp bolt
18. Control cable
19. Clutch pedal
20. Screw and lockwasher
21. Draft pad
22. Pedal pad and shank
23. Retracting spring
24. Pedal to shaft key
25. Washer
26. Pedal shaft
27. Master cylinder tie bar
28. Control lever
29. Bearing carrier

Clutch linkage assembly for Jeeps made prior to 1972

The free pedal clearance is adjusted by lengthening or shortening the clutch fork cable. To make this adjustment, loosen the jam nut on the cable clevis and lengthen or shorten the cable to obtain the proper clearance at the pedal pad, then tighten the jam nut.

NOTE: *On some older Jeeps, a side movement of the clutch and brake pedals may develop. This is the result of wear on the pedals, shafts, and bushings. One way to compensate for this wear is to install a pedal slack adjuster kit.*

Clutch Pressure Plate Adjustment—Prior to 1972

1. Place the thickness spacers between the pressure plate face and the clutch adjusting fixture. Locate the spacers under the pressure plate levers and at the center of the pressure plate face.

2. With the spacers properly installed, bolt the pressure plate to the adjusting fixture. Draw the bolts down evenly a little at a time until they are tight.

3. Using the proper gauge length check the lever adjustment.

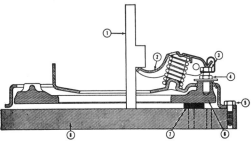

Adjusting the clutch fingers with a spacer installed between the pressure plate and the clutch adjusting fixture

1. Gauge	5. Mounting bolt
2. Clutch lever	6. Clutch pressure plate
3. Adjusting screw	7. Thickness spacer
4. Locknut	8. Clutch adjusting fixture

4. Lever adjustment can be altered by removing the lever clips, loosening the locknut and turning the adjusting screw in or out as required.

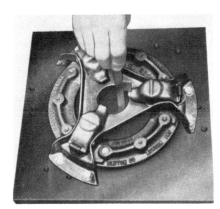

Checking the clutch finger adjustment with a gauge, the pressure plate assembly being mounted on a clutch adjusting fixture

Clutch Adjusting Fixture Data

Make	Disc Diameter	Spacer Thickness	Gauge Length
Auburn	9¼ in.	0.285 in.	1¹⁵⁄₁₆ in.
Rockford	8½ in.	0.305 in.	1¹⁵⁄₁₆ in
Auburn	8½ in.	Not Required	1¹⁵⁄₁₆ in.

Pedal Height Adjustment—1972 Only

The clutch pedal has an adjustable stop located on the pedal support bracket directly behind the instrument cluster.

Adjust the stop to provide the specified clearance between the top of the pedal pad and the closest point on the bare floor pan. The distance must be 8 in.

Control Cable Adjustment—1972 Only

1. Lift up the clutch pedal against the pedal support bracket stop.
2. Unhook the clutch fork return spring.
3. Loosen the ball adjusting nut until some cable slack exists.
4. Adjust the ball adjusting nut until the slack is removed from the cable and the clutch throwout bearing contacts the pressure plate fingers.

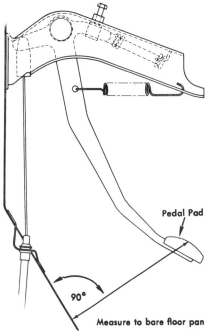

Clutch pedal height adjustment on a 1972 only model

5. Back off the ball adjusting nut ¾ of a turn to provide the proper amount of free play. Tighten the jam nut.
6. Hook the clutch fork return spring.

Clutch Linkage Adjustment—1973–76

1. Adjust the bellcrank outer support bracket to provide approximately ⅛ in. of bellcrank end play.
2. Lift up the clutch pedal against the pedal stop.
3. On the clutch push rod (pedal to bellcrank) adjust the lower ball pivot assembly onto or off the rod (as required) to position the bellcrank inner lever parallel to the front face of the clutch housing (slightly forward from vertical). There is

no lower ball pivot assembly on 1976 models.

4. Adjust the clutch fork release rod (bellcrank to release fork) to obtain the maximum specified clutch pedal free play of ¾ in. on 1973–74 models and 1 in. on 1975–76 models.

Automatic Transmission

The automatic transmission used in all Jeep vehicles is Turbo Hydra-Matic 400, produced by the General Motors Corporation.

Pan Removal

Since the Turbo Hydra-Matic transmission doesn't have a drain plug, the fluid is drained by loosening the pan and allowing the fluid to run out over the top of the pan.

To avoid making a really big mess, place a drain pan under one corner of the transmission pan and remove the two attaching screws nearest to either side of that particular corner. One by one, and in a progressive manner, loosen all of the other attaching screws holding the transmission pan, leaving the ones farthest away from the "drain" corner tighter than the rest. When the majority of the fluid has drained, hold the pan up with one hand, remove the remaining attaching screws and carefully lower the pan. There will be some automatic transmission fluid left in the pan, so be careful not to spill any.

Clean the pan in a suitable solvent and wipe it dry with a clean, lint-free cloth.

Install the pan in the reverse order of removal using a new pan-to-transmission gasket and torquing the bolts in an alternating pattern to 10–13 ft lbs.

Filter Service

The filter is located directly under the oil pan.

There are filter replacement kits available for changing the transmission fluid filter. The kit includes a new filter, pan gasket and, in most cases, a new rubber O-ring to seal the intake pipe. If a new O-ring is not provided, leave the old one in place. If you can see that the old O-ring is cracked or damaged in any way, it is necessary to replace it with a new one, which can be obtained at a Jeep or G.M. dealer.

1. Remove the bottom pan and gasket.
2. Remove the oil filter retainer bolt and remove the oil filter assembly from the transmission.
3. Remove the intake pipe from the filter and the intake pipe-to-case O-ring, if it is to be replaced.
4. Coat the new rubber O-ring with transmission fluid and position it in the groove at the inlet opening.
5. Slide the inlet pipe onto the new filter and position the filter on the transmission, guiding the inlet pipe in place.
6. Install the filter retaining bolt and tighten securely.
7. Install the bottom pan.

Transmission Shift Linkage Adjustment

1. Remove the cotter pin, flat washer and spring washer from the adjusting block at the transmission end of the shift rod and remove the block from the shift lever.
2. Make sure that the transmission shift lever is in the Neutral detent position.
3. Place the selector lever in the Neutral position and hold it firmly forward against the stop.
4. Loosen the locknuts at either end of the adjusting block and position the block on the shift rod, so that it may be freely inserted on the transmission shift lever without moving the lever. Tighten the nuts to 6–12 ft lbs torque.
5. Operate the selector lever to be sure that the transmission detents are engaging in their respective positions.

Transfer Case

Removal and Installation

PRIOR TO 1972—SPICER 18

The transfer case can be removed without removing the transmission.

1. Drain the transfer case and transmission and replace the drain plugs.

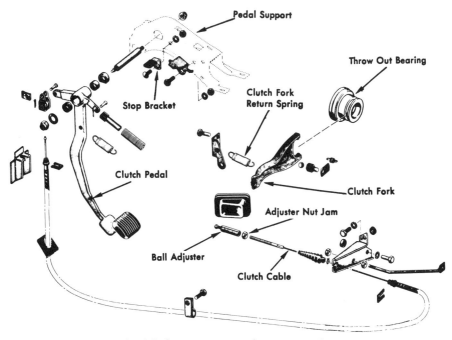

Clutch linkage components for a 1972 model

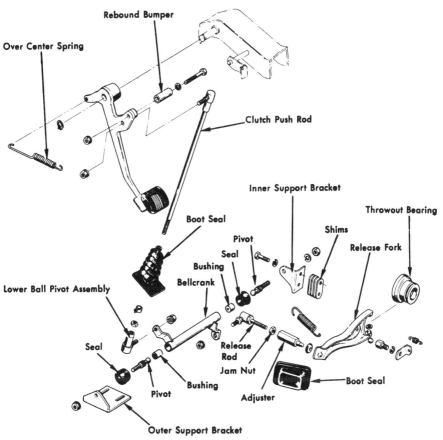

Clutch linkage components for 1973–75 models.
There is no lower ball pivot assembly on 1976 models.

2. Disconnect the brake cable.

3. Disconnect the front and rear propeller shafts at the transfer case.

4. Disconnect the speedometer cable at the transfer case.

5. Disconnect the transfer case shift levers. On vehicles equipped with two shift levers loosen the set screw and remove the pivot pin. Use a screw driver to pry the shift lever springs away from the shift levers. On models equipped with a single shift lever remove the pivot pin cotter key and the adjusting rod attaching nut to remove the shift lever.

6. Remove the cover plate on the rear face of the transfer case or power take-off shift unit. Remove the cotter key, nut and washer from the transmission main shaft.

7. If possible, remove the transfer case main drive gear from the transmission main shaft. If it is not possible, continue on.

8. Remove the transmission-to-transfer case mounting bracket bolt and nut.

9. Remove the transmission-to-transfer case attaching bolts.

10. Remove the transfer case. If the transfer case main drive gear has not been removed in step 7, proceed as follows: Brace the end of the transmission main shaft so that it cannot be moved in the transmission, then pull the transfer case to the rear to loosen the gear. Remove the gear. When separating the two housings, be careful that the transmission main shaft bearing, which bears in both housings, remains in the transmission case.

NOTE: *If the transfer case is being removed from the transmission with the two units out of the vehicle, use the above procedure starting from step 6 and replacing step 10 with the following procedure:*

10A. Remove the transmission shift housing. Install a transmission mainshaft retaining plate to prevent the mainshaft from pulling out of the transmission case. Should this tool be unavailable, loop a piece of wire around the mainshaft directly in back of the mainshaft second speed gear. Install the transmission shift housing right and left front attaching bolts part way into the transmission case. Twist the wire and attach each end to one of the screws. Tighten the wire. With the mainshaft securely in place, support the transfer case and with a rawhide mallet or

Transmission main shaft retaining plate installed for removing the transfer case from the transmission

brass drift and hammer, then tap lightly on the end of the mainshaft to loosen the gear and separate the two units.

11. Install in the reverse order of removal taking note of the following: When installing the rear adapter plate on a four-speed transmission, be sure that the cap screw heads do not protrude beyond the adapter plate face and that they do not interfere with the transfer case fitting tightly against the rear adapter plate. Also, when installing the transfer case gear on the transmission rear splined drive shaft, tighten the large gear nut securely and insert the cotter pin. Sink the cotter pin well into the nut slots so it will clear the power take-off drive (if so equipped).

1972–1975—Spicer 20

1. Remove the transfer case shift lever knob and trim ring and boot.

2. Remove the transfer case shift lever.

3. Lift and support the vehicle.

4. Drain the transfer case lubricant.

5. Mark the yokes for reference during assembly and disconnect the front and rear driveshafts from the transfer case.

6. Install the transfer case drain plug.

7. Disconnect the parking brake cable at the equalizer and mounting bracket.

8. Disconnect the speedometer cable.

9. Remove the screws which attach the

transfer case to the transmission. Install two 16, ⅜ x 4 in. threaded dowel pins, one on each side of the case.

10. Remove the transfer case.

11. Remove the gasket between the transmission and the transfer case.

12. Place a new gasket on the dowel pins in the transmission case before installing the transfer case back onto the transmission.

13. Shift the transfer case to 4WD Low position.

14. Position the transfer case on the dowel pins.

15. Rotate the transfer case output shaft until the gears engage with the output gear on the transmission. Slide the transfer case forward to the transmission.

NOTE: *Be sure that the transfer case fits flush against the transmission. Severe damage will result if the transfer case bolts are tightened while the transfer case is binding.*

16. Install one attaching screw. Remove the dowel pins and install all of the remaining attaching screws.

17. Connect the driveshafts in the same positions from which they were removed.

18. Connect the speedometer cable and parking brake cable.

19. Fill the transfer case with the proper amount of lubricant. See Chapter 1.

20. Lower the vehicle.

21. Install the transfer case lever, trim boot and lever knob.

1976—Spicer 20

1. Remove the shift lever knob, trim ring, and boot.

2. Remove the transmission access cover from the floorpan.

3. Drain the lubricant from the transfer case.

4. Disconnect the torque reaction bracket from the frame crossmember, if so equipped.

5. Support the engine and transmission by placing a jackstand under the clutch housing.

6. Remove the rear frame crossmember.

7. Mark the driveshaft yokes for reference during assembly and disconnect the front and rear driveshafts from the transfer case.

8. Disconnect the speedometer cable from the transfer case.

9. Remove the bolts attaching the transfer case to the transmission and remove the transfer case. Remove the gasket which goes between the transmission and transfer case.

NOTE: *There is one transfer case attaching bolt located at the bottom right corner of the transmission that must be removed from the front end of the case.*

10. Install the transmission-to-transfer case gasket on the transmission.

11. Shift the transfer case into the 4WD low position.

12. Install a ⅜-16 × 4 in. dowel pin on each side of the transmission to assist in guiding the transfer case into place during installation.

13. Position the transfer case on the dowel pins and slide the case forward until it seats against the transmission. It may be necessary to rotate the transfer case output shaft until the mainshaft gear on the transmission engages the rear output shaft gear in the transfer case.

NOTE: *Make sure that the transfer case is flush against the transmission. The case could be cracked if the attaching bolts are tightened while the transfer case is cocked or binded.*

14. Install two transfer case attaching bolts, but do not tighten them completely.

15. Remove the dowel pins and install the remaining attaching bolts, tightening them all to 30 ft lbs.

16. Fill the transfer case with SAE 80W-90 gear lubricant (API GL-4).

17. Assemble the remaining components in the reverse order of removal.

Quadra-Trac—1976 CJ-7

NOTE: *Complete assembly removal is normally not required except when the front output shaft, front annular bearing, transmission output shaft seals or the transfer case (front housing) require service. To service the chain, drive sprocket, differential unit, diaphragm control system, needle bearing, thrust washer or rear output shaft, the rear half of the Quadra-Trac transfer case can be removed, giving access to these components without removing the unit from the vehicle.*

Remove the Quadra-Trac transfer case rear cover assembly in the following manner:

1. Raise and support the vehicle.

2. Remove the reduction unit, if so equipped, as follows:

a. Loosen the bolts attaching the reduction unit to the transfer case cover;

b. Move the reduction unit rearward just far enough to allow the oil to drain from the unit;

c. Disconnect the shift linkage at the reduction unit control lever;

d. After all the oil has drained out, remove the bolts attaching the reduction unit to the transfer case cover;

e. Move the reduction unit rearward to clear the transmission output shaft and pinion cage which is attached to the transfer case drive sprocket.

NOTE: *The pinion cage should not be removed if the transfer case cover assembly is to be removed. The pinion cage assembly may be removed separately for inspection or replacement by removing the snap-ring securing it to the sprocket and sliding the cage rearward.*

3. Remove the transfer case drain plug and drain the lubricant.

4. Mark the rear output shaft yoke and driveshaft universal joint for reference during installation and disconnect the rear driveshaft from the transfer case.

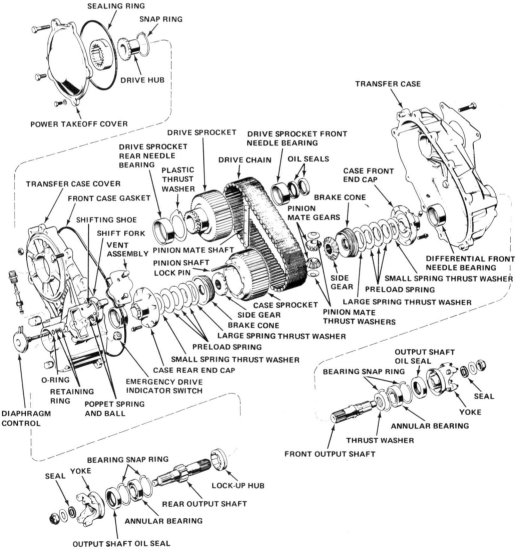

Exploded view of the Warner Quadra-Trac transfer case without the optional reduction unit

5. Identify the diaphragm control vacuum hoses for assembly reference and disconnect the hoses, switch wire, and speedometer cable. Remove the emergency drive indicator switch.

6. Disconnect the parking brake cable guide from the pivot at the right-side frame rail.

7. Support the bellhousing with a jackstand and remove the rear crossmember.

8. Remove the bolts attaching the case cover assembly to the case.

9. Slide the cover assembly backward and off the front output shaft and transmission output shaft.

Disassemble the transfer case cover assembly as follows:

10. Remove the rear output shaft loke.

11. If not equipped with a reduction unit, remove the power takeoff cover from the rear of the transfer case cover. Remove the sealing ring from the transfer case cover.

12. Position the cover and drive sprocket on a $2 \times 4 \times 6$ in. block of wood.

13. If not equipped with a reduction unit, remove the drive hub and sleeve from the drive sprocket rear splines by expanding the internal snap-ring. The expanding tabs are accessible through a slot in the outside edge of the drive sleeve.

14. If equipped with a reduction unit, remove the pinion cage snap-ring and carrier assembly.

15. Remove the case cover from the drive sprocket and differential. The cover, rear output shaft, bearings, and seal, drive sprocket rear needle bearing, and lockup hub may be serviced without disassembling any farther.

16. Slide the drive sprocket toward the differential unit and remove the chain.

Transfer case cover assembly is as follows:

17. Position the drive sprocket on the block of wood.

18. Position the differential assembly about 2 in. from the drive sprocket with the front end down.

19. Install the drive chain on the drive

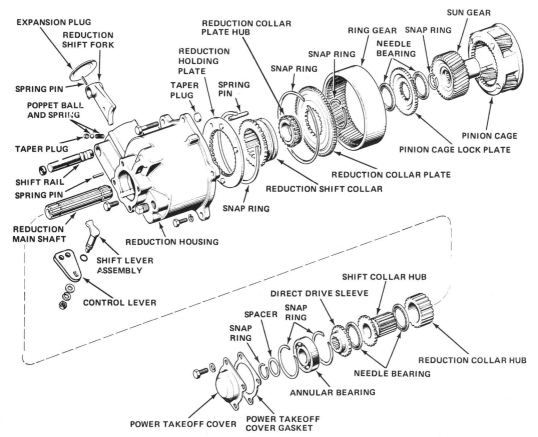

Exploded view of the optional reduction unit for a Warner Quadra-Trac transfer case

sprocket and differential assembly. Make sure that the chain is engaged with the teeth in the sprocket and differential and that all slack is removed.

20. Insert the rear output shaft into the differential.

21. Move the lockup hub rearward in the case cover. Lubricate the drive sprocket thrust washer with petroleum jelly and position the washer on the case cover.

22. Align and position the case cover on the drive sprocket and differential. The output shaft may require slight rotation to align with the lockup hub. Make sure that the drive sprocket thrust washer is not dispositioned.

23. If equipped with a reduction unit, install the pinion cage on the drive sprocket rear splines. Be sure that the retaining snap-ring seats completely in its groove.

24. If the unit is not equipped with a reduction unit, assemble the drive hub, drive sleeve, and snap-ring, and install on the drive sprocket rear splines. Be certain that the retaining snap-ring seats completely in the grove.

25. Rotate the drive sleeve or pinion cage to be sure that the drive sprocket thrust washer did not become misplaced. The unit should turn easily with no binding.

26. If the unit is not equipped with a reduction unit, install the power takeoff sealing ring and cover. Tighten the attaching screws to 20 ft lbs.

27. Install the speedometer gear on the rear output shaft.

28. Install the rear output shaft oil seal, tapping it into place with a wooden dowel and hammer.

29. Install rear yoke and nut, tightening the nut to 120 ft lbs.

Install the rear cover assembly of the Quadra-Trac transfer case as follows:

30. Clean the oil groove around the perimeter of the rear cover and install the sealing ring.

31. Install the $\frac{3}{8}$-16 $\times$ 2 in. long pilot studs in the transfer case front housing.

32. Move the rear cover assembly forward to mesh with the front output shaft and transmission output shaft. It may be necessary to turn the rear output shaft so the two sets of splines engage.

33. Move the cover assembly forward until it seats on the front case housing. Remove the pilot studs and install the cover-to-case attaching bolts, tightening them to 15–25 ft lbs.

34. Install the emergency drive signal switch. Connect the signal switch wire, diaphragm control vacuum hoses, and the speedometer cable.

35. Connect the rear driveshaft to the transfer case. It may be necessary to jack up the rear wheels to properly align the driveshaft universal joint and the yoke on the transfer case.

36. Connect the parking brake cable guide to the pivot.

37. Install the reduction unit, if so equipped, as follows:

a. Clean the sealing ring groove in the rear cover and install the sealing ring;

b. Lift the reduction unit into position and mesh the caged pinion with the sun gear inner splines with the transmission output shaft splines;

c. Move the reduction unit forward until it contacts the sealing ring;

d. Install the attaching bolts, tightening them alternately to 15 ft lbs;

e. Connect the shift lever linkage at the reduction unit control lever.

38. Install the rear crossmember and remove the jackstand supporting the engine and transmission.

39. Install the proper amount of the specified lubricant mixture. It is very important to refer to Chapter 1 with regard to the lubricant mixture.

40. Lower the vehicle.

Transfer Case Overhaul

SPICER MODEL 18

1. Remove the output shaft nuts and washers and remove the rear output shaft flange together with the brake drum, if so equipped. Remove the front output shaft flange also.

2. Remove the bottom cover attaching screws and remove the cover.

3. Remove the lockplate retaining screw and lockwasher and remove the lockplate.

4. Drive the intermediate shaft to the rear of the case with a brass drift and hammer. Do not lose the thrust washers located on the ends of the shaft.

Exploded view of a Spicer Model 18 transfer case with a transmission brake and single shift lever. Some models have two shift levers.

1. Companion flange and oil seal guard	22. Front output shaft bearing cap
2. Parking brake drum	23. Breather
3. Parking brake assembly	24. Shift rod oil seals
4. Parking brake actuating lever	25. Driveshaft yoke
5. Bearing cap oil seal	26. Oil seal gasket
6. Parking brake actuating lever pivot stud	27. Bolt
7. Rear bearing cap	28. Lockwasher
8. Rear bearing cap shims	29. 4WD shift rod
9. Bolt	30. 4WD shift fork
10. Lockwasher	31. Low and 2WD shift fork
11. Bolt	32. Filler plug
12. Rear cover	33. Mainshaft gear
13. Rear cover gasket	34. Mainshaft washer
14. Intermediate shaft lockplate	35. Thrust washer
15. Transfer case housing	36. Intermediate gear
16. Low and 2WD shift rod	37. Shaft bearing snap-ring
17. Poppet plug	38. Output clutch shaft bearing
18. Poppet spring	39. Driveshaft companion flange nut
19. Poppet ball	40. Washer
20. Shift rod interlock	41. Output clutch shaft
21. Bearing cap gasket	42. Output clutch shaft gear
	43. Output shaft gear snap-ring
	44. Thrust washer

45. Output shaft gear
46. Output shaft sliding gear
47. Pilot bushing
48. Output shaft
49. Bearing cone and rollers
50. Output shaft bearing cup
51. Speedometer drive gear
52. Needle bearings
53. Needle bearing spacers
54. Intermediate shaft
55. Drain plug
56. Bottom cover gasket
57. Mainshaft nut
58. Bottom cover
59. Speedometer driven gear sleeve
60. Speedometer driven gear
61. Speedometer driven gear bushing
62. Backing plate gasket
63–66. Bolts
67. Lockwasher
68. Nut
69. Output shaft felt seal

5. Remove the intermediate gear, two thrust washers, needle bearings, and spacers, through the bottom of the case.

6. Remove the poppet plugs, springs, and balls on both sides of the front bearing cap. Shift the 4WD shift lever into the 4WD position (shaft forward).

7. Remove the front bearing cap retaining screws and lockwashers, and remove the cap, clutch shaft, bearing, clutch gear, fork, and shift rod as an assembly. Be careful not to lose the interlock which floats between the shift rods.

8. Remove the attaching screws and lockwashers and remove the brake backing plate assembly, if so equipped, and the rear output cap with the speedometer gear as an assembly. Don't lose or mix the shims.

9. Strike the front end of the output shaft with a soft hammer to drive the rear bearing cup from the case. Tap a wedge-shaped chisel between the output shaft gear and the bearing cone to wedge the front bearing cone and roller assembly from its seat on the front output shaft.

10. Place a spacer on the output shaft

between the front bearing and the output shaft gear.

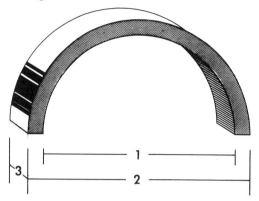

Diagram of a spacer used to remove the front output shaft bearing on a Spicer Model 18 transfer case

1. Output shaft diameter
2. No more than bearing outside diameter
3. Distance between output shaft gear and bearing

NOTE: *A suitable spacer can be fabricated from any number of materials, such as a block of wood, small bolts, a length of pipe cut in half lengthwise, etc. Special tool W-141 is specified for the job, but the availability of the tool is questionable since the Spicer Model 18 transfer case was last used in the CJ in the 1971 model year.*

11. With the spacer in position, use a soft hammer to strike against the rear end of the output shaft to remove the front bearing cup from the boss of the case.

12. Spread the snap-ring which was behind the bearing cup and slide it forward slightly so that it's out of its groove.

13. Drive the shaft through the rear of the case with a soft hammer and drift. As the shaft is removed, the snap-ring, gears, and thrust washer will come off the shaft and fall into the case. Remove these parts from the bottom.

14. Remove the rear bearing cone and roller assembly from the output shaft by striking the end of the shaft lightly against a block of wood.

15. Remove the set screw in the sliding gearshift fork and remove the shift rod.

Disassemble the front bearing cap assembly as follows:

16. Pry the output shaft yoke seal and shift rod oil seals from their bosses with a small screwdriver or other suitable tool.

17. Remove the set screw from the shitt-ing fork and shifting rod. The clutch gear and shifting fork can be removed together.

18. Remove the output clutch shaft assembly by carefully pressing it through the bearing.

19. Remove the bearing retaining snap-ring and the bearing.

Assembly of the Spicer Model 18 transfer case is basically the reversal of disassembly, with the following items requiring special attention:

1. Use a length of copper tubing (any soft metal pipe will do), to press against or strike with a hammer to install the bearing cone and roller assemblies onto the output shaft to prevent damage.

2. When installing the intermediate gear on early model Spicer 18 transfer cases (early models have a 1⅛ in. diameter intermediate shaft and caged needle bearings), insert the bearings in the gear, support the front thrust washer with a pilot tool, position the gears and rear thrust washer, and insert the shaft from the rear of the case.

3. When installing the intermediate gear on later model Spicer 18 transfer cases, which have a 1¼ in. diameter intermediate shaft and individual rollers and spacers, a dummy shaft is required. The dummy shaft should be slightly smaller in diameter than the intermediate shaft and a little shorter than the width of the intermediate gear. First, load the bearing rollers and spacers in the gear, using the dummy shaft to support them. Then, supporting the front thrust washer with your fingers, position the gears and rear thrust washer and insert the intermediate shaft from the rear of the case, driving out the dummy shaft in the same action.

4. After the rear bearing cap assembly is installed, check the end-play of the mainshaft which determines the preload adjustment of the tapered roller bearings. The end-play should be 0.004–0.008 in. The end-play is adjusted by the placement of selective shims between the cap and the case. Shims are available in 0.003, 0.010, and 0.031 in. thicknesses.

5. Do not install the rear cap oil seal until the bearings are correctly adjusted, as previously outlined. Tap the seals into place with a soft hammer and a piece of wooden dowel.

6. When installing the driveshaft yokes

on the output shafts, look for felt seals in each oil seal guard. The oil seal guard is part of each yoke. Felt seals should be installed if they are not present.

SPICER MODEL 20

1. Remove the shift lever assembly.

2. Remove the bottom cover and gasket.

3. Remove the bolts attaching rear bearing cap assembly to the case and remove the assembly.

4. Remove the intermediate shaft lockplate.

5. Drive the intermediate shaft out the rear of the case, using a soft drift pin and a plastic hammer.

6. Remove the intermediate gear assembly and thrust washers from the case.

7. Remove the front output shaft nut and washer and remove the driveshaft yoke. It may be necessary to use a puller to get the yoke off the output shaft.

8. Pry the front oil seal from the boss in the case.

9. Remove the cover plate attaching screws and remove the cover together with the front output shaft rear bearing.

NOTE: *Be careful not to damage the gaskets and shims behind the cover plate while removing it.*

10. Move the rear output shaft shift rail to the rear.

11. Remove the rear output shaft shift fork setscrew.

12. Remove the poppet ball and spring plugs.

13. Insert a punch through the pin hole in the rod and rotate the rear output shaft rod ¼ of a turn counterclockwise and pull the rod out of the case. When the shift fork is free of the rod, catch the poppet ball and spring from under the shift rod in your hand.

14. Remove the front shift rod housing attaching screws and slide the housing off the remaining shift rail.

15. Remove the rear output shaft sliding gear and shift fork.

16. Drive the front output shaft out the rear of the case with a brass drift and hammer. Support the case on blocks of wood when removing the shaft.

17. Remove the gears, spacer, and bearing from the case.

18. Rotate the shift rod to expose the setscrew, remove the setscrew and pull the shift rod out.

19. Remove the shift rail thimbles using a ⅜ in. drive ⁷⁄₁₆ in. socket and an extension to drive the thimbles from the case.

20. Remove the arbor tool, thrust washers, spacers, and roller bearings from the intermediate gear.

21. Remove the front output shaft front bearing cup with a brass drift and hammer.

22. Remove the shift rod seals from the housing.

23. Remove the front output shaft rear bearing. Use the sliding gear as a support. Mount the gear in a vise with the shaft lever groove facing downward. Insert the front output shaft through the rear splines and drive the shaft out of the bearing with a brass drift and a hammer.

24. Wash all of the parts in suitable solvent. Clean all gasket material from the surfaces and dry all of the components with compressed air. Inspect all bearings, thrust washers, shafts and gears for excessive wear, pitting, and scoring. Replace any worn or damaged parts.

25. To begin assembly of the Spicer Model 20 transfer case, install the front output shaft front bearing cup in the case. Seat the cup flush with the exterior surface of the case.

26. Install the shift rail thimbles.

27. Install the shift rod housing. Tighten the attaching bolts to 30 ft lbs.

28. Support the front output shaft rear bearing on a 1¼ in. socket or similar tool and install the shaft into the bearing using a brass drift and hammer.

29. Install the front output shaft shift rail poppet ball and spring.

30. Compress the ball and spring and install the front output shaft rail part way in the case.

31. Install the front output shaft shift fork from the front of the case and slide the shift rail through the shift fork.

32. Align the set screw holes in the shift fork and rail and install the set screw. Tighten the set screw to 14 ft lbs.

33. Install the front output shaft front bearing, bearing spacer, front output shaft sliding gear, and front output shaft gear. Make sure that the shift fork groove in the sliding gear faces the rear of the case.

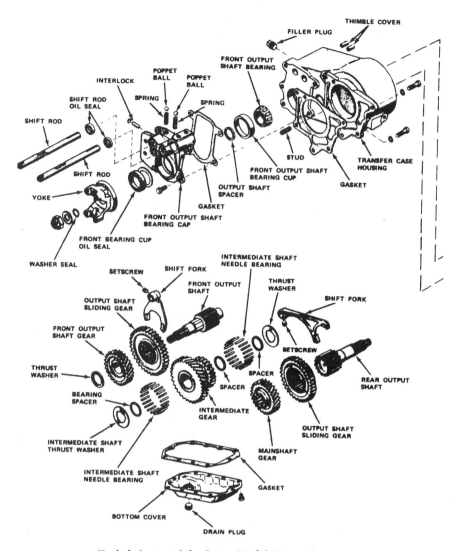

Exploded view of the Spicer Model 20 transfer case

34. Install the front output shaft through the gears, spacer, and bearing.

35. Support the case on blocks of wood and drive the front output shaft into the front housing using a brass drift and hammer. Make sure that the bearing is seated against the shoulder on the front output shaft.

36. Install the front output shaft rear bearing cup, using a block of wood and a hammer.

37. Install the rear bearing, cover plate, and shims. Tighten the cover plate attaching bolts to 30 ft lbs.

38. At this point it is necessary to check the front output shaft end-play in the following manner:

a. Seat the rear bearing cup against the cover plate by striking the end of the front output shaft with a lead hammer or steel hammer cushioned with a block of wood;

b. Mount a dial indicator on the front bearing cap and position the stylus against the end of the output shaft;

c. Pry the shaft rearward, then zero the dial indicator. Pry the shaft forward and observe the dial indicator reading. The end-play should be 0.001–0.003 in.;

The end-play is adjusted by adding or

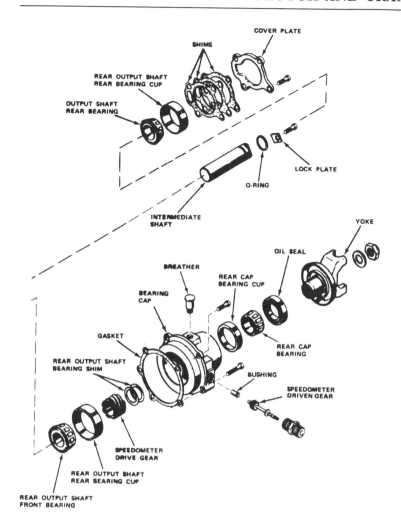

COVER PLATE

SHIMS

REAR OUTPUT SHAFT
REAR BEARING CUP

OUTPUT SHAFT
REAR BEARING

LOCK PLATE

O-RING

INTERMEDIATE
SHAFT

YOKE

OIL SEAL

BREATHER

REAR CAP
BEARING CUP

BEARING
CAP

GASKET

REAR CAP
BEARING

REAR OUTPUT SHAFT
BEARING SHIM

BUSHING

SPEEDOMETER
DRIVEN GEAR

SPEEDOMETER
DRIVE GEAR

REAR OUTPUT SHAFT
REAR BEARING CUP

REAR OUTPUT SHAFT
FRONT BEARING

subtracting between the cover plate and case. If shims are added, it is necessary to seat the rear bearing cup as outlined in Step "a," above, before rechecking endplay.

39. Install the rear output shaft shift rail poppet ball and spring in the shift rod housing.

40. Compress the ball and spring and install the rear output shaft shift rail partway in the case. Before installing the shift rail, make sure that the front output shaft shift rail is in the Neutral position and the interlock is seated in the housing bore.

41. Install the rear output shaft shift fork and sliding gear. Make sure that the

shift fork groove in the gear faces the rear of the case.

42. Align the set screw holes in the fork and rail and install the set screw, tightening it to 14 ft lbs.

43. Assemble the intermediate gear needle bearings and spacers in the intermediate gear. Use either an arbor tool (which will work best), or hold the bearings in place with a light coating of petroleum jelly or grease.

44. Install the intermediate gear thrust washers in the case tangs aligned with the grooves in the case. The rear washer can be held in place with the intermediate shaft started into the case and the front washer

can be held in position with a dab of petroleum jelly.

45. Install the O-ring on the intermediate shaft and install the intermediate gear in the case. Drive the intermediate shaft into the intermediate gear with a soft hammer. This will force the arbor tool, if one is used, out of the gear through the front of the case.

46. Install the intermediate shaft lockplate, identification tag, lockwasher, and bolt, tightening the bolt to 14 ft lbs.

47. Install the rear bearing cap assembly with a new gasket, and slide the rear output shaft through the gear, tightening the bearing cap bolts to 30 ft lbs.

48. Tap the rear yoke seal in place.

49. Install the front driveshaft yoke and tighten the locknut to 240 ft lbs.

50. Install the bottom cover and gasket and tighten the retaining bolts to 14 ft lbs.

51. Install the shift rod oil seals.

52. Install the transfer case in the vehicle after filling with lubricant.

Transmission and Transfer Case Application Chart

Year	Model	Transmission					Transfer Case	
		Make	Model	Speeds	Shifter	Make	Model
1953–1957	CJ-3B CJ-5 CJ-6	Warner	T-90C	3	Floor	Spicer	18
1958–1964	CJ-3B CJ-5 CJ-6	Warner	T-90C	3	Floor	Spicer	18
	CJ-5 CJ-6	Warner	T-98A	4	Floor	Spicer	18
1965–1968①	CJ-5 CJ-6 CJ-5A CJ-6A	Warner	T-90C	3	Floor Steering Column	Spicer	18
	CJ-5 CJ-6	Warner	T-98A	4	Floor	Spicer	18
All years with V6 engine	CJ-5 CJ-6 CJ-5A CJ-6A	Warner	AS7-T86AA	3	Floor Steering Column	Spicer	18
	Late CJ-5 CJ-6	Warner	T-14A	3	Floor	Spicer	18
1972–1975	CJ-5	Warner	T-14A	3	Floor	Spicer	20
	CJ-6	Warner	T-15A②	3	Floor		
		Warner	T-18③	4	Floor		

Transmission and Transfer Case Application Chart (cont.)

Year	Model	Transmission				Transfer Case	
		Make	*Model*	*Speeds*	*Shifter*	*Make*	*Model*
1976	CJ-5, CJ-7	Warner	T-150	3	Floor	Spicer	20
		Warner	T-18③	4	Floor	Spicer	20
		GM Turbo Hydra-Matic	400④	3	Steering Column	Warner	Quadra-Trac⑤

① Vehicles with the F-Head engine only
② Installed on the 304 V8 only
③ The T-18 4 speed transmission was an option for all engines in 1972. From 1973–76, it was only installed on the 232 and 258 Sixes.

④ CJ-7 with 258 six or 304 V8 only
⑤ With automatic transmission only

7 · Drive Train

Driveline

FRONT AND REAR DRIVESHAFTS

Removal and Installation

In order to remove the front and rear driveshafts, unscrew the holding nuts from the universal joint's U-bolts, remove the U-bolts and slide the shaft forward or backward toward the slip joint. The shaft can then be removed from the end yokes and removed from under the vehicle.

Each shaft is equipped with a splined slip joint at one end to allow for variations in length caused by vehicle spring action. Some slip joints are marked with arrows at the spline and sleeve yoke. When installing, align the arrows. If the slip joint is not marked with arrows, align the yokes at the

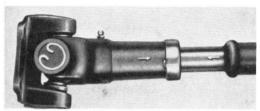

Alignment markings on a drive shaft. Universal joint is of the snap ring type

front and rear of the shaft in the same horizontal plane. This is necessary in order to avoid vibration in the drive train.

U-JOINTS

All the universal joints used are similar in construction except that some use U-bolts and others use snap rings. This difference is only in the attachment of the joints.

The universal joints have needle bearings and are designed so that correct as-

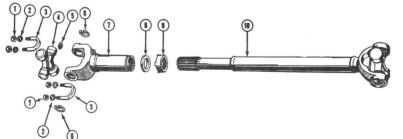

1. U-bolt nut
2. U-bolt washer
3. U-bolt
4. Universal joint journal
5. Lubrication fitting
6. Snap ring
7. Universal joint steeve yoke
8. Rubber washer
9. Dust cap
10. Propeller shaft tube

Drive shaft and U-bolt type universal joint assembly

192

sembly is very simple. No hand fitting or special tools are required.

Removal and Installation

SNAP RING

1. Remove the snap rings by pinching the ends together with a pair of pliers. If the rings do not readily snap out of the groove, tap the end of the bearing lightly to relieve pressure against the rings.

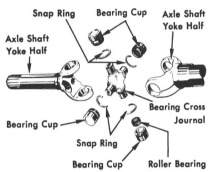

An exploded view of a Cardan Cross universal joint used in 1972–1976 models (snap-ring type)

2. After removing the snap rings, press on the end of one bearing until the opposite bearing is pushed from the yoke arm. Turn the joint over and press the first bearing back out of that arm by pressing on the exposed end of the journal shaft. To drive it out, use a soft ground drift with a flat face, about 1/32 in. smaller in diameter than the hole in the yoke; otherwise there is danger of damaging the bearing.

3. Repeat this procedure for the other two bearings, then lift out the journal assembly by sliding it to one side.

4. Wash all parts in cleaning solvent and inspect the parts after cleaning. Replace the journal assembly if it is worn extensively. Make sure that the grease channel in each journal trunnion is open.

5. Pack all of the bearing caps 1/3 full of grease and install the rollers (bearings).

6. Press one of the cap/bearing assemblies into one of the yoke arms just far enough so that the cap will remain in position.

7. Place the journal in position in the installed cap, with a cap/bearing assembly placed on the opposite end.

8. Position the free cap so that when it is driven from the opposite end it will be inserted into the opening of the yoke. Re-

peat this operation for the other two bearings.

9. Install the retaining clips. If the U-joint binds when it is assembled, tap the arms of the yoke slightly to relieve any pressure on the bearings at the end of the journal.

U-BOLT

1. Removal of the attaching U-bolt releases one set of bearing races. Slide the drive shaft into the yoke flange to remove that set of bearing races being careful not to lose the rollers (bearings).

2. After removal of the first set of bearings, release the other set by pinching the ends of the snap rings with pliers and removing them from the sleeve yoke. Should the rings fail to snap readily from the groove, tap the end of the bearing lightly, to relieve the pressure against them.

3. Press on the end of one bearing, until the opposite bearing is pushed out of the yoke arm.

4. Turn the universal joint over and press the first bearing out by pressing on the exposed end of the journal assembly. Use a soft ground drift with a flat face about 1/32 in. smaller in diameter than the hole in the yoke arm. Then drive out the bearing.

5. Lift the journal out by sliding it to one side.

6. Install in the reverse order of removal, using the procedures for the snap ring U-joints from step 4 on as a guide.

Rear Axle

AXLE SHAFT

Removal and Installation

PRIOR TO 1972

1. Jack up the wheel and remove the hub cap.

2. Remove the axle shaft nut.

3. Use a puller to remove the wheel hub and key.

4. Remove the screws which attach the brake dust shield, grease and bearing retainers, and brake assembly. Remove the shield and retainer.

5. Pull out the axle shaft with a puller, being careful not to lose the adjusting

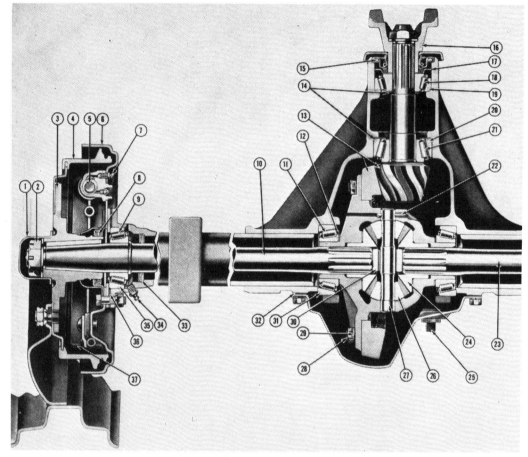

A cutaway view of a rear axle assembly installed in models prior to 1972

1. Hub cap	14. Pinion bearing shims	26. Pinion mate
2. Hex nut	15. Drive pinion oil seal	27. Pinion mate shaft
3. Rear wheel hub	16. Universal joint end yoke	28. Drive gear screw
4. Wheel brake drum	17. Drive pinion oil slinger	29. Drive gear screw strap
5. Brake wheel cylinder	18. Drive pinion outer bearing cone	30. Axle shaft spacer (center block)
6. Backing plate	and roller	31. Differential bearing cup
7. Brake cylinder bleeder screw	19. Drive pinion outer bearing cup	32. Axle housing cover gasket
8. Axle shaft outer grease retainer	20. Drive pinion inner bearing cup	33. Axle shaft oil seal (inboard)
9. Axle shaft bearing cone and roller	21. Drive pinion inner bearing cone	34. Lubrication fitting
10. Axle shaft—left	and roller	35. Axle shaft bearing cup
11. Differential bearing cone and	22. Pinion mate shaft pin and lock	36. Rear axle shaft bearing shims
roller	23. Axle shaft—right	37. Brake shoe and lining
12. Differential shims	24. Side gear	
13. Axle drive gear and pinion	25. Pipe plug (filler)	

shims. Should the axle shaft be broken, the inner end can usually be drawn out of the housing with a wire loop, after the outer seal is removed. However, if the broken end is less than 8″ long, it will be necessary to remove the differential.

If both shafts are to be removed, keep the shims from each shaft separate and replace them on the shaft from which they were removed in order to maintain the correct bearing adjustment.

6. Install in the reverse order of re-moval. Use a new grease seal when installing the hub assembly. Install the hub assembly, then the key.

1972–1975

1. Jack up the vehicle and remove the wheels.

2. Remove the brake drum spring lock nuts and remove the drum.

3. Remove the axle shaft flange cup plug by piercing the center with a sharp tool and prying it out.

Pulling the wheel hub with a puller

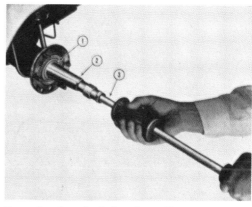

Removing the axle shaft with a puller

1. Cone and roller   2. Axle   3. Tool

4. Using the access hole in the axle shaft flange, remove the nuts which attach the backing plate and retainer to the axle tube flange.

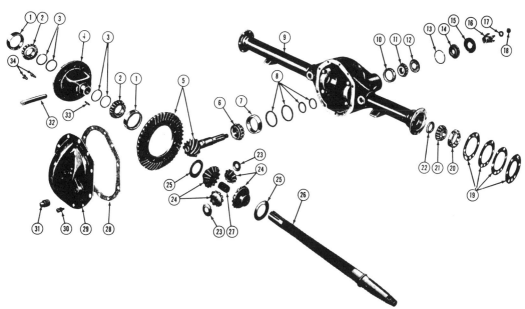

An exploded view of a rear axle assembly installed in models prior to 1972

1. Differential bearing cup
2. Differential bearing cone and rollers
3. Shims
4. Differential case
5. Ring gear and pinion
6. Pinion inner bearing cone and rollers
7. Pinion inner bearing cup
8. Pinion shims
9. Axle housing
10. Pinion outer bearing cup
11. Pinion outer bearing cone and rollers

12. Oil slinger
13. Gasket
14. Pinion oil seal
15. Dust shield
16. Yoke
17. Flat washer
18. Pinion nut
19. Wheel bearing shims
20. Bearing cup
21. Bearing cone and rollers
22. Oil seal
23. Thrust washer
24. Differential pinion gears
25. Thrust washer

26. Axle shaft
27. Spacer
28. Gasket
29. Housing cover
30. Screw and lockwasher
31. Filler plug
32. Differential shaft
33. Lock pin
34. Ring gear screw

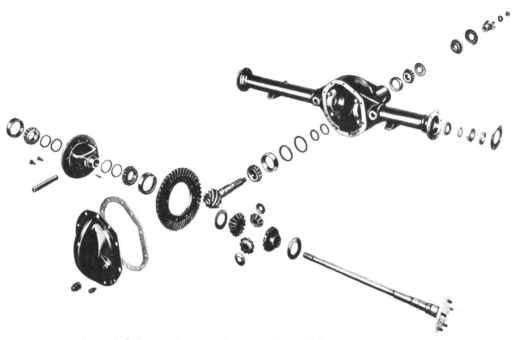

An exploded view of a rear axle assembly installed in 1972–1975 models

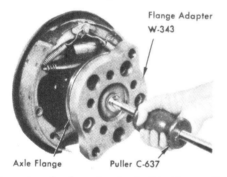

Flange Adapter
W-343

Axle Flange   Puller C-637

Removing the flanged axle shaft with a puller—
1972–1975 models

5. Remove the axle shaft from the housing with an axle puller.

6. Install in reverse order of removal.

1976

1. With the wheel on the ground, remove the axle shaft cotter pin and nut. Loosen the wheel nuts.

2. Raise and support the rear of the car, preferably with jackstands under the axle housing.

3. Remove the wheel.

4. Remove the drum retaining screws, 3 per drum.

5. Remove the drum from the hub. If the brake shoes hold the drum, the brake adjustment will have to be backed off slightly.

6. Attach a puller to the wheel bolts and pull off the hub.

CAUTION: *Don't use a knock-out type puller. It could damage the rear wheel bearings or the differential.*

7. Disconnect the parking brake cable at the equalizer. The equalizer is where the single cable from the parking brake pedal joins the double cable from the rear wheels.

8. Disconnect the brake tube at the wheel cylinder and remove the brake support plate assembly (backing plate), oil seal, and shims (left-side only).

9. Use a puller to remove the axle shaft and bearing.

10. Remove and discard the axle shaft inner oil seal.

11. The bearing cone is pressed onto the shaft. A hydraulic press must be used to remove it.

12. Before installation, pack the axle shaft bearings with high quality grease. Place a healthy glob of grease in the palm of one hand and force the edge of the bearing into it so that grease fills the bearing. Do this until the whole bearing is packed. Grease packing tools are available which make this task much easier.

13. Press the axle shaft bearings onto the axle shafts with the small diameter of the cone toward the outer end of the shaft.

CAUTION: *Always press on the inner bearing race.*

14. Coat the inner axle shaft seal with light oil.

15. Coat the outer surface of the metal seal retainer with sealant.

16. Use a seal driver to install the inner oil seal in the axle housing.

17. Install the axle shaft(s), turning them as necessary to fit the splines into the differential.

18. Install the outer bearing cup.

19. Apply sealant to the axle housing flange and brake support plate mounting areas. Install the original shims in their original locations, oil seal assembly, and brake support plate. Tighten the retaining bolts to 35 ft lbs.

NOTE: *The oil seal and retainer go on the outside of the brake support plate.*

20. Axle shaft end-play can be measured by installing the hub retaining nut on the shaft so that it can be pushed and pulled with relative ease. Strike the end of each axle shaft with a lead hammer to seat the bearing cups against the support plate. Mount a dial indicator on the left-side support plate with the stylus resting on the end of the axle shaft. Check the end-play while pushing and pulling on the axle shaft. End-play should be within 0.004–0.008 in., with 0.006 in. ideal. Add shims to increase end-play. Remove the hub retaining nut when finished checking end-play.

NOTE: *When a new axle shaft is installed, a new hub must also be installed. However, a new hub can be installed on an original axle shaft if the serrations on the shaft are not worn or damaged. The procedures for installing an original hub and a new hub are different.*

21. Install an original hub in the following manner:

a. Align the keyway in the hub with the axle shaft key;

b. Slide the hub onto the axle shaft as far as possible;

c. Install the axle shaft nut and washer;

d. Install the drum, drum retaining screws, and wheel;

e. Lower the vehicle onto its wheels and tighten the axle shaft nut to 250 ft lbs. If the cotter pin hole is not aligned, tighten the nut to the next castellation

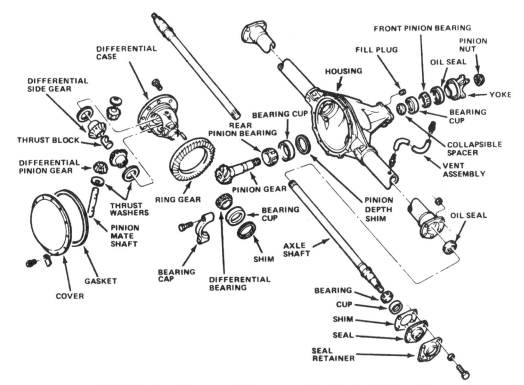

Exploded view of American Motors rear axle installed on 1976 models

and install the pin. Do not loosen the nut to align the cotter pin hole.

22. Install a new hub in the following manner:

a. Align the keyway in the hub with the axle shaft key;

b. Slide the hub onto the axle shaft as far as possible;

c. Install two well-lubricated thrust washers and the axle shaft nut;

d. Install the brake drum, drum retaining screws, and wheel;

e. Lower the vehicle onto its wheels;

f. Tighten the axle shaft nut until the distance from the outer face of the hub to the outer end of the axle shaft is $1^{19}\!/\!_{84}$ in. Pressing the hub onto the axle to the specified distance is necessary to form the hub serrations properly;

g. Remove the axle shaft nut and one thrust washer;

h. Install the axle shaft nut and tighten it to 250 ft lbs. If the cotter pin hole is not aligned, tighten the nut to the next castellation and install the pin. Do not loosen the nut to install the cotter pin.

23. Connect the brake line to the wheel cylinder and bleed the brake hydraulic system and adjust the brake shoes.

Front Axle

FRONT HUB

Removal and Installation

PRIOR TO 1972

The front axle shaft and universal joint assembly is removed as an assembly.

1. Remove the wheel.

2. Remove the hub with a puller.

3. Remove the axle shaft driving flange bolts.

4. Apply the foot brakes and remove the axle shaft flange with a puller.

5. Release the locking lip on the lockwasher and remove the outer nut, lockwasher, adjusting nut, and bearing lockwasher.

6. Remove the wheel hub and drum assembly with the bearings. Be careful not to damage the oil seal.

7. Remove the hydraulic brake tube and the brake backing plate screws.

Removing the hub cap with a puller

8. Remove the spindle.

9. Remove the axle shaft and universal joint assembly.

1972–1976

1. Remove the hub cap.

2. Remove the drive flange snap ring.

3. Remove the axle flange bolts, lockwashers, and flatwashers.

4. If the axle is on the vehicle, apply the foot brakes. Remove the axle flange with a puller.

5. Release the locking lip of the lockwasher, and remove the outer nut, lock-

Removing the axle shaft drive flange with a puller

Removing the wheel bearing nut with a special wrench

Removal of the front axle shaft on 1972–1976 models with a dry steering knuckle

washer, adjusting nut, and bearing lock-washer.

6. Back off on the brake adjusting star wheel adjusters and remove the brake drum assembly with the bearings. Be careful not to damage the oil seal.

7. Remove the brake backing plate. If the axle is on the vehicle, it will first be necessary to disconnect the brake hose be-tween the front brake line and the flexible connection.

8. Remove the spindle and spindle bushing.

9. Remove the axle shaft and universal joint assembly.

10. Clean all parts.

11. Insert the universal joint and axle shaft assembly into the axle housing, being careful not to knock out the inner seal. Insert the splined end of the axle shaft into the differential and push into place.

12. Install the wheel bearing spindle and bushing.

Specifications for Driveshafts and Universal Joints Prior to 1972

DRIVESHAFTS

Make	Spicer			
	Front		Rear	
Dimensions:	O.D. (in.)	Length (in.)	O.D. (in.)	Length (in.)
F-Head Engine Vehicles:				
CJ-5, CJ-5A				
3 Speed	$1\frac{1}{4}$	$22\frac{3}{4}$	$1\frac{3}{4}$	$18\frac{3}{32}$
4 Speed	$1\frac{1}{4}$	$28\frac{1}{4}$	$1\frac{3}{4}$	$13\frac{7}{16}$
CJ-6, CJ-6A				
3 Speed	$1\frac{1}{4}$	$22\frac{3}{4}$	$1\frac{3}{4}$	$38\frac{1}{2}$
4 Speed	$1\frac{1}{4}$	$28\frac{1}{4}$	$1\frac{3}{4}$	$33\frac{11}{32}$
CJ-3B	$1\frac{1}{4}$	$33\frac{1}{16}$	$1\frac{3}{4}$	$19\frac{5}{16}$
V6 Engine Vehicles:				
CJ-5, CJ-5A				
3 Speed	$1\frac{1}{4}$	$20\frac{13}{16}$	2	$20\frac{3}{16}$
CJ-6, CJ-6A				
3 Speed	$1\frac{1}{4}$	$20\frac{13}{16}$	2	40

UNIVERSAL JOINTS:

Make: Spicer   **Type:** Cardean Cross   **Bearing:** Antifriction

13. Install the brake backing plate.

14. Grease and assemble the wheel bearings and oil seal.

15. Install the wheel hub and drum on the wheel bearing spindle. Install the wheel bearing washer and adjusting nut. Tighten the nut until there is a slight drag on the bearings when the hub is turned. Then back off approximately ⅛ of a turn. Install the lockwasher and nut, tighten the nut into place, and then bend the lip of the lockwasher over onto the locknut.

16. Install the drive flange and gasket onto the hub and attach with six capscrews and lockwashers. Install the snap ring onto the outer end of the axle shaft.

17. Install the hub cap.

18. Install the wheel, lug nuts, and wheel disc.

19. If the tube was installed with the axle assembly on the vehicle, check the front wheel alignment, bleed the brakes and lubricate the front axle universal joints.

8 · Suspension and Steering

Front and Rear Suspension

All springs should be examined periodically for broken or shifted leaves, loose or missing clips, angle of the spring shackles, and position of the springs on the saddles. Springs with shifted leaves do not retain their normal strength. Missing clips may permit the spring leaves to fan out or break on rebound. Broken leaves may make the vehicle hard to handle or permit the axle to shift out of line. Weakened springs may break causing difficulty in steering. Spring attaching clips or bolts must be tight. It is suggested that they be checked at each vehicle inspection.

All front springs on models made prior to 1972, except as noted below, have shackles at the front of the springs and pivot bolts at the rear of the springs. Model CJ-5 up to serial number 44437 and Model CJ-6 up to serial number 11981 have shackles at the rear of the front springs, and pivot bolts at the front.

All rear springs have shackles at the rear and pivot bolts at the front.

NOTE: *On 1972 and later models, all spring ends have silent block-type rubber bushings. Never lubricate these rubber bushings.*

SPRINGS

Removal and Installation

Prior to 1972

1. Raise the vehicle with a jack under the axle and place a jackstand under the frame side rail. Then lower the axle jack

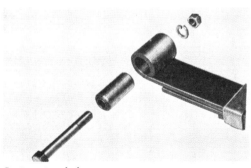

Spring pivot bolt

Front spring shackle

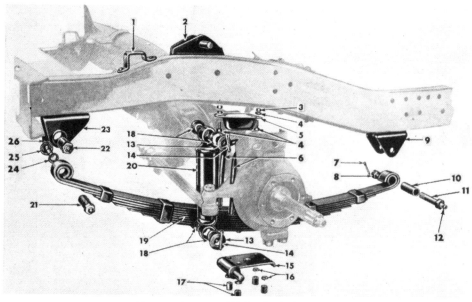

Front spring assembly for the early CJ-3B

1. Bracket
2. Bracket and shaft
3. Nut
4. Screw and lockwasher
5. Axle bumper
6. Left clip
7. Cotter pin

8. Nut
9. Bracket
10. Eye bushing
11. Pivot bolt
12. Lubrication fitting
13. Washer
14. Cotter pin

15. Plate and shaft
16. Lockwasher
17. Nut
18. Bushing
19. Front spring
20. Shock absorber
21. Lower bushing

22. Upper bushing
23. Bracket
24. Grease seal retainer
25. Grease seal
26. U-bolt

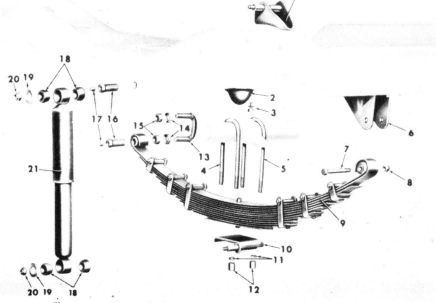

Front spring assembly for the early CJ-5 and CJ-6 (Prior to 1972)

1. Front shock absorber bracket
2. Front axle bumper
3. Bolt
4. U-bolt
5. U-bolt
6. Spring pivot bracket
7. Pivot bolt

8. Nut
9. Front spring assembly
10. Front spring clip plate
11. Lockwasher
12. U-bolt nut
13. Shackle
14. Retainer

15. Grease seal
16. Threaded shackle bushing
17. Lube fitting
18. Mounting pin bushing
19. Washer
20. Lock nut
21. Shock absorber assembly

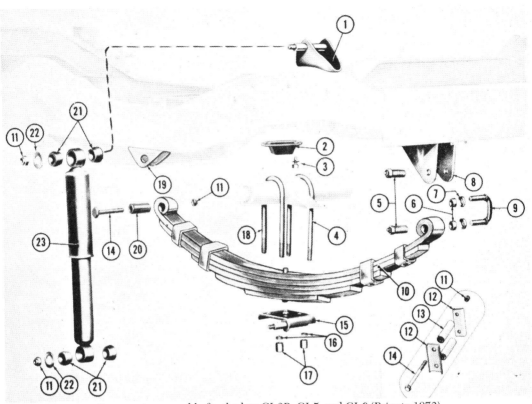

Front spring assembly for the late CJ-3B, CJ-5, and CJ-6 (Prior to 1972)

1. Bracket and shaft	9. Spring shackle	17. Nut
2. Axle bumper	10. Spring	18. Spring clip
3. Bolt and lockwasher	11. Nut	19. Bracket
4. Spring clip	12. Plate	20. Bushing (spring)
5. Bushing	13. Bearing	21. Bushing
6. Grease seal	14. Bolt	22. Washer
7. Grease retainer	15. Plate and shaft	23. Shock absorber
8. Bracket	16. Lockwasher	

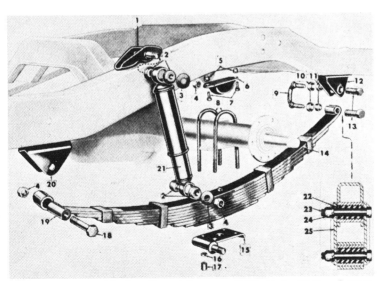

1. Bracket
2. Bushing
3. Washer
4. Lock nut
5. Nut and lockwasher
6. Axle bumper
7. Bolt
8. Spring clip
9. U-bolt
10. Grease retainer
11. Grease seal
12. Bracket
13. Bushing
14. Spring
15. Plate and shaft
16. Lockwasher
17. Nut
18. Bolt
19. Bearing
20. Bracket
21. Shock absorber
22. Silent block bearing
23. Bolt
24. Nut
25. Side plate

Rear spring assembly for all models up to 1972. Early CJ-5 and CJ-6 models had a grease fitting in the threaded shackle bushings

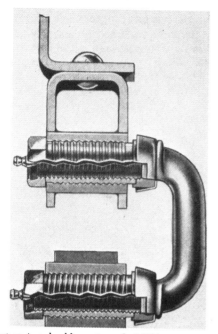

Front spring shackle up to early 1957

so that the load is relieved from the spring and the wheels rest on the floor.

2. Remove the nuts which secure the spring clip bolts. Remove the spring plate and clip bolts. Free the spring from the axle by raising the axle jack.

3. Remove the pivot bolt nut and drive out the pivot bolt. Disconnect the shackle either by removing the lower nuts and bolts on the rubber-bushed shackles, or by removing the threaded bushings on the U-shackles.

4. To replace, first install the pivot bolt. Then, connect the shackle using the following procedures.

5. On bronze-bushed pivot bolts, install the bolt and nut and tighen the nut. Then back it off two cotter pin slots and install the cotter pin. The nut must be drawn up tightly but must be sufficiently loose to allow the spring to pivot freely. Otherwise the spring might break.

6. On rubber-bushed pivot bolts and locknuts (or lockwasher and nut) only tighten the bolt enough to hold the bushings in position until the vehicle is lowered from the jack.

7. Connect the shackle. On rubber-bushed shackles install the bolts as in step 6 above. For U-shackles, insert the shackle through the frame bracket and eye of the spring. Holding the U-shackle tightly against the frame, start the upper bushing

on the shackle, taking care that when it enters the thread in the frame it does not crossthread. Screw the bushing on the shackle tightly against the spring eye, and thread the bushing in approximately half way. Then, alternately from top bushing to lower bushing, turn them in until the head of the bushing is snug against the frame bracket and the bushing in the spring eye is 1/32 in. away from the spring as measured from the inside of the hexagon head to the spring. Lubricate the bushing and then try the flex of the shackle, which must be free. If a shackle is tight, rethread the bushings on the shackle.

8. Move the axle into position on the spring by lowering or raising the axle jack. Install the spring clip bolts, spring plate, lockwashers, and nuts. Torque the nuts to 50–55 ft lbs. Avoid over-tightening. Be sure the spring is free to move at both ends.

9. Remove both jacks. On rubber bushed shackles and pivot bolts, allow the weight of the vehicle to seat the bushings in their operating positions. Then torque the nuts to 27–30 ft lbs.

1972–1976

1. Raise the vehicle with a jack under the axle. Place a jackstand under the frame side rail. Then lower the axle jack so the load is relieved from the spring and the wheels just touch the floor.

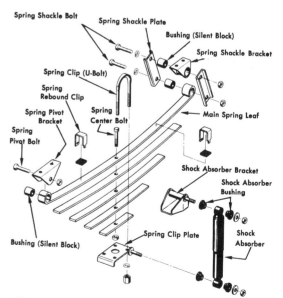

Front spring assembly for 1972–1975 models; 1976 models have one less leaf.

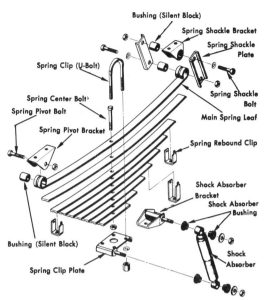

Bushing (Silent Block)
Spring Shackle Bracket
Spring Shackle Plate
Spring Clip (U-Bolt)
Spring Center Bolt
Spring Pivot Bolt
Spring Shackle Bolt
Main Spring Leaf
Spring Pivot Bracket
Spring Rebound Clip
Shock Absorber Bracket
Shock Absorber Bushing
Bushing (Silent Block)
Shock Absorber
Spring Clip Plate

Rear spring assembly for 1972–1975 models; 1976 models have only four leaves.

2. Disconnect the shock absorber from the spring clip plate.

3. Remove the nuts which secure the spring clips (U-bolts). Remove the spring plate and spring clips. Free the spring from the axle by raising the axle.

4. Remove the pivot bolt nut and drive out the pivot bolt. Disconnect the shackle from the shackle bracket by removing the lock nut, lock nut and bolt or nut, or lock-washer and bolt.

5. With the spring removed, the spring shackle and/or shackle plate may be removed from the spring by removing the lock nut, or lock nut and shackle bolt or nut, or lockwasher and shackle bolt.

6. Inspect the bushings in the eye of the main spring leaf and the bushings of the spring shackle for excessive wear. Replace if necessary.

7. The spring can be disassembled for replacing an individual spring leaf, by removing the clips and the center bolts.

8. To install the spring on the vehicle, with the bushings in place and the spring shackle attached to the springs, position the spring in the pivot hanger and install the pivot bolt and lock nut. Only tighten the lock nut enough to hold the bushings in position until the vehicle is lowered from the jack.

9. Position the spring and install the shackle, shackle bolts, shackle plate if ap-

plicable, lockwasher, and nut. Only finger tighten the nuts at this time.

10. Move the axle into position on the spring by lowering the axle jack. Place the spring center bolt in the axle saddle hole. Install the spring clips, spring plate, lock-washers and nuts. Torque the $\frac{7}{16}$ in. nuts to 36–42 ft lbs and the $\frac{1}{2}$ in. nuts to 45–65 ft lbs.

NOTE: *Be sure that the center bolt is properly centered in the axle saddle.*

11. Connect the shock absorber.

12. Remove the axle and allow the weight of the vehicle to seat the bushings in their operating positions. Then torque the $\frac{7}{16}$ in. spring pivot bolt nuts and spring shackle nuts to 25–40 ft lbs. Torque the $\frac{5}{8}$ in. shackle nuts 55–75 ft lbs.

SHOCK ABSORBERS

Removal and Installation

1. Remove the locknuts and washers. The CJ-3B has cotter pins instead of lock-nuts. Remove the cotter pins and washers on the CJ-3B.

2. Pull the shock absorber eyes and rubber bushings from the mounting pins.

3. Install the shocks in reverse order of the removal procedure.

NOTE: *Squeaking usually occurs when movement takes place between the rubber bushings and the metal parts. The squeaking may be eliminated by placing the bushings under greater pressure. This is accomplished either by adding additional washers where the cotter pins are used or by tightening the locknuts. Do not use mineral lubricant to stop the squeaking as it will deteriorate the rubber.*

Steering

STEERING KNUCKLE PIVOT PINS

PRIOR TO 1972

The steering knuckle pivot pins take the place of ball joints in a conventional vehicle. The pins pivot on tapered roller bearings located in the axle yoke. Replacement of these bearings requires removal of the hub and brake drum assembly, wheel bearings, axle shaft, spindle, steering tie

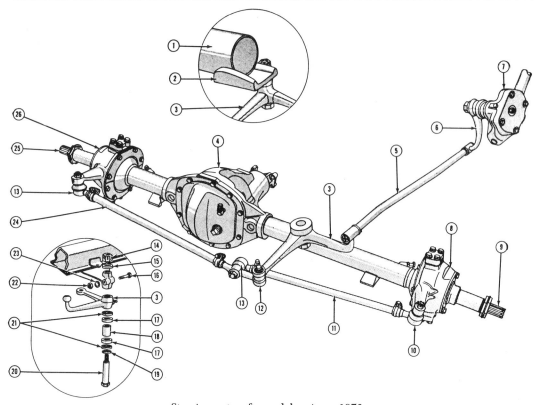

Steering system for models prior to 1972

1. Frame cross tube (CJ-3B)	10. Left tie rod socket	19. Washer
2. Steering bellcrank bracket	11. Left steering tie rod	20. Bellcrank shaft
3. Steering bellcrank	12. Left tie rod socket	21. Bearing seal
4. Front axle assembly	13. Right tie rod socket	22. Nut
5. Steering connecting rod	14. Bellcrank nut	23. Lockwasher
6. Steering gear arm	15. Washer	24. Right steering tie rod
7. Steering gear	16. Bolt	25. Right shaft and universal joint
8. Left steering knuckle and arm	17. Bellcrank bearing	26. Right steering knuckle and arm
9. Left shaft and universal joint	18. Bearing spacer	

rod, and steering knuckle. Disassemble the steering knuckle as follows:

Removal and Installation

1. Remove the eight screws that hold the oil seal retainer in place.

2. Remove the four screws which secure the lower pivot pin bearing cap.

3. Remove the four screws which hold the upper bearing cap in place.

4. Remove the bearing cap.

5. The steering knuckle can now be removed from the axle.

6. Wash all of the parts in cleaning solvent.

7. Replace any worn or damaged parts. Inspect the bearings and races for scores, cracks, or chips. Should the bearing cups be damaged, they may be removed and installed with a driver.

8. To install, reverse the removal procedure. When reinstalling the steering knuckle sufficient shims must be installed under the top bearing cap to obtain the correct preload on the bearing. Shims are available in 0.003, 0.005, 0.010, and 0.030 in. thicknesses. Install only one shim of the above thicknesses at the top only. Install the bearing caps, lockwashers, and screws, and tighten securely.

You can check the preload on the bearings by hooking a spring scale in the hole in the knuckle arm for the tie rod socket. Take the scale reading when the knuckle has just started its sweep.

The pivot pin bearing preload should be 12–16 lbs with the oil seal removed. Remove or add shims to obtain a preload within these limits. If all shims are removed and adequate preload is still not

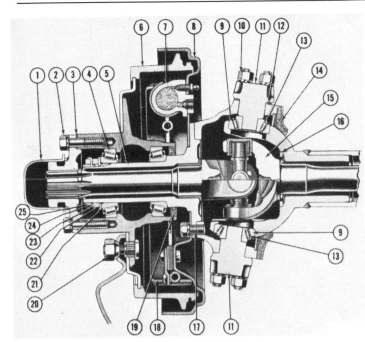

1. Wheel hub cap
2. Driving flange capscrew
3. Axle shaft drive flange gasket
4. Wheel bearing cup
5. Front wheel spindle
6. Brake drum
7. Front brake wheel cylinder
8. Brake backing plate
9. Pivot pin bearing cap
10. Pivot pin bearing capnut
11. Pivot pin
12. Pivot bearing adjusting shims
13. Pivot pin cone and rollers
14. Steering knuckle oil seal
15. Front axle universal joint (Spicer)
16. Thrust washer
17. Brake backing plate screw
18. Brake shoe and lining
19. Hub oil seal
20. Wheel hub bolt nut
21. Wheel bearing cone and rollers
22. Wheel bearing washer
23. Wheel bearing retainer nut
24. Wheel adjusting nut lockwasher
25. Wheel bearing retaining nut

A cutaway view of the front steering knuckle with a Spicer universal joint

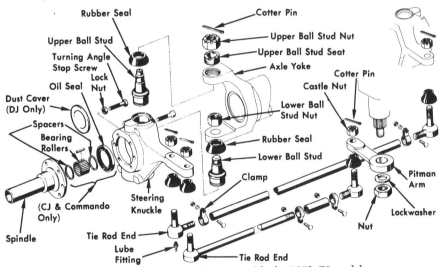

Front axle and steering linkage assembly for 1972–76 models

obtained, a washer may be used under the top bearing cap to increase preload. When a washer is used, shims may have to be reinstalled to obtain proper adjustment.

OPEN TYPE
STEERING KNUCKLE
BALL JOINTS—1972–1976

Removal and Installation

1. Replacement of the ball joints, or ball stud, as they will be called from here on, requires the removal of the steering knuckle. To remove the steering knuckle, first remove the wheel, brake drum, and hub as an assembly. Remove the brake assembly from the spindle. Position the brake assembly on the front axle in a convenient place. Remove the snap ring from the axle shaft.

2. Remove the spindle and bearing assembly. It may be necessary to tap the spindle with a soft mallet to disengage it from the steering knuckle.

3. Slide the axle shaft out through the steering knuckle.

Removing the lower stud nut

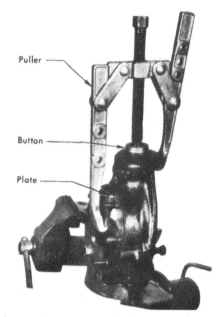

Using a puller to remove the lower ball stud

Unseating the upper and lower ball studs from the yoke so the knuckle can be removed from the vehicle

4. Disconnect the steering tie-rods from the knuckle arm.

5. Remove the lower ball stud nut.

6. Remove the cotter pin from the upper stud. Loosen the upper stud until the top edge of the nut is flush with the top end of the stud.

7. Use a lead hammer to unseat the upper and lower studs from the yoke. Remove the upper nut and the knuckle assembly.

8. Remove the ball stud seat from the upper hole in the axle yoke. It is threaded in the hole. There are special wrenches available for removing the seat.

9. On 1974–76 models, remove the lower ball stud snap-ring.

10. Securely clamp the knuckle assembly in a vise with the upper ball stud pointed down.

11. Using a large socket or drift, of approximately the same size as the ball stud, and a mallet, drive the lower stud out of the knuckle.

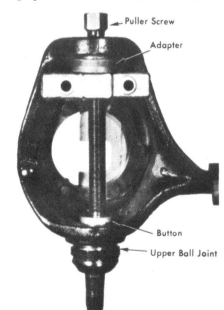

Removing the upper ball stud

NOTE: *Throughout this procedure, where a ball stud is either removed or installed, a hydraulic press or a two jawed gear puller can be used and, if at all possible, should be used to make the job easier. However it is possible to complete the job using a mallet, drift and a large socket the same size as the ball studs.*

12. Place the socket on the bottom surface of the upper ball stud. Place the drift through the hole where the lower ball stud

was and place it on the socket. Drive the upper ball stud out of the knuckle with a mallet.

13. Before installing the lower ball stud, run the lower ball stud nut onto the stud just far enough so the head of the stud is flush with the top edge of the nut.

14. Invert the knuckle in the vise. Position the lower ball stud in the knuckle with the nut in place. Place the same size socket over the nut and drive the ball stud into place with the drift and mallet.

15. Install the lower ball stud snap-ring on 1974–76 models.

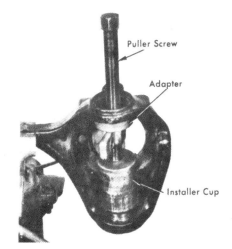

Installing the lower ball stud

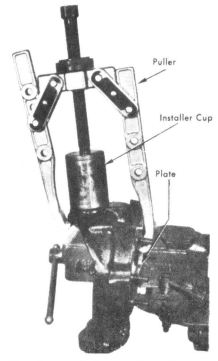

Installing the upper ball stud with a puller

16. Use the same procedure for installing the upper ball stud. The drift will not be needed to install the upper ball stud.

17. Install the upper ball stud seat into the axle yoke. Use a new one if the old one shows evidence of wear. The top of the seat should be flush with the top of the yoke.

18. Install the knuckle assembly onto the axle yoke. Install the lower stud nut. Tighten it to 70–90 ft lbs.

19. Install the upper stud nut and tighten it to 100 ft lbs. Install the cotter pin. If the cotter pin holes do not align, tighten the nut until the pin can be installed. Do not loosen the nut to align the holes.

20. Install the axle shaft, spindle and bearing assembly, and brake assembly. Connect the steering rods. Install the drum and hub, and wheel assembly. Adjust the wheel bearings. Check the turning angle. Adjust the stop screw to permit the proper turning angle of 31°.

Turning angle adjusting screw

1. Stop screw

STEERING KNUCKLE OIL SEAL

Remove the old steering knuckle oil seal by removing the eight screws which hold it in place. Earlier production vehicles have two-piece seals. Later production vehicles have a split oil seal and backing ring assembly, an oil seal felt, and two seal retainer plate halves.

Examine the spherical surface of the axle for scores or scratches which could damage the seal. Smooth any roughness with emery cloth.

Before installing the oil seal felt, make a diagonal cut across the top side of the felt so that it may be slipped over the axle. Install the oil seal assembly in the sequence mentioned above, making sure the backing ring (of the oil seal and backing ring assembly) is toward the wheel.

After driving in wet, freezing weather swing the front wheels from side to side to remove moisture adhering to the oil seal and the spherical surface of the axle housing. This will prevent freezing with resultant damage to the seals. Should the vehicle be stored for any period of time, coat the surfaces with light grease to prevent rusting.

FRONT END ALIGNMENT

Proper alignment of the front wheels must be maintained in order to ensure ease of steering and satisfactory tire life.

The most important factors of front wheel alignment are wheel camber, axle caster, and wheel toe-in.

Wheel toe-in is the distance by which the wheels are closer together at the front than at the rear.

Wheel camber is the amount the top of the wheels incline outward from the vertical.

Front axle caster is the amount in degrees that the steering pivot pins are tilted toward the rear of the vehicle. Positive caster is inclination of the top of the pivot pin toward the rear of the vehicle.

These points should be checked at regular intervals, particularly when the front axle has been subjected to a heavy impact. When checking wheel alignment, it is important that wheel bearings and knuckle bearings (pre-1972) be in proper adjustment. Loose bearings will affect instrument readings when checking the camber, pivot pin inclination, and toe-in.

Front wheel camber is preset and cannot be adjusted. Caster is also preset, but can be altered by use of shims between the axle pad and the springs. Wheel toe-in is adjustable.

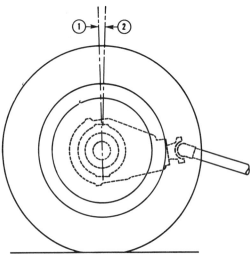

Axle caster

1. Vertical line   2. Caster angle

Caster Adjustment

Caster angle is established in the axle design by tilting the top of the kingpins toward the rear and the bottom of the kingpins forward so that an imaginary line through the center of the kingpins would strike the ground at a point ahead of the point of the contact.

The purpose of caster is to provide steering stability which will keep the front wheels in the straight ahead position and also assist in straightening up the wheels when coming out of a turn.

If the angle of caster, when accurately measured, is found to be incorrect, correct it to the specification given at the end of this section by either installing new parts or installing caster shims between the axle pad and the springs.

If the camber and toe-in are correct and it is known that the axle is not twisted, a satisfactory check may be made by testing the vehicle on the road. Before road testing, make sure all tires are properly inflated, being particularly careful that both front tires are inflated to exactly the same pressure.

If the vehicle turns easily to either side but is hard to straighten out, insufficient caster for easy handling of the vehicle is indicated. If correction is necessary, it can usually be accomplished by installing shims between the springs and axle pads to secure the desired result.

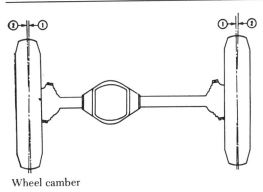

Wheel camber

1. Vertical line   2. Camber angle

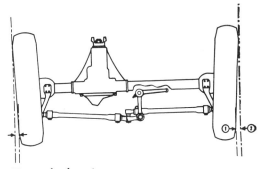

Front wheel toe-in

1. Vertical line   2. Toe-in angle

Camber Adjustment

The purpose of camber is to more nearly place the weight of the vehicle over the tire contact patch on the road to facilitate ease of steering. The result of excessive camber is irregular wear of the tires on the outside shoulders and is usually caused by bent axle parts.

The result of excessive negative or reverse camber will be hard steering and possibly a wandering condition. Tires will also wear on the inside shoulders. Negative camber is usually caused by excessive wear or looseness of the front wheel bearings, axle parts or the result of a sagging axle.

Unequal camber may cause any or a combination of the following conditions: unstable steering, wandering, kick-back or road shock, shimmy or excessive tire wear. The cause of unequal camber is usually a bent steering knuckle or axle end.

Correct wheel camber is set in the axle at the time of manufacture and cannot be altered by any adjustment. It is important that the camber be the same on both front wheels. Heating of any parts to facilitate straightening usually destroys the heat treatment given them at the factory. Cold bending may cause a fracture of the steel and is also unsafe. Replacement with new parts is insisted upon rather than any straightening of damaged parts.

Toe-in Adjustment

Prior to 1972

The toe-in may be adjusted with a line or straight edge as the vehicle tread is the same in the front and rear. To set the adjustment both tie rods must be adjusted as outlined below:

Set the tie rod end of the steering bell-crank at right angles with the front axle. Place a straight edge or line against the left rear wheel and left front wheel to determine if the wheel is in a straight ahead position. If the front wheel tire does not touch the straight edge at both the front and rear, it will be necessary to adjust the left tie rod by loosening the clamps on each end and turning the rod until the tire touches the straight edge.

Check the right hand side in the same manner, adjusting the tie rod if necessary making sure that the bell-crank remains at right angles to the axle. When it is determined that the front wheels are in the straight ahead position, set the toe-in by shortening each tie rod approximately ½ turn.

1972–1976

First raise the front of the vehicle to free the front wheels. Turn the wheels to the straight ahead position. Use a steadyrest to scribe a pencil line in the center of each tire tread as the wheel is turned by hand. A good way to do this is to first coat a strip with chalk around the circumference of the tread at the center to form a base for a fine pencil line.

Measure the distance between the scribed lines at the front and rear of the wheels using care that both measurements are made at an equal distance from the floor. The distance between the lines should be greater at the rear than at the front by $\frac{3}{64}$ in. to $\frac{3}{32}$ in. To adjust, loosen the clamp bolts and turn the tie rod with a small pipe wrench. The tie rod is threaded with right and left hand threads to provide equal adjustment at both wheels. Do not overlook retightening the clamp bolts.

It is common practice to measure between the wheel rims. This is satisfactory providing the wheels run true. By scribing

Wheel Alignment Specifications

Year	Model	CASTER Pref Setting (deg)	CAMBER Pref Setting (deg)	Toe-in (in.)	Steering Axis Inclin.
1953–1976	CJ-3B CJ-5 CJ-5A CJ-6 CJ-6A CJ-7	3	1½	³⁄₆₄– ³⁄₃₂	7½

a line on the tire tread, measurement is taken between the road contact points reducing error caused by wheel run-out.

STEERING WHEEL

Removal and Installation

1953–75

1. Disconnect the negative battery cable.

2. Set the front tires in a straight ahead position.

3. Pull the horn button from the steering wheel.

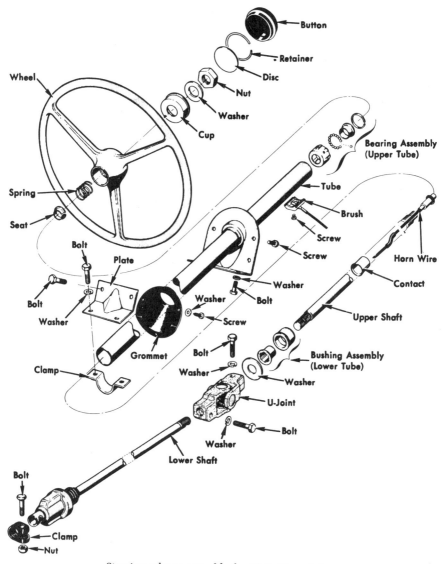

Steering column assembly for 1972–75 models

4. Remove the steering wheel nut and horn button contact cup.

5. Scribe a line mark on the steering wheel and steering shaft if there is not one already. Release the turn signal assembly from the steering post and install a puller.

6. Remove the steering wheel and spring.

7. To install, align the scribe marks on the steering shaft with the steering wheel and secure the steering wheel spring, steering wheel, and horn button contact cup with the steering wheel nut.

8. Install the horn button.

9. Connect the battery cable and test the horn.

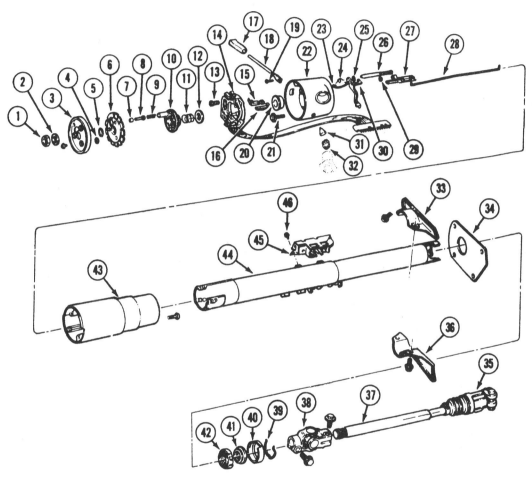

Exploded view of the steering column on 1976 models

1. Steering wheel nut
2. Washer
3. Anti-theft cover
4. Anti-theft cover screw and retainer
5. Steering shaft snap-ring
6. Lockplate
7. Bushing
8. Horn contact pin
9. Spring
10. Concelling cam
11. Upper bearing preload spring
12. Thrust washer
13. Turn signal switch screw
14. Turn signal switch
15. Buzzer switch
16. Buzzer switch spring

17. Turn signal lever knob
18. Turn signal lever
19. Turn signal lever screw
20. Upper bearing
21. Housing retaining screw
22. Housing
23. Rack preload spring
24. Key release lever spring
25. Wave washer
26. Lockbolt
27. Lock rack
28. Remote rod
29. Spring washer
30. Key release lever
31. Hazard warning switch knob
32. Sector

33. Upper half of toe plate
34. Seal
35. Intermediate shaft coupling
36. Lower half of toe plate
37. Intermediate shaft
38. U-joint
39. Snap-ring
40. Retainer
41. Lower bearing
42. Lower bearing adapter
43. Shroud
44. Jacket
45. Ignition switch
46. Ignition switch screw

1976

1. Disconnect the negative battery cable.

2. Place the front wheels in the straight-ahead position.

3. Remove the rubber boot and horn button from the steering wheel. Turn the button until the locktabs on the button align with the notches in the contact cup and pull upward to remove it.

4. Remove the steering wheel nut and washer.

5. If the Jeep is equipped with a sport style steering wheel, remove the horn button, nut and washer, bottom retaining ring, and horn contact ring.

6. Remove the plastic horn contact cup retainer and remove the cup and contact plate from the steering wheel.

7. Remove the horn contact pin and bushing from the steering wheel.

8. Paint or scribe alignment marks on the steering wheel and shaft for reference during assembly.

9. Remove the steering wheel using a puller.

10. Install the steering wheel in the reverse order, tightening the nut to 20 ft lbs.

TURN SIGNAL SWITCH REPLACEMENT

1953–75

The turn signal switch is attached to the steering column; the whole unit is

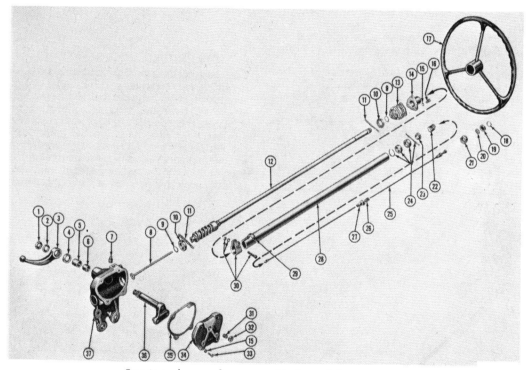

Steering column and gear assembly for models prior to 1972

1. Nut	14. Upper cover	27. Spring cap
2. Lockwasher	15. Lockwasher	28. Steering column
3. Steering gear arm	16. Bolt	29. Oil hole cover
4. Lever shaft oil seal	17. Steering wheel	30. Clamp
5. Outer housing bushing	18. Horn button retainer	31. Adjusting screw
6. Inner housing bushing	19. Horn button	32. Nut
7. Filler plug	20. Horn button cap	33. Bolt
8. Cover and tube	21. Nut	34. Side cover
9. Ball retainer ring	22. Spring	35. Gasket
10. Cup	23. Spring seat	36. Shaft and lever
11. Ball (steel)	24. Bearing	37. Housing
12. Tube and cam	25. Horn cable	
13. Shims	26. Horn button spring	

mounted externally. To remove the switch assembly, remove the attaching screws, unfasten the wires and remove the unit from the steering column.

The most frequent causes of failure in the directional signal system are loose connections and burned out bulbs. A flashing rate of approximately twice normal usually indicates a burned-out bulb in the circuit.

When trouble in the signal switch is suspected, it is advisable to make a few checks to definitely locate the trouble before going to the effort of removing the signal switch.

First check the fuse. There is an inline fuse located between the ignition switch and the turn signal flasher.

If the fuse checks out OK, next eliminate the flasher unit by substituting a known good flasher. If a new flasher does not cure the trouble, check the signal system wiring connections at the fuse and at the steering column connector.

NOTE: *If the right front parking light and the right rear stop light are inoperative, switch failure is indicated. If the brake lights function properly, the rear signal lights are OK.*

To check the switch on models prior to 1972, first put the control lever in the neutral position. Then disconnect the wire to the right side circuit and bridge it to the "L" terminal, thus by-passing the signal switch. If the right side circuit lights, the signal switch is inoperative and must be replaced.

To check out the switch on the 1972 and 1973 models, disconnect the switch at the six wire connector. Use a jumper wire from the white (battery feed) wire to the other wires. Circuitry is as follows:

White to Orange—Right rear
White to Black—Right front
White to Yellow—Left front
White to Blue—Left rear

If the lights in any of these circuits light then the switch is bad and must be replaced.

1976

1. Disconnect the negative battery cable.

2. Remove the steering wheel.

3. Loosen the anti-theft cover retaining screws and lift the cover from the steering column. It is not necessary to completely remove these screws.

4. Depress the lockplate and pry the round wire snap-ring from the steering shaft groove. A lockplate compressor tool J-23653 is available for compressing the lockplate.

5. Remove the lockplate, directional signal canceling cam, upper bearing preload spring, and thrust washer from the steering shaft.

6. Move the directional signal actuating lever to the right turn position and remove the lever.

7. Depress the hazard warning light switch and remove the button by turning it counterclockwise.

8. Remove the directional signal wiring harness connector block from its mounting bracket on the right-side of the lower column.

9. On vehicles equipped with an automatic transmission, use a stiff wire, such as a paper clip, to depress the lock tab which retains the shift quadrant light wire in the connector block.

10. Remove the directional signal switch retaining screws and pull the switch and wiring harness from the steering column.

11. Guide the wiring harness of the new switch into position and carefully align the switch assembly. Make sure that the actuating lever pivot is correctly aligned and seated in the upper housing pivot boss prior to installing the retaining screws.

12. Install the directional signal lever and actuate the directional signal switch to assure correct operation.

13. Place the thrust washer, spring, and directional signal canceling cam on the upper end of the steering shaft.

14. Align the lockplate splines with the steering shaft splines and place the lockplate in position with the directional signal canceling cam shaft protruding through the dogleg opening in the lockplate.

15. Install the snap-ring.

16. Install the anti-theft cover.

17. Install the steering wheel and connect the negative battery cable.

18. Check the operation of the turn signal switch.

STEERING COLUMN

Removal and Installation

This procedure applies primarily to 1972 and later models. It will be necessary to adapt this procedure to models prior to 1972.

NOTE: *When the steering column is removed from the vehicle, handle it with special care. Sharp blows on the end of the steering shaft or shift levers, leaning on the column assembly, or dropping the assembly could shear or loosen the plastic fasteners that maintain the rigidity of the steering column. The steering column is designed to collapse in the event of a collision. This applies only to 1976 models.*

1. Disconnect the negative battery cable.

2. Disconnect the steering column wiring connector from the wiring harness located underneath the instrument panel.

NOTE: *The steering wheel does not have to be removed to remove the steering column on the 1972–76 models.*

3. Scribe a line mark on the steering shaft and upper steering shaft-to-lower shaft U-joint. Remove the U-joint pinch bolt.

4. Disconnect the gear shift linkage from the shift lever, on vehicles equipped with automatic transmissions.

Disconnect the steering column toeboard-to-the-tube plate and clamp. Remove the rubber grommet attaching screws.

5. Disconnect the steering column at the instrument panel.

6. Pull the steering column out of the floor pan and remove.

7. Install in the reverse order of removal.

MANUAL STEERING GEAR

Adjustments

PRIOR TO 1972

The cam lever steering gear consists of a spiral cam, and a cross shaft and lever assembly with two lever studs. When the steering wheel is turned, the cam moves the studs, causing rotary movement of the cross shaft, which in turn causes angular movement of the steering arm.

Two adjustments of the steering gear are necessary: up and down play of the steering shaft, and adjustment of the lever studs (tapered pins) in the cam groove.

Adjustment of the ball thrust bearings to eliminate up and down play of the steering shaft is accomplished by removing the shims which are installed between the steering gear housing and the upper cover. Before making this adjustment, loosen the housing side cover adjusting screw to free the pins in the cam groove. Loosen the housing cover to cut and remove a shim or more as required. Install the screws and tighten. Adjustment should be made to have a slight drag but allow the steering wheel to turn freely with thumb and forefinger lightly gripping the rim.

Shims installed for adjustment are 0.002, 0.003, and 0.010 in. in thickness.

Adjustment of the tapered pins in the cam groove is accomplished by adjusting the screw located on the side cover of the steering gear housing. Unlock the adjusting screw and turn it in until a very slight drag is felt through the mid-position when turning the steering wheel slowly from one extreme position to the other.

Backlash of the pins in the groove shows up as end play of the lever shaft and also as backlash of the steering arm.

The cam groove is purposely cut shallow in the straight ahead position for each pin. This feature permits a close adjustment for normal straight ahead driving and permits take up of backlash at this point after wear occurs without causing a bind elsewhere. Always adjust within the high range through the mid position of the pin travel. Do not adjust off the "straight ahead" position. Backlash in turned positions is not objectionable.

1972–1976

Attach a torque wrench to the splined end of the worm shaft and turn the shaft to either extreme left or right position. Do not hit the travel stops. Tighten the worm bearing adjuster until the torque wrench registers 8 in. lbs. Make sure the adjustment is made within ½ turn of either extreme position of the shaft. Tighten the adjuster lock nut to 70–110 ft lbs. Recheck the torque of the worm shaft.

Turn the steering gear from one extreme position to the opposite position, counting the number of turns. Turn back one-half the total number of turns. This places the steering gear on the "high" point or straight ahead position. The total number of turns should be 6.14.

With the torque wrench on the pitman shaft, tighten the lash adjuster screw until the torque registered is 4 to 10 in. lbs more

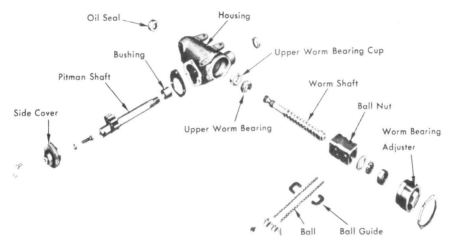

An exploded view of a non-power steering gear for 1972–76 models

than worm bearing preload, and total torque is less than 18 in. lbs. Make sure the torque does not exceed this value over the center range. Tighten the nut on the adjuster screw to 18–27 ft lbs. Recheck the torque.

POWER STEERING GEAR

Adjustments

1972–1976

Under normal conditions, the thrust bearing adjustment and the worm-to-rack preload need never be changed. If lash does develop in the steering gear, the pit-man shaft should be adjusted in the vehicle as follows:

Disconnect the pitman arm from the pitman shaft and remove the horn button from the steering wheel hub.

Turn the gear ½ of a turn off center in either direction. Using an inch pound torque wrench on the steering wheel nut, determine the torque required to rotate the shaft slowly through a 20 degree arc.

Turn the gear back to center and loosen the lash adjuster locknut. Turn the screw until the reading is equal to 6 in. lbs in excess of that noted above, and retighten the lock nut while holding the screw in place.

Recheck the readings and replace the pitman arm and hub cover.

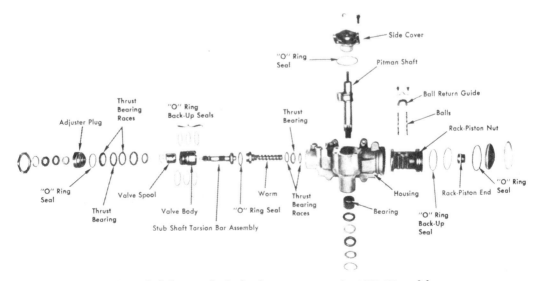

An exploded view of a hydraulic steering gear for 1972–76 models

POWER STEERING PUMP

Removal and Installation

If the power steering pump has to be removed to service another component, it is not necessary to remove the hoses from the pump. Just disconnect the mounting fixtures and lift the pump away from the engine and lay it out of the way. The only time the power steering hoses have to be removed from the pump is when the pump has to be removed from the vehicle for service or replacement.

1. Remove the pump drive belt tension adjusting bolt. Disconnect the belt from the pump.

2. Disconnect the return and pressure hoses from the pump. Cover the hose connector and union on the pump and open ends of the hoses to avoid the entrance of dirt.

3. On the 304 V8, remove the front bracket from the engine.

4. Remove the two nuts which secure the rear of the pump to the bracket, and the two bolts which secure the front of the pump to the bracket and remove the pump.

5. To install, position the pump in the bracket and install the rear attaching screws. On the 304 V8, install the front bracket.

6. Connect the hydraulic hoses. Adjust the drive belt to the correct tension of about 125 lbs.

7. Fill the pump reservoir to the correct level.

8. Start the engine and wait for at least three minutes before turning the steering wheel. Check the level frequently during this time.

9. Slowly turn the steering wheel through its entire range a few times with the engine running. Recheck the level and inspect for possible leaks.

NOTE: *If air becomes trapped in the fluid, the pump may become noisy until all of the air is out. This may take some time since trapped air does not bleed out rapidly.*

9 · Brakes

Brake System

ADJUSTMENT

The method of brake adjustment varies somewhat depending on whether the vehicle is equipped with cam adjustment brakes, star wheel adjustment brakes or star wheel adjustment brakes with self adjusters. When the brake linings become worn, effective brake pedal travel is reduced. Adjusting the brake shoes will restore the necessary travel.

Before adjusting the brakes, check the spring nuts, brake dust shield to axle flange bolts, and wheel bearing adjustments. Any looseness in these parts will cause erratic brake operation. Also on models prior to 1972 make sure that the brake pedal has the correct amount of free travel without moving the master cylinder piston (free play). There should be about ½ in. of free play at the master cylinder eye bolt. Turn the eye bolt to adjust free play.

Release the parking brakes and centralize the brake shoes in the drums by depressing the brake pedal hard and then releasing it. It is best to have all four wheels off the ground when the brakes are adjusted so that you can go back to each wheel to double check your adjustments.

BRAKE SHOE INITIAL ADJUSTMENT

If the brake assemblies have been disassembled, an initial adjustment must be made before the drum is installed. It may also be necessary to back off the adjustment to remove the drums.

When the brake parts have been installed in their correct position, adjust the adjusting screw assemblies to a point where approximately ⅜ in. of threads are exposed between the star wheel and the star wheel nut.

Cam Adjustment Brakes

1. Jack up the vehicle until all of the wheels, or at least the one to be adjusted first, are off the ground.

2. Turn the forward shoe adjusting cams on the left side of the vehicle clockwise until the shoes are tight against the drums. Then turn the cams in the opposite direction until the wheels rotate freely without brake drag.

3. Turn the rear adjusting cams on the left side counter-clockwise until the shoes are tight against the drums. Then turn the cams in the opposite direction until the wheels rotate freely without brake drag.

4. Repeat the two steps given above on the right side of the vehicle, turning the forward shoe adjusting cams counter-

Cam adjustment brakes

clockwise and the rear shoe adjusting cams clockwise to tighten.

Star Wheel Adjusting Type Brakes (without self-adjuster)

1. Jack up the vehicle.
2. Remove the adjusting hole dust clip from the back of the brake backing plate.
3. Use a brake adjusting tool to turn the star wheel. Raise the handle of the tool to tighten the shoes against the drum.

Star wheel adjustment brakes

4. When the brake shoes are tight against the drum, turn the star wheel in the opposite direction until the wheel rotates freely without brake drag.
5. Repeat the above procedure for all four wheels.

Star Wheel Adjusting Type Brakes (with self-adjusters)

1. Jack up the vehicle.
2. Remove the access slot cover and using a brake adjusting tool or screw driver, rotate the star wheel until the wheel is locked and can't be turned by hand. To tighten, rotate the star wheel in the clockwise direction.
3. Back off the star wheel at least 15 to 20 notches. To back off the star wheel on the brake, insert an ice pick or thin screw driver in the adjusting screw slot to hold the automatic adjusting lever away from the star wheel. Do not attempt to back off on the adjusting screw without holding the adjusting lever away from the star wheel as the adjuster will be damaged.

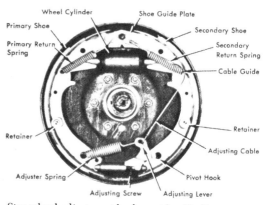

Star wheel adjustment brakes with self adjusters

Hydraulic System

MASTER CYLINDER

Removal and Installation

To remove the master cylinder, disconnect and plug the brake lines, disconnect the wires from the stoplight switch, disconnect the master cylinder pushrod at the brake pedal (manual brakes only—1972–76), remove all attaching bolts and nuts and lift the assembly from the vehicle.

Installation is the reverse of the removal procedure. Bleed the hydraulic system.

Overhaul

SINGLE SYSTEM

1. After the master cylinder has been removed it should be dismantled and

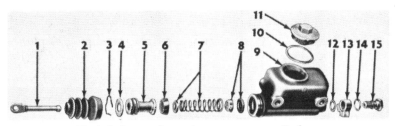

Exploded view of a single system master cylinder

1. Pushrod	7. Valve spring assembly	13. Outlet fitting
2. Boot	8. Valve seat	14. Outlet fitting bolt
3. Piston stop lock wire	9. Supply tank	gasket
4. Stop plate	10. Filler cap gasket	15. Oulet fitting bolt
5. Piston	11. Filler cap	
6. Master cylinder cup	12. Outlet fitting gasket	

washed in alcohol. Never wash any part of the hydraulic braking system in gasoline or kerosene.

2. After all the parts have been thoroughly cleaned with alcohol, make a careful inspection, replacing those parts which show signs of deterioration.

3. Inspect the cylinder bore. If it is rough it should be honed out or a new cylinder installed.

4. Clean out the cylinder with alcohol. Pass a wire through the ports that open from the supply reservoir into the cylinder bore to make sure that these passages are free of any foreign matter.

5. Install a new piston, primary cup, valve, and valve seat when rebuilding the master cylinder.

6. When reassembling the master cylinder, dip all internal parts in clean brake fluid. Install the valve seat in the end of the cylinder with the flat surface toward the valve.

7. Install the valve assembly.

8. Install the return spring and primary cup. The flat side of the cup goes toward the piston.

9. Install the piston and the piston stop snap ring.

10. Install the fitting connection.

11. Fill the reservoir half full with brake fluid and operate the piston with the piston rod until fluid is ejected at the fitting.

12. Install the master cylinder to the firewall or in position under the floor pan. Fill it to a level ½ in. below the top of the fill hole.

13. Make the necessary connections and adjust the pedal clearance.

14. Bleed the brake lines.

15. Recheck the entire hydraulic brake system to make sure there are no leaks.

DUAL SYSTEM—1972-75

1. Remove the filler cap and empty all the fluid.

2. The stop light switch and primary piston stop, located in the stop light switch outlet hole, must be removed before removing the snap ring from the piston bore. Remove the snap ring, pushrod assembly and the primary and secondary piston assemblies. Air pressure applied in the piston stop hole will help facilitate the removal of the secondary piston assembly.

3. The residual check valves are located under the front and rear fluid outlet tube seats.

4. The tube seats must be removed with self tapping screws to permit the removal of the check valves. Screw the self-

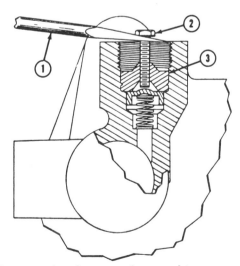

Removing the tube seats with a screwdriver

1. Screwdriver
2. Self-tapping screw
3. Tube seat

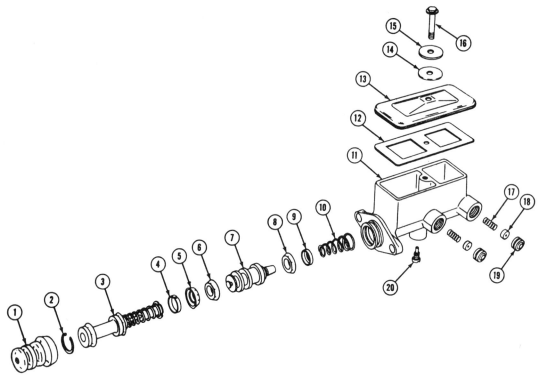

Exploded view of a double system master cylinder. (Prior to 1972)

tapping screws into the tube seats and place two screw driver tips under the screw head and force the screw upward.

5. Remove the expander in the rear secondary cup, secondary cups, return spring, cup protector, primary cup, and washer from the secondary piston.

6. Immerse all of the metal parts in clean brake fluid and clean them. Use an air hose to blow out dirt and cleaning solvent from recesses and internal passages.

7. After cleaning, place all of the parts on clean paper in a clean pan.

8. Inspect all parts for damage or excessive wear. Replace any damaged, worn, or chipped parts. Inspect the hydraulic cylinder bore for signs of scoring, rust, pitting, or etching. Any of these will require replacement of the hydraulic cylinder.

9. Prior to assembling the master cylinder, dip all of the components in clean brake fluid and place them on clean paper or in a clean pan.

10. Install the primary cup washer, primary cup, cup protector, and return spring on the secondary piston.

11. Install the piston cups in the double groove end of the secondary piston, so the flat side of the cups face each other (lip of

the cups away from each other). Install the cup expander in the lip groove of the end cup.

12. Coat the cylinder bore and piston assemblies with clean brake fluid before installing any parts in the cylinder.

13. Install the secondary piston assembly first and then the primary piston.

14. Install the pushrod assembly, which includes the pushrod, boot, and rod retainer, and secure with the snap ring. Install the primary piston stop and stop light switch.

15. Place new rubber check valves over the check valve springs and install in the outlet holes, spring first.

16. Install the tube seats, flat side toward the check valve, and press in with tube nuts or the master cylinder brake tube nuts.

17. Before the master cylinder is installed on the vehicle it must be bled. Support the cylinder assembly in a vise and fill both fluid reservoirs with brake fluid.

18. Loosely install a plug in each outlet of the cylinder. Depress the push rod several times until air bubbles cease to appear in the brake fluid.

19. Tighten the plugs and attempt to de-

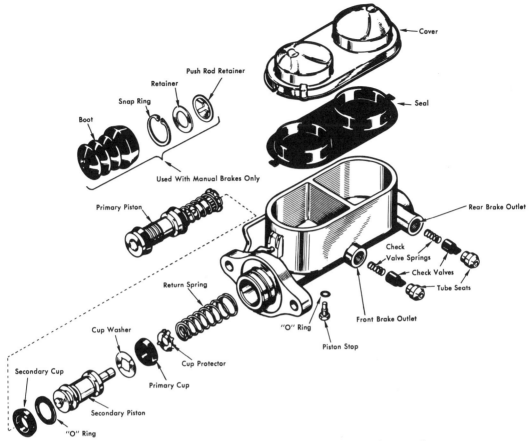

An exploded view of a double system master cylinder. (1972–75)

press the piston. The piston travel should be restricted after all of the air is expelled.

20. Install the master cylinder in the vehicle and bleed all the hydraulic lines at the wheel cylinders.

DUAL SYSTEM—1976

1. Remove the master cylinder from the vehicle and remove the cover and diaphragm seal. Drain the brake fluid from the reservoir and mount it in a vise.

2. On vehicles with manual brakes remove the boot, pushrod, and pushrod retainer. Straighten the locktab in the side of the retainer in order to remove it.

3. Push the primary piston inward with a phillips screwdriver, remove the snap-ring from the groove in the cylinder bore, and remove the primary and secondary piston assemblies. Air pressure applied through the piston stop hole will help in the removal of the secondary piston.

4. Remove the piston seal and piston cups from the secondary piston. It is not

necessary to disassemble the primary piston because a new complete primary piston assembly is supplied in the rebuilding kit.

5. Clean and inspect the master cylinder. Replace the master cylinder body if the bore is severely scored, corroded, or pitted, cracked, porous, or is otherwise damaged. Check the by-pass and compensator ports to make sure that they are open and not plugged or dirty. Use brake fluid and air pressure to open these passages. Do not use wire.

NOTE: *Use only clean brake fluid or an approved cleaning solvent to wash the master cylinder. Do not use any solvent containing mineral oil such as gasoline, kerosene, alcohol, or carbon tetrachloride. Mineral oil harms rubber components.*

6. Check the tube seats in the outlet ports. Replace the seats only if they are cracked, scored, cocked in the bore, or loose. Replace the tube seats as follows:

7. Enlarge the hole in the tube seat

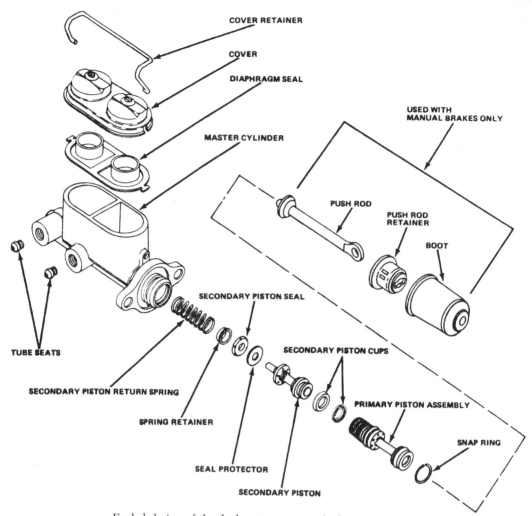

Exploded view of the dual system master cylinder on 1976 models

with a $1\frac{3}{16}$ in. drill. Place a flat washer on each outlet port and thread a $\frac{1}{4}$-20 x $\frac{3}{4}$ in. long screw into the seat. Tighten the screw until the seat is loosened. Remove the seat, screw, and washer. Flush any metal chips away with brake fluid and compressed air.

8. Install the replacement tube seats, if removed, using spare tube fitting nuts to press the seats into place. Be careful that the seats don't become cocked during installation. Make sure that the seats are bottomed. Remove the tube fitting nuts and check for burrs or chips. Rinse the master cylinder in brake fluid and blow out all passages with compressed air.

9. Install the piston cups on the secondary piston. The piston cup installed in the groove at the end of the piston should have its lip facing away from the piston.

Install the next cup so that its lip faces the piston.

10. Install the seal protector, piston seal, spring retainer, and return spring on the secondary piston. Install the piston seal so that its lip faces the interior of the master cylinder bore when the assembly is installed. Make sure that the return spring seats against the retainer and that the retainer is located inside the lip of the piston seal.

11. Lubricate the master cylinder bore and secondary piston seal and cups with brake fluid and install the secondary piston assembly in the cylinder bore.

12. Lubricate the seals on the primary piston assembly with brake fluid and install the assembly in the master cylinder bore.

13. Push the primary piston inward with

a phillips screwdriver and install the retaining snap-ring in the groove of the master cylinder bore.

14. On vehicles with manual brakes, install the pushrod, pushrod retainer, and boot. Bend the small locktab in the side of the retainer into the groove at the end of the master cylinder and install the boot.

15. Install the diaphragm seal on the master cylinder cover.

16. Install the master cylinder in the vehicle.

BLEEDING THE BRAKES

The hydraulic brake system must be bled whenever a fluid line has been disconnected because air gets into the system. A leak in the system may sometimes be indicated by the presence of a spongy brake pedal. Air trapped in the system is compressible and does not permit the pressure applied to the brake pedal, to be transmitted solidly through to the brakes. The system must be absolutely free from air at all times. When bleeding brakes, bleed at the wheel most distant from the master cylinder first, the next most distant second, and so on. During the bleeding operation the master cylinder must be kept at least $3/4$ full of brake fluid.

To bleed the brakes, first carefully clean all dirt from around the master cylinder filler cap. If a bleeder tank is used follow the manufacturer's instructions. Remove the filler cap and fill the master cylinder

View of the inside surface of a front backing plate prior to 1972

1. Brake adjuster cam
2. Brake line leading to the wheel cylinder
3. Bleeder screw
4. Brake adjuster cam

to the lower edge of the filler neck. Clean off the bleeder connections at all four wheel cylinders. Attach the bleeder hose to the right rear wheel cylinder bleeder screw and place the end of the tube in a glass jar, submerged in brake fluid. Open the bleeder valve $1/2$–$3/4$ of a turn.

Have an assistant depress the brake pedal slowly and allow it to return. Continue this pumping action to force any air out of the system. When bubbles cease to appear at the end of the bleeder hose, close the bleeder valve and remove the hose.

Check the level of fluid in the master cylinder reservoir and replenish as necessary.

After the bleeding operation at each wheel cylinder has been completed, fill the master cylinder reservoir and replace the filler plug.

Do not reuse the fluid which has been removed from the lines through the bleeding process because it contains air bubbles and dirt.

Drum Brakes

BRAKE DRUMS

Removal and Installation

FRONT

The front brake drums are attached to the wheel hubs by five bolts. These bolts are also used for mounting the wheels on the hub. Remove the wheel and press or drive out the bolts to remove the drum from the hub.

When placing the drum on the hub, make sure that the contacting surfaces are clean and flat. Line up the holes in the drum with those in the hub and put the drum over the shoulder on the hub. Insert five new bolts through the drum and hub and drive the bolts into place solidly. Place a round piece of stock approximately the diameter of the head of the bolt, in a vise; next place the hub and drum assembly over it so that the bolt head rests on it. Then flatten the bolt head into the countersunk section of the hub with a punch.

The runout of the drum face should be

within 0.030 in. If the runout is found to be greater than 0.030 in., it will be necessary to reset the bolts to correct the condition.

The left hand hub bolts have an L stamped on the head of the bolt.

The left hand threaded nuts may have a groove cut around the hexagon faces, or the word LEFT stamped on the face.

Hubs with left hand threaded hub bolts are installed on the left hand side of the vehicle. Late production vehicles are equipped with right hand bolts and nuts on all four hubs.

REAR

The rear brake drums are held in position by spring clip-type locknuts on pre-1976 models and by three drum-to-hub retaining screws on 1976 models. After the spring-type locknuts or retaining screws are removed, the drum can be slid off the axle shaft or hub and brake shoes. It may be necessary to back off the brake shoe adjustment so that any lip on the inside of the brake drum clears the brake shoes.

Inspection

Using a brake drum micrometer, check all drums. Should a brake drum be scored or rough, it may be reconditioned by grinding or turning on a lathe. Do not remove more than 0.030 in. thickness of metal. The maximum allowable oversize for any brake drum is 0.060 in. over the original diameter. Hard spots in a brake drum can and should be removed by grinding. A normal cutting tool will ride over hard spots, dulling the tool and leaving high spots on the drum friction surface. If a drum is reconditioned in this manner, either the correct factory supplied, 0.030 in. oversize lining should be installed, or a shim equal in thickness to the metal removed should be placed between the lining and the brake shoe so that the arc of the lining will be the same as that of the drum.

Use compressed air and a clean cloth to clean dirt from the brake drums. If further cleaning is required, use soap and water. Do not use brake fluid, gasoline, kerosene, or any other similar solvents.

BRAKE SHOES

Removal and Installation

1. Jack up the vehicle so that all four wheels are off the ground.

2. On vehicles equipped with cam adjustment brakes, turn all eccentrics to the lower side of the cam. On vehicles equipped with star wheel adjustment, turn the star adjuster all the way in.

3. Remove the wheels and the hubs and drums to give access to the brake shoes.

4. Install wheel cylinder clamps to retain the wheel cylinder pistons in place and prevent leakage of brake fluid while replacing the shoes.

5. Remove the return springs with a brake spring remover tool.

6. On models with self adjusters, remove the adjuster cable, cable guide, adjuster lever and adjuster springs.

7. Remove the hold down clips or springs and remove the brake shoes.

8. Before installing the new shoes, now would be a good time to inspect the oil seals in the hubs. If the condition of the seals is doubtful, replace them. Also check the wheel cylinders for leakage. Pull back the dust covers. If there is fluid present behind the dust cover the wheel cylinder must be rebuilt or replaced.

NOTE: *Always replace brake lining in axle sets. Never replace linings on one side or just on one wheel.*

9. Install the brakes in the reverse order of removal.

WHEEL CYLINDERS

Overhaul

Wheel cylinder rebuilding kits are available reconditioning wheel cylinders. The kits usually contain new cup springs, cylinder cups and in some, new boots. The most important factor to keep in mind when rebuilding wheel cylinders is cleanliness. Keep all dirt away from the wheel cylinders when you are reassembling them.

1. To remove the wheel cylinder, jack up the vehicle and remove the wheel, hub, and drum.

2. Disconnect the brake line at the fitting on the brake backing plate.

3. Remove the brake assemblies.

4. Remove the screws or nuts that hold the wheel cylinder to the backing plate

and remove the wheel cylinder from the vehicle.

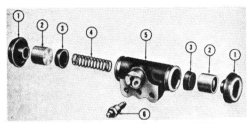

A wheel cylinder from a model prior to 1972

1. Boot   3. Cylinder cup   5. Cylinder
2. Piston   4. Cup spring   6. Bleeder screw

5. Remove the rubber dust covers on the ends of the cylinder. Remove the pistons and piston cups and the spring. Remove the bleeder screw and make sure it is not plugged.

6. Discard all of the parts that the rebuilding kit will replace.

7. Examine the inside of the cylinder. If it is severely rusted, pitted or scratched, then the cylinder must be replaced as the piston cups won't be able to seal against the walls of the cylinder.

8. Using emery cloth or crocus cloth, polish the inside of the cylinder. Do not polish in a lengthwise direction; polish by rotating the wheel cylinder around the polishing cloth supported on your fingers. The purpose of this is to put a new surface on the inside of the cylinder. Keep the inside of the cylinder coated with brake fluid while polishing.

NOTE: *Honing the wheel cylinders is not recommended due to the possibility of removing too much material from the bore, making it too large to seal.*

9. Wash out the cylinder with clean brake fluid after polishing.

10. When reassembling the cylinder dip all of the parts in clean brake fluid. Reassemble in the reverse order of removal.

FRONT WHEEL BEARINGS

Removal and Installation

To remove the front wheel bearings, remove the hub cap, snap ring, drive flange, and the two nuts and lockwashers. The outer wheel bearing can then be removed. To remove the inner wheel bearing, the outer wheel bearing must be removed and the hub removed from the spindle. Turn the hub over and drive out the inner bear-

ing with a hammer and a block of wood, using the block of wood as a drift, having it placed through the center of the hub and up against the inner side of the inner wheel bearing. Discard the grease seal and replace it.

Before handling the bearings there are a few things that you should remember to do and not to do.

Remember to DO the following:

1. Remove all outside dirt from the housing before exposing the bearing.

2. Treat a used bearing as gently as you would a new one.

3. Work with clean tools in clean surroundings.

4. Use clean, dry canvas gloves, or at least clean, dry hands.

5. Clean solvents and flushing fluids are a must.

6. Use clean paper when laying out the bearings to dry.

7. Protect disassembled bearings from rust and dirt. Cover them up.

8. Use clean rags to wipe bearings.

9. Keep the bearing in oil-proof paper when they are to be stored or are not in use.

10. Clean the inside of the housing before replacing the bearing.

Do NOT do the following:

1. Don't work in dirty surroundings.

2. Don't use dirty, chipped, or damaged tools.

3. Try not to work on wooden work benches or use wooden mallets.

4. Don't handle bearings with dirty or moist hands.

5. Do not use gasoline for cleaning; use a safe solvent.

6. Do not spin-dry bearings with compressed air. They will be damaged.

7. Do not spin unclean bearings.

8. Avoid using cotton waste or dirty cloths to wipe bearings.

9. Try not to scratch or nick bearing surfaces.

10. Do not allow the bearing to come in contact with dirt or rust at any time.

Place all of the bearings, nuts, washers, and dust caps in a container of solvent. Cleanliness is basic to wheel bearing maintenance. Use a soft brush to thoroughly clean each part. Make sure that every bit of dirt and grease is rinsed off, then place each cleaned part on an absorbent cloth and let them dry completely.

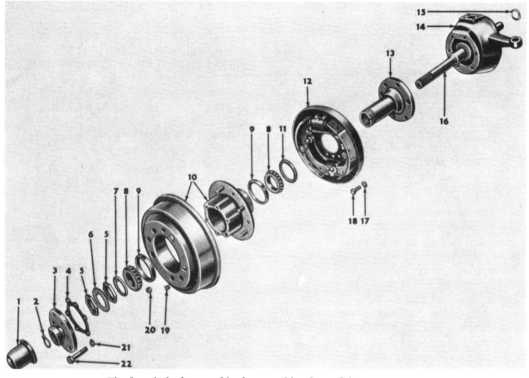

The front hub, drum and brake assembly of a model prior to 1972

1. Hub cap	9. Cup	17. Lockwasher
2. Snap ring	10. Hub and drum	18. Bolt
3. Drive flange	11. Oil seal	19. Screw
4. Gasket	12. Left front brake	20. Nut
5. Nut	13. Spindle and bushing	21. Lockwasher
6. Lockwasher	14. Left knuckle and arm	22. Bolt
7. Lockwasher	15. Thrust washer	
8. Cone and rollers	16. Universal joint shaft	

Inspect the bearings for pitting, flat spots, rust, and rough areas. Check the races on the hub and the spindle for the same defects and rub them clean with a rag that has been soaked in solvent. If the races show hairline cracks or worn, shiny areas, they must be replaced with new parts. Replacement seals, bearings, and

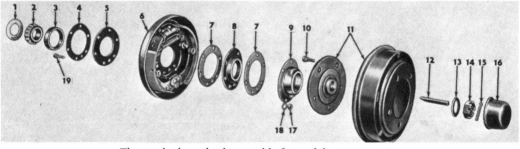

The rear brake and axle assembly for models prior to 1972

1. Oil seal	8. Grease retainer	15. Cotter pin
2. Cone and rollers	9. Grease protecter	16. Hub cap
3. Cup	10. Bolt	17. Nut
4. Shims	11. Hub and drum	18. Lockwasher
5. Bearing retainer	12. Shaft key	19. Bolt
6. Brake	13. Oil seal	
7. Gasket	14. Nut	

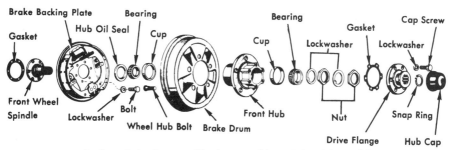

The front hub, drum and brake assembly—1972–1976 models

other required parts can be bought at an auto parts store. The old parts that are to be replaced should be taken along to be compared with the replacement part to ensure a perfect match.

Pack the wheel bearings with grease. There are special devices made for the specific purpose of greasing bearings, but, if one is not available, pack the wheel bearings by hand. Put a large dab of grease in the palm of your hand and push the bearing through it with a sliding motion. The grease must be forced through the side of the bearing and in between each roller. Continue until the grease begins to ooze out the other side and through the gaps between the rollers; the bearing must be completely packed with grease.

Turn the hub assembly over, making sure that it is perfectly clean, and drop the inner wheel bearing into place. Using a hammer and a block of wood, tap the new seal in place. Do not hit the seal with the hammer directly. Move the block of wood around the circumference until it is seated properly.

Slide the hub assembly onto the spindle, and push it as far as it will go, making sure that it has completely covered the brake shoes.

Place the outer bearing in place over the spindle. Press it in until it is snug. Place the washer on the spindle behind the bearing. Put on the spindle adjusting nut. While turning the wheel by hand, turn the nut down until a slight binding is felt, then back off about $\frac{1}{6}$ of a turn. Bend the lip on the lockwasher over the edge of the nut. Place the second washer and nut on the spindle and tighten them up against the adjusting nut, being careful not to turn the adjusting nut further onto the spindle.

Reassemble the rest of the hub assembly in the reverse order of removal.

If the bearings are correctly adjusted, wheel shake will be just perceptible when the wheel is gripped by hand and shaken from side to side. The wheel will also turn freely with no drag.

If the bearing adjustment is too tight, the rollers may break or become overheated. Loose bearings may cause excessive wear and possible noise.

Bearing Diagnosis

This section will help in the diagnosis of bearing failure. Such a diagnosis can be helpful in determining the cause of axle failure. The illustrations will help to take some of the guesswork out of deciding when to use an old bearing and when to replace it with a new one.

When disassembling an axle, the general condition of all bearings should be noted and classified where possible. Proper recognition of the cause will help in correcting the problem and avoiding a repetition of the failure.

Some of the common causes of bearing failure are:

a. Abuse during assembly or disassembly;

b. Improper assembly methods;

c. Improper or inadequate lubrication;

d. Bearing contact with dirt or water;

e. Wear caused by dirt or metal chips;

f. Corrosion or rust;

g. Seizing due to overloading;

h. Overheating;

i. Frettage of the bearing seats;

j. Brinelling from impact or shock loading;

k. Manufacturing defects;

l. Pitting due to fatigue.

To avoid damage to the bearing from improper handling, it is best to treat a used bearing the same as a new bearing.

Always work in a clean area with clean tools. Remove all outside dirt from the housing before exposing a bearing and clean all bearing seats before installing a bearing.

CAUTION: *Never spin a bearing, either by hand or with compressed air. This will lead to almost certain bearing failure.*

Transmission Brake

ADJUSTMENT

Make sure that the brake handle on the instrument panel is fully released. Check the operating linkage and the cable to make sure that they don't bind. If necessary, free the cable and lubricate it. Rotate the brake drum until one pair of the three sets of holes are over the shoe adjusting screw wheels in the brake. Use the edge of the holes in the brake drum as a fulcrum for the brake adjusting tool or a screwdriver. Rotate each notched adjusting

Transmission brake adjustment

1. Ball nut
2. ³⁄₃₂ in. clearance
3. Adjusting screw

screw by moving the handle of the tool away from the center of the drive shaft until the shoes are snug against the drum. Back off seven notches on the adjusting screw wheels to secure the proper running clearance between the shoes and the drum.

Bearing Failure Chart

General Wear

Cause	Serviceability
Wear on races and rollers caused by fine abrasives	Clean all parts and check seals. Install new bearing if old one is rough or noisy.

Normal wear pattern. (© Chevrolet Div. G.M. Corp.)

Step Wear

Step wear. (© Chevrolet Div. G.M. Corp.)

Cause	Serviceability
Wear pattern on roller ends caused by fine abrasives	Clean all parts and check seals. Install new bearings if old one is rough or noisy.

Indentations

Cause	Serviceability
Surface depressions on races and rollers caused by hard foreign particles	Clean all parts and check seals. Install new bearing if old one is rough or noisy.

Indentations. (© Chevrolet Div. G.M. Corp.)

Galling. (© Chevrolet Div. G.M. Corp.)

Galling

Cause	Serviceability
Metal smears on roller ends due to overheating from improper lubricant or overloading	Install a new bearing. Check seals and use proper lubricant.

Etching

Cause	Serviceability
Bearing surfaces appear gray or gray-black with related etching	Install new bearing and check seals. Use proper lubricant.

Etching. (© Chevrolet Div. G.M. Corp.)

Cage wear. (© Chevrolet Div. G.M. Corp.)

Cage Wear

Cause	Serviceability
Wear around outside diameter of cage and rollers caused by foreign material and poor lubrication	Clean all parts, check seals, and install new bearing.

Bearing Failure Chart (cont.)

Fatigue Spalling

Cause	*Serviceability*
Flaking of surface metal due to fatigue	Clean all parts and install new bearing.

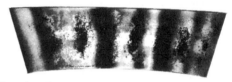

Fatigue spalling. (© Chevrolet Div. G.M. Corp.)

Heat discoloration. (© Chevrolet Div. G.M. Corp.)

Heat Discoloration

Cause	*Serviceability*
Discoloration from faint yellow to dark blue due to overload or lubricant breakdown. Softening of races or rollers also	Check for softening of parts by drawing a file over suspected area. The file will glide easily over hard metal, but will cut soft metal. If overheating is evident, install new bearings. Check seals and other parts.

Stain Discoloration

Cause	*Serviceability*
Stain discoloration ranging from light brown to black, caused by lubricant breakdown or moisture	Reuse bearings if stains can be removed by light polishing and no overheating exists. Check seals.

Stain discoloration. (© Chevrolet Div. G.M. Corp.)

Brinelling. (© Chevrolet Div. G.M. Corp.)

Brinelling

Cause	*Serviceability*
Surface indentations in race caused by rollers under impact load or vibration while the bearing is not rotating	If the old bearing is rough or noisy, install a new bearing.

Bent Cage

Cause	Serviceability
Improper handling	Install a new bearing.

Bent cage. (© Chevrolet Div. G.M. Corp.)

Bent cage. (© Chevrolet Div. G.M. Corp.)

Bent Cage

Cause	Serviceability
Improper handling	Install a new bearing.

Misalignment

Cause	Serviceability
Outer race misaligned as shown	Install a new bearing and be sure races and bearing are properly seated.

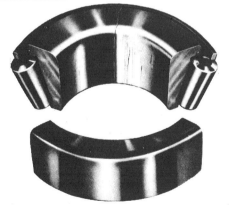

Misalignment. (© Chevrolet Div. G.M. Corp.)

Cracked inner race. (© Chevrolet Div. G.M. Corp.)

Cracked Inner Race

Cause	Serviceability
Crack due to improper fit, cocked bearing, or poor bearing seats	Install a new bearing and be sure it is seated properly.

Bearing Failure Chart (cont.)

Frettage

Cause	Serviceability
Corrosion due to small movement of parts with no lubrication	Clean parts and check seals. Install a new bearing and be sure of proper lubrication.

Frettage. (© Chevrolet Div. G.M. Corp.)

Smears. (© Chevrolet Div. G.M. Corp.)

Smears

Cause	Serviceability
Metal smears due to slippage caused by poor fit, improper lubrication, overloading, or handling damage	Clean parts, install new bearing, and check for proper fit and lubrication.

Brake Specifications
(All measurements are in Inches.)

Model	Master Cylinder Bore	Wheel Cylinder		Drum Diameter	
		Front	Rear	Front	Rear
CJ-3B	1	1	¾	9	9
Prior to 1972 CJ-5 CJ-5A CJ-6 CJ-6A	1	1	13⁄16	10	10
1972–76 CJ-5 CJ-6 CJ-7	1	1⅛	15⁄16	10	10

10 · Body

Windshield Assembly

Removal and Installation

The windshield and frame may be lowered to the hood by unlatching the two clamps at each side of the windshield. When in the lowered position, always secure the windshield with the strap provided, running it through the loop at the top of the windshield and the one at the radiator guard or hood, and drawing it tight.

To remove the windshield and frame as an assembly, remove the wiper control switch from the dash (1972–74). On the older models pull the windshield wiper vacuum hose from the fitting on the wiper motor. Disconnect the windshield wiper motor electric wires from the switch, and remove them from the grommetted hole.

Unlatch the two windshield clamps on each side of the windshield. Fold the windshield forward until the slot in the windshield hinges aligns with the flat side of the pin in the body hinges. Slip the windshield off the pins and remove it from the body.

Install the windshield assembly in the reverse order of removal.

Removal and Installation

Before attempting to remove the glass from the windshield frame, make sure that the weatherstripping is at a temperature of at least 75° F or warmer. This is to make sure that it is pliable and won't break. Remove the windshield wiper arms from the shafts.

On models prior to 1972, the windshield glass is mounted in a rubber weatherstrip which is mounted in the frame. A rubber locking strip, which holds the glass firmly in place, is inserted in a moulded groove around the rear face of the weatherstrip. To remove the glass it is necessary to first remove the locking strip which may be pried out with a screwdriver or a similar tool.

To install, coat the locking strip and the groove in which it is placed with a thin coat of light oil or liquid soap to facilitate installation. Place the glass in the weatherstripping and place it in position in the frame. Insert the locking strip in the groove.

On the 1972–76 models the weatherstripping around the edge of the windshield is the locking type. Use a wedge shaped fiber or hardwood stick or wand to

235

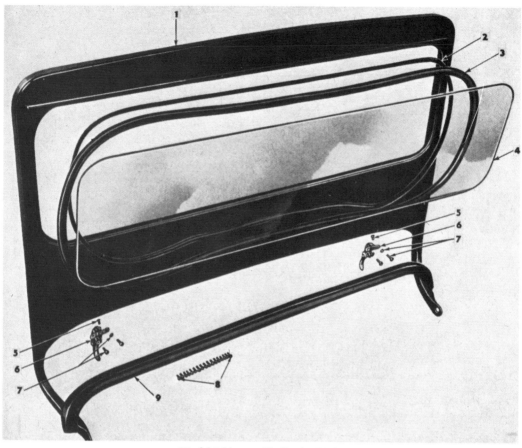

Windshield assembly for the CJ-3B

1. Windshield assembly	4. Windshield glass	7. Screw and lockwasher
2. Filler strip	5. Screw	8. Screw
3. Weatherstrip	6. Clamp	9. Weatherstrip

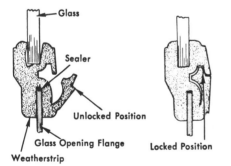

Cross-sectional view of the windshield weatherstrip (1972–1976)

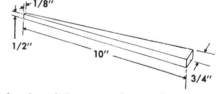

Wedge shaped fiber or wooden wand

unlock the weatherstripping, starting at a bottom corner and working across the bottom first, then around the rest of the frame.

Use the fiber stick to break the seal between the glass and the weatherstrip and also to unlock the weatherstrip.

Removing the windshield from the weatherstrip should be done by two persons, one pushing the lower inside corner, and one lifting the windshield as it comes free.

Remove the weatherstrip from the opening of the frame. Inspect the weatherstrip and clean any old sealer from the glass cavity and the flange cavity. Inspect for uneven surfaces or irregularities in the windshield opening flange that could cause stress damage to the glass.

If the windshield removed is to be reinstalled, clean any hardened sealer from the edges of the glass.

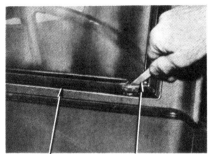

Rubber Weatherstrip   Wood Wand or
                       Fiber Stick   72802

Breaking the seal between the window glass and the weatherstrip with a wedge shaped stick. The stick is also used to unlock the weatherstrip

Using a medium body sealer, apply a $\frac{3}{16}$ in. bead of sealer completely around the weatherstrip flange cavity.

Install the weatherstrip on the windshield flange (frame). Apply a liberal amount of liquid soap solution or light lubricating oil in the glass cavity of the weatherstrip.

With two people working on the outside of the vehicle, work the windshield into the upper glass cavity and into each side. Check for equal side clearance. Position the wooden stick under the bottom of the glass and lift the windshield up and into the lower glass cavity.

Use the wooden wand to lock the weatherstrip in position.

Using a pressure applicator, apply a bead of sealer between the weatherstrip and the glass around the entire outside perimeter of the glass.

Hood

Alignment

The hood hinge mounting holes are oversized for a range of adjustments; forward, backward, and from side to side.

If the hood must be moved to either side, the hood lock loop striker, hood lever lock, and the safety hook assembly must first be loosened.

Slightly loosen the hinge mounting bolts on one side and tap the hinge in the opposite direction the hood is to be moved. Secure the bolts and repeat the operation on the opposite hinge.

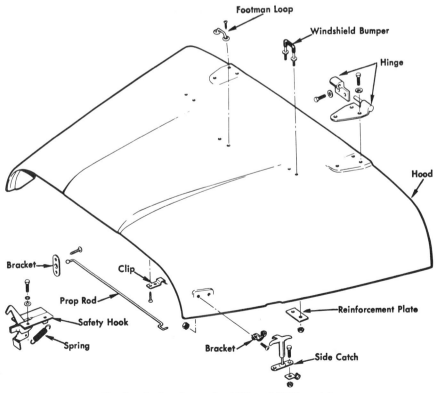

Hood and related parts for 1972 and 1973 models

Tailgate assembly for the CJ-5A and CJ-6A

Move the hood lock loop striker, hood lever lock and safety hook assembly to ensure positive locking.

Tighten all of the attaching bolts.

Tailgate

Removal, Installation
and Alignment

CJ-5 AND CJ-6

To remove the tailgate, rotate it about 45° from the full up position and disengage the right hinge. Rotate the tailgate an additional few degrees and then disengage the left hinge. Install it in the same manner.

To adjust the tailgate, loosen the hinge attaching bolts and slide the body half of the hinge up, down or to either side as needed. Tighten the bolts.

CJ-7

The tailgate on a CJ-7 is hinged at the bottom and is held in the closed position by two latches on either side. The tailgate is supported in the open position by two steel cables.

To remove the tailgate, disconnect the support cables from the tailgate, then, with the tailgate closed, remove the screws attaching the hinges to the tailgate. Disengage the latches and remove the tailgate. Install the tailgate in the reverse order.

To adjust the alignment of the tailgate, loosen the hinge-to-body screws and align the tailgate to the body. Retighten the hinge-to-body screws.

Fuel Tank

Removal and Installation

PRIOR TO 1972

To remove the fuel tank, first make sure that the tank is either completely drained or that the level is at least below any of the vent lines or filler openings so that when these lines are disconnected fuel will not run out.

Remove the driver's seat from the vehicle.

Disconnect all of the ventline hoses, the fuel gauge electrical lead, the fill hose and the fuel outlet line at the tank.

Remove the tank hold down screws from the mounting brackets, or the hold down strap, and lift the tank from the vehicle.

If there is still gas in the tank, be careful not to spill any fuel when lifting it out of the vehicle. Also, empty the tank of all fuel and flush it with water before soldering or welding the tank.

Install the tank in the reverse order of removal.

1972–76

The fuel tank on 1972–76 model CJs is attached to the frame by brackets and bolts. The brackets are attached to the tank at the seam flange.

Before removing the fuel tank, make sure that the level of the fuel inside the tank is at least below any of the various hoses connected. It is best to either drain or siphon the majority of fuel out of the tank to make it easier to handle while removing it.

To remove the tank, loosen all of the clamps retaining hoses to the tank and disconnect the hoses from the tank. It may be necessary to remove the fuel tank-to-mounting bracket screws and lower the tank slightly to gain access to some of the connecting hoses. Disconnect the tank from the mounting brackets, if not already done, and lower the tank from under the vehicle. Be careful not to spill any fuel in the tank while removing it.

Empty the tank of all fuel and flush it with water before soldering or welding.

Install the fuel tank in the reverse order of removal.

Fenders

Removal and Installation

1. Remove all items attached to the apron of the fender.

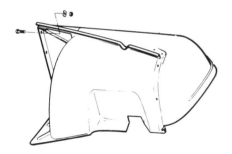

Fender assembly for the CJ-5, CJ-6, and CJ-7 (1972–76)

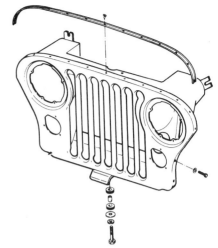

Grille panel assembly for the CJ-5, CJ-6, and CJ-7 (1972–76)

2. Remove the hood retaining latch and, on the 1972–76 models, remove the side marker light.

3. Remove the bolts, nuts and washers which retain the fender and the fender brace to the firewall.

4. Remove the bolts, nuts and washers which secure the fender to the radiator grille guard panel.

5. Pull the fender outward and remove it from the vehicle.

6. Install in the reverse order of removal, applying sealer evenly over and along surfaces where the fender and the apron make contact with other sheet metal parts.

Appendix

General Conversion Table

Multiply by	To convert	To	
2.54	Inches	Centimeters	.3937
30.48	Feet	Centimeters	.0328
.914	Yards	Meters	1.094
1.609	Miles	Kilometers	.621
.645	Square inches	Square cm.	.155
.836	Square yards	Square meters	1.196
16.39	Cubic inches	Cubic cm.	.061
28.3	Cubic feet	Liters	.0353
.4536	Pounds	Kilograms	2.2045
4.546	Gallons	Liters	.22
.068	Lbs./sq. in. (psi)	Atmospheres	14.7
.138	Foot pounds	Kg. m.	7.23
1.014	H.P. (DIN)	H.P. (SAE)	.9861
——	To obtain	From	Multiply by

Note: 1 cm. equals 10 mm.; 1 mm. equals .0394″.

Conversion—Common Fractions to Decimals and Millimeters

INCHES			INCHES			INCHES		
Common Fractions	Decimal Fractions	Millimeters (approx.)	Common Fractions	Decimal Fractions	Millimeters (approx.)	Common Fractions	Decimal Fractions	Millimeters (approx.)
1/128	.008	0.20	11/32	.344	8.73	43/64	.672	17.07
1/64	.016	0.40	23/64	.359	9.13	11/16	.688	17.46
1/32	.031	0.79	3/8	.375	9.53	45/64	.703	17.86
3/64	.047	1.19	25/64	.391	9.92	23/32	.719	18.26
1/16	.063	1.59	13/32	.406	10.32	47/64	.734	18.65
5/64	.078	1.98	27/64	.422	10.72	3/4	.750	19.05
3/32	.094	2.38	7/16	.438	11.11	49/64	.766	19.45
7/64	.109	2.78	29/64	.453	11.51	25/32	.781	19.84
1/8	.125	3.18	15/32	.469	11.91	51/64	.797	20.24
9/64	.141	3.57	31/64	.484	12.30	13/16	.813	20.64
5/32	.156	3.97	1/2	.500	12.70	53/64	.828	21.03
11/64	.172	4.37	33/64	.516	13.10	27/32	.844	21.43
3/16	.188	4.76	17/32	.531	13.49	55/64	.859	21.83
13/64	.203	5.16	35/64	.547	13.89	7/8	.875	22.23
7/32	.219	5.56	9/16	.563	14.29	57/64	.891	22.62
15/64	.234	5.95	37/64	.578	14.68	29/32	.906	23.02
1/4	.250	6.35	19/32	.594	15.08	59/64	.922	23.42
17/64	.266	6.75	39/64	.609	15.48	15/16	.938	23.81
9/32	.281	7.14	5/8	.625	15.88	61/64	.953	24.21
19/64	.297	7.54	41/64	.641	16.27	31/32	.969	24.61
5/16	.313	7.94	21/32	.656	16.67	63/64	.984	25.00
21/64	.328	8.33						

Conversion—Millimeters to Decimal Inches

mm	inches	mm	inches	mm	inches	mm	inches	mm	inches
1	.039 370	31	1.220 470	61	2.401 570	91	3.582 670	210	8.267 700
2	.078 740	32	1.259 840	62	2.440 940	92	3.622 040	220	8.661 400
3	.118 110	33	1.299 210	63	2.480 310	93	3.661 410	230	9.055 100
4	.157 480	34	1.338 580	64	2.519 680	94	3.700 780	240	9.448 800
5	.196 850	35	1.377 949	65	2.559 050	95	3.740 150	250	9.842 500
6	.236 220	36	1.417 319	66	2.598 420	96	3.779 520	260	10.236 200
7	.275 590	37	1.456 689	67	2.637 790	97	3.818 890	270	10.629 900
8	.314 960	38	1.496 050	68	2.677 160	98	3.858 260	280	11.032 600
9	.354 330	39	1.535 430	69	2.716 530	99	3.897 630	290	11.417 300
10	.393 700	40	1.574 800	70	2.755 900	100	3.937 000	300	11.811 000
11	.433 070	41	1.614 170	71	2.795 270	105	4.133 848	310	12.204 700
12	.472 440	42	1.653 540	72	2.834 640	110	4.330 700	320	12.598 400
13	.511 810	43	1.692 910	73	2.874 010	115	4.527 550	330	12.992 100
14	.551 180	44	1.732 280	74	2.913 380	120	4.724 400	340	13.385 800
15	.590 550	45	1.771 650	75	2.952 750	125	4.921 250	350	13.779 500
16	.629 920	46	1.811 020	76	2.992 120	130	5.118 100	360	14.173 200
17	.669 290	47	1.850 390	77	3.031 490	135	5.314 950	370	14.566 900
18	.708 660	48	1.889 760	78	3.070 860	140	5.511 800	380	14.960 600
19	.748 030	49	1.929 130	79	3.110 230	145	5.708 650	390	15.354 300
20	.787 400	50	1.968 500	80	3.149 600	150	5.905 500	400	15.748 000
21	.826 770	51	2.007 870	81	3.188 970	155	6.102 350	500	19.685 000
22	.866 140	52	2.047 240	82	3.228 340	160	6.299 200	600	23.622 000
23	.905 510	53	2.086 610	83	3.267 710	165	6.496 050	700	27.559 000
24	.944 880	54	2.125 980	84	3.307 080	170	6.692 900	800	31.496 000
25	.984 250	55	2.165 350	85	3.346 450	175	6.889 750	900	35.433 000
26	1.023 620	56	2.204 720	86	3.385 820	180	7.086 600	1000	39.370 000
27	1.062 990	57	2.244 090	87	3.425 190	185	7.283 450	2000	78.740 000
28	1.102 360	58	2.283 460	88	3.464 560	190	7.480 300	3000	118.110 000
29	1.141 730	59	2.322 830	89	3.503 903	195	7.677 150	4000	157.480 000
30	1.181 100	60	2.362 200	90	3.543 300	200	7.874 000	5000	196.850 000

To change decimal millimeters to decimal inches, position the decimal point where desired on either side of the millimeter measurement shown and reset the inches decimal by the same number of digits in the same direction. For example, to convert .001 mm into decimal inches, reset the decimal behind the 1 mm (shown on the chart) to .001; change the decimal inch equivalent (.039" shown) to .00039".

Tap Drill Sizes

National Fine or S.A.E.			National Coarse or U.S.S.		
Screw & Tap Size	Threads Per Inch	Use Drill Number	Screw & Tap Size	Threads Per Inch	Use Drill Number
No. 5	44	37	No. 5	40	39
No. 6	40	33	No. 6	32	36
No. 8	36	29	No. 8	32	29
No. 10	32	21	No. 10	24	25
No. 12	28	15	No. 12	24	17
1/4	28	3	1/4	20	8
5/16	24	1	5/16	18	F
3/8	24	Q	3/8	16	5/16
7/16	20	W	7/16	14	U
1/2	20	29/64	1/2	13	27/64
9/16	18	33/64	9/16	12	31/64
5/8	18	37/64	5/8	11	17/32
3/4	16	11/16	3/4	10	21/32
7/8	14	13/16	7/8	9	49/64
1 1/8	12	1 3/64	1	8	7/8
1 1/4	12	1 11/64	1 1/8	7	63/64
1 1/2	12	1 27/64	1 1/4	7	1 7/64
			1 1/2	6	1 11/32

Decimal Equivalent Size of the Number Drills

Drill No.	Decimal Equivalent	Drill No.	Decimal Equivalent	Drill No.	Decimal Equivalent
80	.0135	53	.0595	26	.1470
79	.0145	52	.0635	25	.1495
78	.0160	51	.0670	24	.1520
77	.0180	50	.0700	23	.1540
76	.0200	49	.0730	22	.1570
75	.0210	48	.0760	21	.1590
74	.0225	47	.0785	20	.1610
73	.0240	46	.0810	19	.1660
72	.0250	45	.0820	18	.1695
71	.0260	44	.0860	17	.1730
70	.0280	43	.0890	16	.1770
69	.0292	42	.0935	15	.1800
68	.0310	41	.0960	14	.1820
67	.0320	40	.0980	13	.1850
66	.0330	39	.0995	12	.1890
65	.0350	38	.1015	11	.1910
64	.0360	37	.1040	10	.1935
63	.0370	36	.1065	9	.1960
62	.0380	35	.1100	8	.1990
61	.0390	34	.1110	7	.2010
60	.0400	33	.1130	6	.2040
59	.0410	32	.1160	5	.2055
58	.0420	31	.1200	4	.2090
57	.0430	30	.1285	3	.2130
56	.0465	29	.1360	2	.2210
55	.0520	28	.1405	1	.2280
54	.0550	27	.1440		

Decimal Equivalent Size of the Letter Drills

Letter Drill	Decimal Equivalent	Letter Drill	Decimal Equivalent	Letter Drill	Decimal Equivalent
A	.234	J	.277	S	.348
B	.238	K	.281	T	.358
C	.242	L	.290	U	.368
D	.246	M	.295	V	.377
E	.250	N	.302	W	.386
F	.257	O	.316	X	.397
G	.261	P	.323	Y	.404
H	.266	Q	.332	Z	.413
I	.272	R	.339		

ANTI-FREEZE INFORMATION

Freezing and Boiling Points of Solutions
According to Percentage of Alcohol or Ethylene Glycol

Freezing Point of Solution	Alcohol Volume %	Alcohol Solution Boils at	Ethylene Glycol Volume %	Ethylene Glycol Solution Boils at
20°F.	12	196°F.	16	216°F.
10°F.	20	189°F.	25	218°F.
0°F.	27	184°F.	33	220°F.
−10°F.	32	181°F.	39	222°F.
−20°F.	38	178°F.	44	224°F.
−30°F.	42	176°F.	48	225°F.

Note: above boiling points are at sea level. For every 1,000 feet of altitude, boiling points are approximately 2°F. lower than those shown. For every pound of pressure exerted by the pressure cap, the boiling points are approximately 3°F. higher than those shown.

ANTI-FREEZE CHART

Temperatures Shown in Degrees Fahrenheit
+32 is Freezing

Cooling System Capacity Quarts	Quarts of ETHYLENE GLYCOL Needed for Protection to Temperatures Shown Below													
	1	2	3	4	5	6	7	8	9	10	11	12	13	14
10	+24°	+16°	+ 4°	−12°	−34°	−62°								
11	+25	+18	+ 8	− 6	−23	−47								
12	+26	+19	+10	0	−15	−34	−57°							
13	+27	+21	+13	+ 3	− 9	−25	−45							
14			+15	+ 6	− 5	−18	−34							
15			+16	+ 8	0	−12	−26							
16			+17	+10	+ 2	− 8	−19	−34	−52°					
17			+18	+12	+ 5	− 4	−14	−27	−42					
18			+19	+14	+ 7	0	−10	−21	−34	−50°				
19			+20	+15	+ 9	+ 2	− 7	−16	−28	−42				
20				+16	+10	+ 4	− 3	−12	−22	−34	−48°			
21				+17	+12	+ 6	0	− 9	−17	−28	−41			
22				+18	+13	+ 8	+ 2	− 6	−14	−23	−34	−47°		
23				+19	+14	+ 9	+ 4	− 3	−10	−19	−29	−40		
24				+19	+15	+10	+ 5	0	− 8	−15	−23	−34	−46°	
25				+20	+16	+12	+ 7	+ 1	− 5	−12	−20	−29	−40	−50°
26					+17	+13	+ 8	+ 3	− 3	− 9	−16	−25	−34	−44
27					+18	+14	+ 9	+ 5	− 1	− 7	−13	−21	−29	−39
28					+18	+15	+10	+ 6	+ 1	− 5	−11	−18	−25	−34
29					+19	+16	+12	+ 7	+ 2	− 3	− 8	−15	−22	−29
30					+20	+17	+13	+ 8	+ 4	− 1	− 6	−12	−18	−25

For capacities over 30 quarts divide true capacity by 3. Find quarts Anti-Freeze for the ⅓ and multiply by 3 for quarts to add.

For capacities under 10 quarts multiply true capacity by 3. Find quarts Anti-Freeze for the tripled volume and divide by 3 for quarts to add.

To Increase the Freezing Protection of Anti-Freeze Solutions Already Installed

Cooling System Capacity Quarts	Number of Quarts of ETHYLENE GLYCOL Anti-Freeze Required to Increase Protection												
	From +20°F. to					From +10°F. to					From 0°F. to			
	0°	−10°	−20°	−30°	−40°	0°	−10°	−20°	−30°	−40°	−10°	−20°	−30°	−40°
10	1¾	2¼	3	3½	3¾	¾	1½	2¼	2¾	3¼	¾	1½	2	2½
12	2	2¾	3½	4	4½	1	1¾	2½	3¼	3¾	1	1¾	2½	3¼
14	2¼	3¼	4	4¾	5½	1¼	2	3	3¾	4½	1	2	3	3½
16	2½	3½	4½	5¼	6	1¼	2½	3½	4¼	5¼	1¼	2¼	3¼	4
18	3	4	5	6	7	1½	2¾	4	5	5¾	1½	2½	3¾	4¾
20	3¼	4½	5¾	6¾	7½	1¾	3	4¼	5½	6½	1½	2¾	4¼	5¼
22	3½	5	6¼	7¼	8¼	1¾	3¼	4¾	6	7¼	1¾	3¼	4½	5½
24	4	5½	7	8	9	2	3½	5	6½	7½	1¾	3½	5	6
26	4¼	6	7½	8¾	10	2	4	5½	7	8¼	2	3¾	5½	6¾
28	4½	6¼	8	9½	10½	2¼	4¼	6	7½	9	2	4	5¾	7¼
30	5	6¾	8½	10	11½	2½	4½	6½	8	9½	2¼	4¼	6¼	7¾

Test radiator solution with proper hydrometer. Determine from the table the number of quarts of solution to be drawn off from a full cooling system and replace with undiluted anti-freeze, to give the desired increased protection. For example, to increase protection of a 22-quart cooling system containing Ethylene Glycol (permanent type) anti-freeze, from +20°F. to −20°F. will require the replacement of 6¼ quarts of solution with undiluted anti-freeze.

Off-Road Equipment Manufacturers and Distributors

The function of this list is to assist the owner in locating manufacturers and distributors of off-road improvement items made specifically for his vehicle. The publisher has neither tested nor used, and therefore cannot endorse, these firms or their products. Furthermore, the exclusion of any product or company is unintentional but obviously it would be impossible to list them all. We recognize that this list will soon become outdated and therefore recommend that the numerous off-road and camping magazines be consulted for the latest innovations and information.

Advance Adaptors
P.O. Box 206
Bell, California 90201

Archer Brothers
Off-Road Specialists
19745 Meedland Ave.
Hayward, Cal. 94541

Berens Associates
6046 Claremont Avenue
Oakland, California 94618

Dick Cepek, Inc.
9201 California Ave.
South Gate, California 90280

Con-Fer Inc.
300 N. Victory Blvd.
Burbank, Calif. 91502

Desert Dynamics
6230 Maywood Ave.
Bell, California 90201

Fairway Ford
1350 Yorba Linda
Placenta, Calif.

Hickey Enterprises, Inc.
1645 Callens Rd.
Ventura, Calif. 93003

Man-A-Fre Co.
18736 Parthenia St.
Northridge, Calif. 91423
or
107 West 43rd. St.
Boise, Idaho 83704

Novak Enterprises
Engine Conversion Components
Specialists
Box 1324
Whittier, Calif. 90609

Bill Stroppe & Associates
P.O. Box 1891
Long Beach, California 90801

MAGAZINES

Camping Journal
Davis Publications
229 Park Ave. S.
New York, New York 10003

Four Wheeler
Four Wheeler Publishing Co.
P.O. Box 978
11044 McCormick St.
North Hollywood, Calif. 91603

Off-Road Vehicles Magazine
131 Barrington Place
Los Angeles, Calif. 90049

PV4
Bond/Parkhurst Publications
1499 Monrovia Ave.
Newport Beach, Calif. 92663

Hot Rod
Petersen Publishing Co.
8490 Sunset Blvd.
Los Angeles, Calif. 90069

Jeep Model Identification

MODEL- MB MILITARY

Year MFG - 1941 - 1945
Distinguishing Characteristics - 4 cyl. L Head
Engine, No Tailgate, 6 Volt Electrical System,
Timing Chain Split Windshield, Rear Mounted
spare tire.

MODEL - MC - M38 MILITARY

Year MFG - 1950 - 1951
Distinguishing Characteristics - 4 cyl. L Head
Engine w/24 Volt waterproof Electrical System. No Tailgate. Brushguards over Head-
lamps. One piece windshield. Rear mounted
spare tire.

MODEL - MD - M38A1 MILITARY

Year MFG - 1951 - 1968
Distinguishing Characteristics - 4 cyl. F Head
Engine, No Tailgate. 24 Volt Waterproof Electrical System. Rounded Fenders. One piece
windshield. Rear mounted spare tire.

MODEL - M715 CARGO TRUCK

Year MFG - 1967 - 1968
Distinguishing Characteristics - Militarized version of 'Jeep' Gladiator. 6-230 OHC Engine.
24 Volt Electrical System w/60 Amp. Alternator. Soft Top Cab. Fold down windshield.

MODEL - CJ-2A UNIVERSAL JEEP

Year MFG - 1945 - 1949
Distinguishing Characteristics - 4 cyl. L Head Engine. Split Windshield. Has Tailgate. 6 Volt Electrical System. Side mounted spare tire.

MODEL - CJ-3A UNIVERSAL JEEP

Year MFG - 1948 - 1953
Distinguishing Characteristics - 4 cyl. L Head Engine. One piece windshield. 6 Volt Electrical System, Has Tailgate. Side mounted spare tire.

MODEL - CJ-3B UNIVERSAL JEEP

Year MFG - 1953 - 1964
Distinguishing Characteristics - 4 cyl. F Head Engine, Has tailgate, angular fenders, high flat hood, 6 or 12 Volt Electrical System. One piece windshield. Side mounted spare tire.

MODEL - CJ-5 UNIVERSAL JEEP

Year MFG - 1955 - 1968
Distinguishing Characteristics - Has Tailgate, rounded fenders. 6 or 12 Volt electrical system. Engines - 4 cyl. F Head or V-6. 81" wheelbase. Side mounted spare tire.

MODEL - CJ-6 UNIVERSAL JEEP

Year MFG - 1955 - 1968
Distinguishing Characteristics - Has Tailgate, Rounded fenders, 6 or 12 Volt electrical system. Engines 4 cyl. F Head or V6. Extended body. 101" wheelbase. Side mounted spare tire.

MODEL - DJ-3A DISPATCHER, 2WD

Year MFG - 1955 - 1964
Distinguishing Characteristics - "I" beam front axle. Hard top or soft top. 4 L engine.

MODEL - VJ2 OR 3 VJ3-6 JEEPSTER

Year MFG - 1948 - 1950
Distinguishing Characteristics - 4L - 6L Engine. All 2 wheel drive. Folding canvas top. Clear plastic windows, side and rear.

MODEL - 2WD, 4WD TRUCK
Year MFG - 1947 - 1950
Distinguishing Characteristics - Flat grille, flat fenders. 2 piece windshield glass. 4L Engine.

MODEL - 4-73 TRUCK
Year MFG - 1950 - 1951
Distinguishing Characteristics - 2 WD, 4 WD. V type radiator guard with chrome trim. Rounded fender top. 2 piece windshield glass.

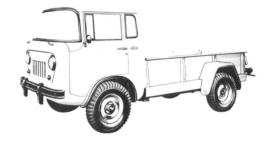

MODEL - FC-150 TRUCK
Year MFG - 1957 - 1964
Distinguishing Characteristics - Cab over engine. F4 Engine. All 4 wheel drive. 6 & 12 Volt systems.

MODEL - FC-170 TRUCK
Year MFG - 1957 - 1964
Distinguishing Characteristics - Cab over engine. 6-226 Engine. All 4 wheel drive. 6 & 12 Volt systems.

MODEL - 2400 - 3400
GLADIATOR TRUCK

Year MFG - 1962 - 1968
Distinguishing Characteristics - Town side or
Thrift side pick-up box. 2400 series 120''
wheelbase, 3400 series 126'' wheelbase. Square
radiator grille. Engines 6-230 OHC, 6-232 Hi-
Torque, V8-327 Vigilante, V8-350 Dauntless.

MODEL-1413 JEEP PANEL DELIVERY

Year MFG - 1962 - 1967
Distinguishing Characteristics - Engines 6-230
OHC, 6-232 Hi-Torque, V8-327 Vigilante. 4
wheel drive. Square radiator grille.

MODEL - 4-63 (2 WHEEL DRIVE),
4X4-63 (4 WHEEL DRIVE)

Year MFG -   4-63 1947 - 1950
         4X4-63 1949 - 1950
Distinguishing Characteristics - 4L Engine.
Single front springs. 2WD. Planadyne front
suspension. 2 piece windshield and tailgate
glass.

MODEL - 6-63 STATION SEDAN

Year MFG - 1950
Distinguishing Characteristics - 6 cyl. Solid
rear seat. L head. Spare tire mounted on floor.
Basket weave outside body trim.

MODEL - 473 2WD, 4X473 4WD

Year MFG - 1950 - 1951
Distinguishing Characteristics - F4 and 6-73
Engine. V type radiator guard w/chrome trim.
Rounded front fender top. 2 piece windshield
and tailgate glass.

MODEL - 4-75 JEEP
4 X 4 UTILITY WAGON

Year MFG - 1956 - 1964
Distinguishing Characteristics - Engines F4,
6-226, 6-230. All 4 wheel drive. One piece
windshield and tailgate glass. Outside body
trim moulding.

MODEL - MAVERICK, 2 WHEEL DRIVE

Year MFG - 1958
Distinguishing Characteristics - Four captive
air tires - no spare. External body length dress
up mouldings. One piece windshield and tailgate glass. F4 engine.

MODEL - 1414 JEEP WAGONEER

Year MFG - 1962 - 1965
Distinguishing Characteristics - OHC 6-230
Engine, V8-327 Engine. Standard or automatic transmission. 4 wheel drive. Square
radiator grille.

MODEL - 1414 JEEP WAGONEER

Distinguishing Characteristics - Engines 6-232 with low wide grille, 2 & 4 wheel drive, mfg 1965 - 1968. V8-327 with low wide grille, 2 & 4 wheel drive mfg 1965 - 1967. V8-350 with low wide grille, 4 wheel drive only mfg 1968.

MODEL - 1414 SUPER WAGONEER

Year MFG - 1965 - 1968
Distinguishing Characteristics - Deluxe interior trim including bucket seats and console shift. Deluxe exterior trim and mouldings. Tilt steering wheel. 4 wheel drive. Engine V8-327 with 4 barrel carburetor.

MODEL - C-101
JEEPSTER CONVERTIBLE

Year MFG - 1966 - 1968
Distinguishing Characteristics - Bucket seats, soft top, rear mounted spare tire. Standard or automatic transmission. 4 wheel drive. Engine 4 cyl. F head or V6.

MODEL - C-101
JEEPSTER COMMANDO

Year MFG - 1966 - 1968
Distinguishing Characteristics - Standard or automatic transmission, 4 wheel drive. Engine 4 cyl. F Head or V6. Models: Convertible, Roadster, Pick-Up, Station Wagon.

WHEN A PROBLEM DRINKER DRIVES, IT'S YOUR PROBLEM.

Problem drinkers were responsible for 19,000 highway deaths last year. That is your problem.

Because they didn't kill only themselves. They killed people they loved, people they'd never met, people like you.

And they didn't only kill. They crippled and maimed and destroyed lives without actually taking them.

If your friend has a drinking problem, there are many ways you can help him. But first you must help him stay alive. So others may live.

If you are really his friend, don't help him drink. Admittedly, you alone probably can't stop a problem drinker from drinking.

But you can discourage it.

If he has been drinking, don't let him drive. Drive him yourself. Call a cab. Take his car keys.

It won't be easy. After all, he is your friend. You don't want to hurt him or insult him. But the alternative is perhaps losing him.

Everything you think you can't do, you must do.

Write Drunk Driver, Box 2345, Rockville, Maryland 20852.

U.S. DEPARTMENT OF TRANSPORTATION
NATIONAL HIGHWAY TRAFFIC SAFETY ADMINISTRATION